AS/A-LEVEL Geography

Michael Raw

E
R
Notes

Philip Allan Updates
Market Place
Deddington
Oxfordshire
OX15 0SE

tel: 01869 338652
fax: 01869 337590
e-mail: sales@philipallan.co.uk
www.philipallan.co.uk

ISBN 0 86003 426 7

Cover illustration by John Spencer
Typeset by Magnet Harlequin, Oxford
Printed by Raithby, Lawrence & Co. Ltd, Leicester

Contents

Introduction

About this book

This book provides core knowledge and understanding of the major topics in geography at AS and A2 level. Two special features are the additional notes in the margin and the insets within the text. The marginal notes are intended to reinforce ideas developed in the main text, summarise major themes, and offer clarification where possible misunderstandings could arise. The insets have two purposes. Some explore topics in more depth, while others provide exemplar material. Reading and learning the insets is not essential, but if you require extra detail and understanding you should find them useful.

What examiners are looking for

Examiners mark written papers using four criteria or *assessment objectives*, namely: *knowledge*, *understanding*, *application of knowledge and understanding*, and *skills* outlined below. Each module puts a slightly different weighting on the assessment objectives. Coursework and decision-making exercises (DMEs), for example, particularly test the skills.

Knowledge and understanding

Your answers will have to demonstrate both knowledge and understanding of the topics you have studied. The difference between knowledge and understanding is not always clear. As a rule of thumb, questions which test knowledge ask you to 'describe'. Those which test understanding require you to 'explain'. For example, if you described the shape of a cumulus cloud you would draw on your knowledge. But if you explained how the shape of a cumulus cloud related to the processes which formed it you would show understanding. Because explanation is based on prior knowledge, it is a higher-order skill than description, and carries higher marks.

Application of knowledge and understanding

To do well at AS/A2 level your answers must not only demonstrate good knowledge and understanding but also show that you can apply this knowledge and understanding relevantly to a question. What often sets apart A/B grade candidates from the rest is their ability to apply knowledge and understanding. Consider the question: *why do rates of coastal erosion vary from one stretch of coast to another?* An answer might show *knowledge* of erosion, erosion rates and different stretches of coastline. It might also show *understanding* of the complex processes which influence erosion rates. However, *application of knowledge and understanding* requires you to explain how different combinations of processes operate at different locations, and therefore give rise to variable rates of erosion.

Skills

The appropriate way to assess many geographical skills is through coursework. However, some skills can be assessed in written papers, and some specifications offer a geographical techniques module as an alternative to coursework. Written papers cover both literacy and numeracy skills (including quality of English). In geographical techniques modules you will have to use skills such as data presentation (e.g. charts, map-making), data interpretation (OS maps, extracting information from tables, charts, etc.) and data analysis (e.g. statistical skills). Other modules include DMEs which require skills such as data assimilation, data synthesis, the ability to write summary reports, and decision-making.

Types of question in written examinations

Examiners use a range of question types to assess your knowledge, understanding and skills. It is important that you know the type of question used in assessing each module in your specification. The main types of question are:

- short answer: data-response and stimulus-response questions

- structured essays divided into several sub-sections
- unstructured, discursive essays
- DMEs

When revising topics assessed by short-answer questions you should appreciate the need for concise and accurate knowledge and understanding. While examples and case studies have limited importance for short-answer questions, they are essential for essay-type questions. Learning how to plan and structure essays is also a vital component of revision. DMEs place heavy demands on skills of assimilation and synthesis. Here your revision will focus on practice answers to past exercises.

Responding to command words and phrases

Examination questions spell out what you must do by using simple command words and phrases. These commands are crucial and must be followed explicitly. They vary in their level of difficulty and are the principal way in which examiners achieve differentiation in their marking. Too often candidates ignore the more demanding command words and phrases such as 'discuss', 'evaluate', 'under what circumstances', etc. and instead resort to description or narrative. Answers of this type fail to apply knowledge and understanding effectively and are penalised heavily. Study the command words in Table 1 and make absolutely sure that you understand what each one is asking you to do.

Common command words	Meaning
Describe	Description is the simplest skill and carries the fewest marks. The examiner is assessing your knowledge of a topic. Descriptions should be precise, accurate and structured. 'Outline' is an alternative command to 'describe'.
Explain	Explanation demands understanding as well as knowledge. Explanation is a higher-level skill than description, requiring you to understand processes and causes.
Discuss/assess/evaluate	These skills are of the highest order and are likely to be tested at A2 level. To discuss, assess and evaluate you are required to consider different viewpoints/outcomes/strategies, etc. and reach some overall synthesis/conclusion.
Amplify	The command word 'amplify' is asking you to describe and explain something in more detail. Some of the extra detail will probably include case studies and examples.

Table 1 Common command words and their meanings

In your revision you should refer constantly to past papers. You should identify the key commands and phrases. How often does each word/phrase appear in each paper? Do the AS examinations have a different frequency of command words to A2? In which papers (and modules) are the more demanding command words and phrases found? Practise your response to these key words and phrases by preparing planned answers to past questions.

How to revise

Your revision of a particular topic should follow a logical sequence:

- Choose a revision topic.
- Read the section of your specification which deals with that topic.
- Make a list of past examination questions on the topic and identify the main themes.
- Get copies of mark schemes for these questions (your teacher should have copies; if not you can purchase them from the examining boards) so that you understand how the questions are marked.
- Read and learn the relevant notes in this textbook using the themes of past questions and examiners' mark schemes to guide your learning.

- Learn appropriate examples and case studies from the following sources: this book, other texts recommended by your teacher, articles in *Geography Review* and class notes and hand-outs.
- Write and/or prepare planned answers to all past examination questions on the topic.

Structuring your revision

Most topics at AS/A2 level normally have three dimensions:

- the main features of geographical forms, patterns and processes, including their variations in space and over time
- the impact of geographical processes on the human and/or physical environment
- the human response to this impact

You should adapt your revision of topics to fit this structure. An example is given in Table 2.

Dimensions	Example: soil erosion
Main characteristics, including descriptions of form, causes, variations in space and time	Soil erosion by wind and water. Physical and human causes of soil erosion.
Impact on the human and/or physical environment	Loss of soil cover: gulleying, impact on crop yields, land degradation, etc.
Human responses	Terraces, contour ploughing, maintaining soil fertility, shelter belts, land abandonment, etc.

Table 2 Structuring revision topics: the example of soil erosion

Points to remember

In your revision you must:

- Have a thorough systematic knowledge and understanding of the subject.
- Learn a wide range of examples and case studies with which to illustrate your answers.
- Adopt an intelligent approach to learning, structuring your revision around past examination questions and mark schemes.
- Apply knowledge and understanding so that your answers reflect accurately (and therefore relevantly) the demands of the question.
- Practise writing answers under timed conditions, and prepare planned answers for those that you do not wish to write out in full.

In the examination you must:

- Plan and give structure to your answers – essay-type questions will require 5 minutes of planning to organise and specify their content (factual content, arguments and exemplification).
- Manage your time efficiently; remember that if you spent excessive time on one question, the extra marks you gain are unlikely to compensate for the loss of time (and marks) on other questions.
- Convey knowledge and understanding through sketch maps, diagrams and charts, as well as text.
- Never write generalised answers to essay-type questions: geography is about the real world and this should be reflected through your use of examples and case studies.
- Write answers which show good knowledge and understanding and an ability to apply knowledge and understanding accurately to the questions set.
- Make a conscious effort to write clear and concise English, with accurate punctuation, grammar and spelling.
- Use appropriate geographical terminology accurately.

Michael Raw

UNIT 1 Tectonic activity

1 The Earth's structure

Earth is the third planet from the Sun and the largest of the four inner planets. It has a diameter at the equator of 12,756 kilometres. With an average density of 5.5, Earth is jointly the densest planet in the solar system.

In cross-section the Earth consists of a series of concentric shells (see Figure 1.1). Each shell has different physical and chemical properties (Table 1.1).

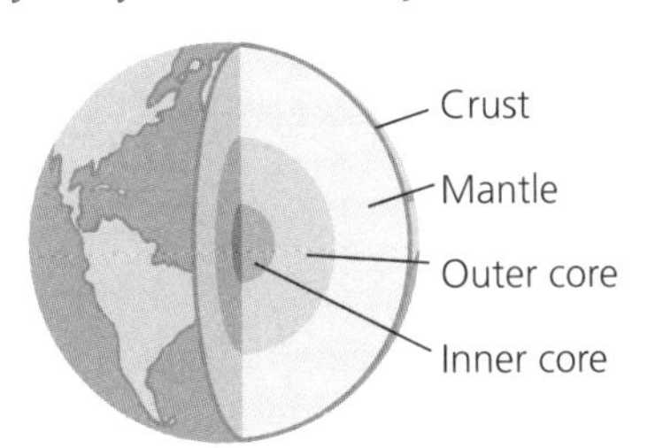

Figure 1.1 Earth's structure

Layer	Depth (km)	Density (gm/cm^3)	Rock type	Temperature (°C)
Crust				**10**
Continental	30–70	2.7	granite	
Oceanic	5–10	3.0	basalt	
Mantle	**2,900**	**5.5**	**peridotite**	**375**
Core				**3,000**
Outer	2,000	10.0	iron/nickel (liquid)	
Inner	1,450	13.3	iron/nickel (solid)	

Table 1.1 Chemical properties of the Earth

INSET 1

Determining the Earth's internal structure from seismic evidence

Knowledge of the Earth's internal structure comes from the study of earthquake (seismic) waves. The velocities and paths of earthquake waves depend on the materials they pass through. There are two types of wave: primary or **P-waves** and secondary or **S-waves**. P-waves can be transmitted through any material, but S-waves can pass only through solids. From the behaviour of these waves it is possible to determine the physical composition (density and make-up) of the interior.

1.1 The upper mantle or asthesnosphere

Most of the mantle appears to be solid rock, with minerals of high density dominated by magnesium and iron. However, the upper part of the mantle (100–300 kilometres from the surface) has plastic properties that allow it to flow under pressure. This zone is called the **asthenosphere**.

1.2 The crust and lithosphere

The crust is the Earth's thin, rocky outer shell, between 5 and 70 kilometres thick. The crust and the immediate underlying part of the mantle form a single unit known as the **lithosphere**. As Figure 1.2 shows, there are two types of crust and lithosphere: **oceanic** and **continental**. The oceanic crust/lithosphere is thinner, denser and much younger than the continental crust/lithosphere (Table 1.1). Nowhere is the oceanic crust more than 200 million years old. By comparison, the oldest rocks on the continents are up to 3,500 million years old – three-quarters as old as the Earth itself.

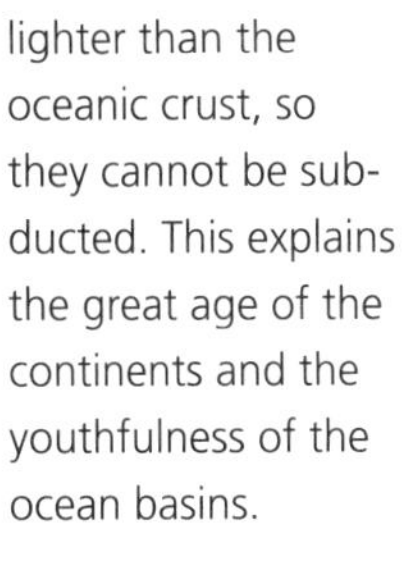
The continents are lighter than the oceanic crust, so they cannot be subducted. This explains the great age of the continents and the youthfulness of the ocean basins.

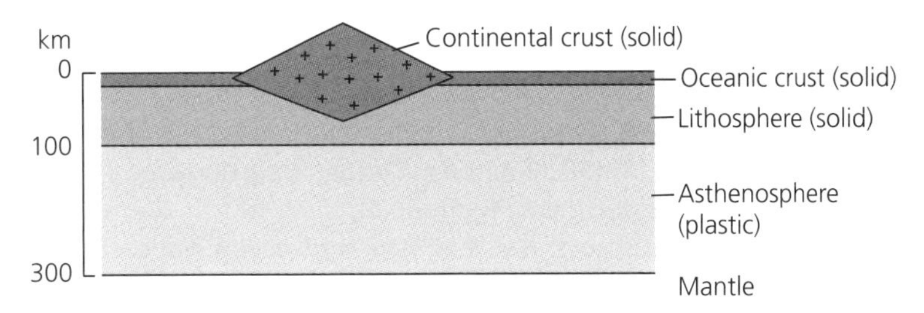

Figure 1.2 Cross-section through the Earth's crust, lithosphere and upper mantle

2 Continental drift

The idea that the continents are not stationary, but have shifted their position on the Earth's surface, goes back to the seventeenth century and the completion of the first accurate charting of the Atlantic coastline. The shapes of the coastlines of Africa and South America, and Europe and North America, seemed to match. This suggested that at some time the continents might have formed a single landmass.

In 1912 Alfred Wegener provided further evidence that the continents might once have been joined:

- ancient glacial deposits in the southern continents (evidence of a past glacial episode) now widely dispersed;
- similarities in fossil plants and animals from Africa and South America;
- similar rock types and geological structures on opposite sides of the Atlantic: in Brazil and west Africa, and in north-west Europe and eastern North America.

Using this evidence, Wegener argued that 300 million years ago the continents formed a single supercontinent. He called this continent Pangaea and it is shown in Figure 1.3. About 200 million years ago this continent split apart. Africa, South America, India, Australia and Antarctica formed the southern supercontinent of Gondwanaland. Eurasia and North America formed the northern supercontinent known as Laurasia. Eventually the two supercontinents also broke up and the continental landmasses drifted (at a rate of just 2 or 3 cm a year) to their present position.

Despite Wegener's evidence, with no mechanism to explain how continents could move, scientists remained sceptical about the theory of continental drift. Plate tectonics, developed in the 1960s, eventually provided an explanation and forced the scientific community to accept the reality of continental drift.

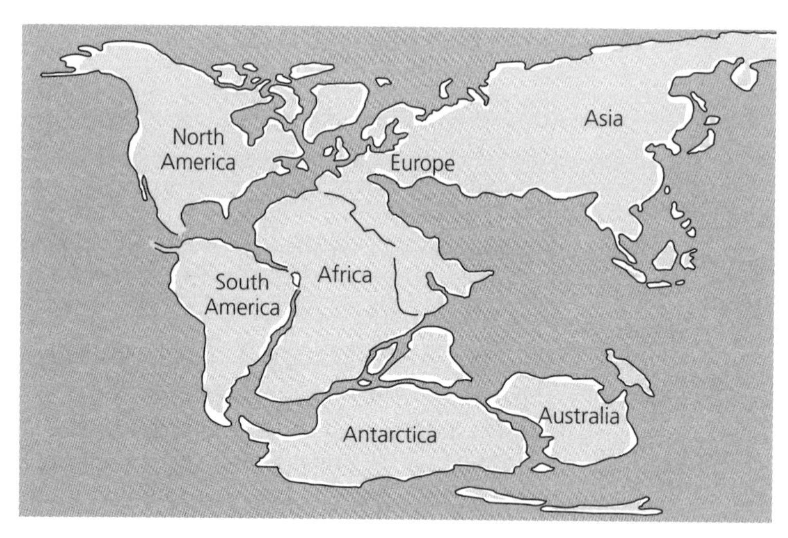

Figure 1.3 The Pangaea supercontinent

2.1 Palaeomagnetism

The crucial evidence supporting the idea of continental drift came from **palaeomagnetism**. This describes how iron particles in lava were 'frozen' in the direction of the Earth's magnetic field at the time they cooled and solidified. Studies of palaeomagnetism showed that the Earth reverses its polarity at regular intervals: on average, every 400,000 years.

2.2 Sea floor spreading

Investigation of palaeomagnetism in the basalt rocks in the North Atlantic Ocean revealed a remarkable pattern. Regular reversals of the Earth's magnetic field showed up as 'stripes' 20–30 kilometres across and hundreds of kilometres long. The stripes had alternate north and south polarity. Moreover, identical striped patterns were discovered on either side of the Atlantic's **mid-ocean ridge** of submerged mountains. This finding led to the notion of **sea floor spreading**.

One consequence of sea floor spreading is that oceanic crust increases in age with distance from its origin.

Sea floor spreading starts at the mid-ocean ridges. Here, convection currents in the mantle cause magma to rise to the surface where it forms new oceanic crust. Pressure from the newly formed crust causes the older crust to spread laterally away from the mid-ocean ridge. Eventually the oceanic crust reaches an island arc or a continent. Here it descends into the mantle, where it is destroyed. The whole process, from the formation of new oceanic crust to its destruction, takes around 200 million years. The movement of oceanic crust is like a slow conveyor belt. As the oceanic crust moves, the continents 'ride' this natural conveyor. Thus sea floor spreading is the process that drives continental drift.

3 Plate tectonics

The Earth's crust and lithosphere are broken into seven large slabs and a dozen or more minor ones known as **lithospheric plates**. The distribution of the main tectonic plates is shown in Figure 1.4. The plate boundaries are zones of tectonic activity, including volcanism, earthquakes, mountain building and faulting and folding. The global distribution of active volcanoes and earthquakes defines the plate boundaries. There are three types of plate boundary: constructive, destructive and conservative.

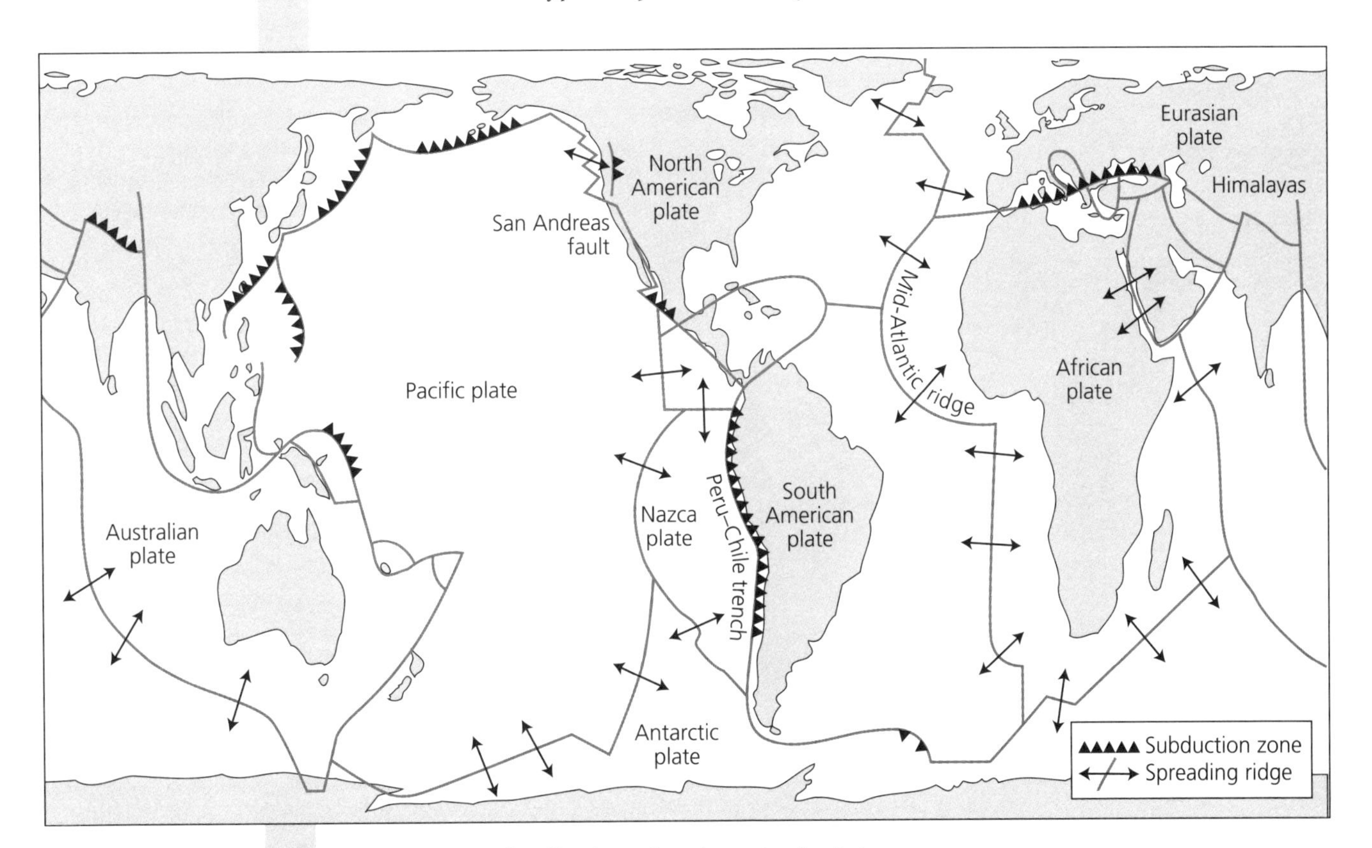

Figure 1.4 Distribution of main tectonic plates

3.1 Constructive plate boundaries

Constructive (or divergent) plate boundaries are the mid-ocean ridges where new crust forms. Here, as Figure 1.5 shows, rising plumes of magma from the Earth's mantle stretch the crust and lithosphere. Active volcanoes form where lava reaches the surface. Most volcanic activity takes place on the ocean floor, where it forms the submarine mountain ranges of the mid-ocean ridges. Faulting (see Unit 2) associated with volcanism has produced huge rifts that form valleys between the mountains of the mid-ocean ridges.

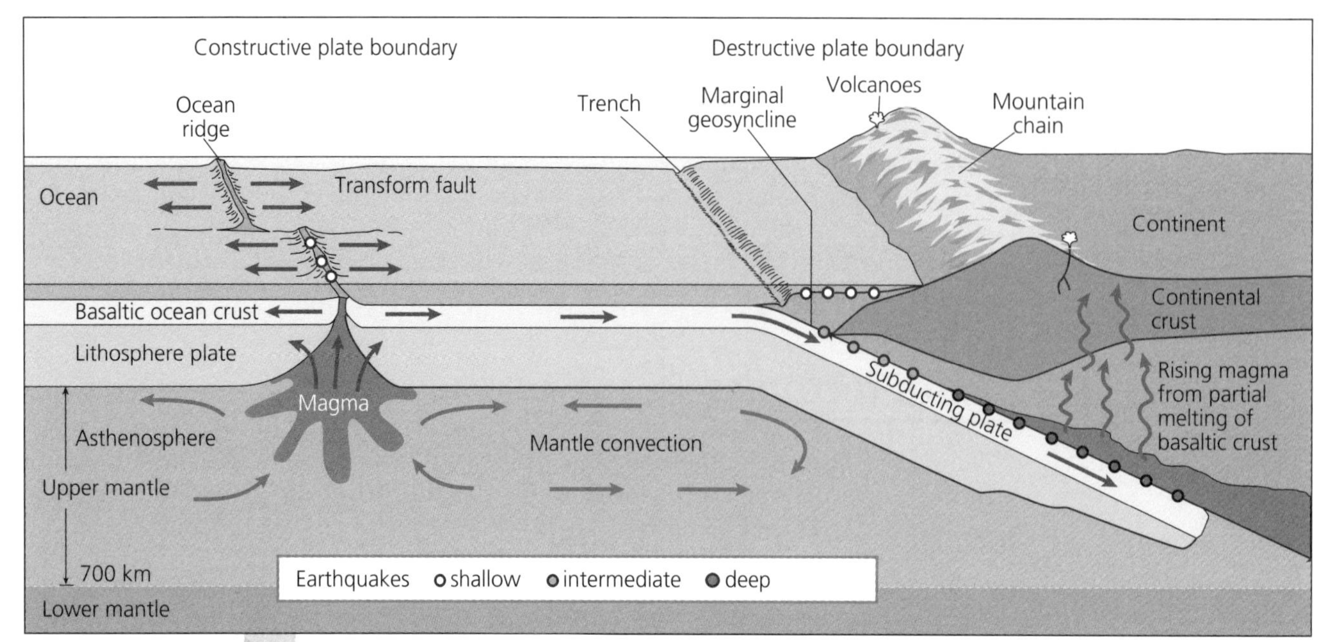

The mid-ocean ridges are offset at regular intervals by faults at right angles to the axis of the ridge. These transform faults have caused displacements of 1,000 kilometres or more.

Figure 1.5 Constructive and destructive plate boundaries

INSET 2

Iceland – a spreading ridge

Volcanic activity at mid-ocean ridges largely occurs unseen on the ocean floor. As Figure 1.6 shows, Iceland sits astride the North American and Eurasian plates. It is part of the mid-Atlantic ridge above sea level and is being torn apart by the spreading ridge. A huge rift valley called Thingvellir marks the location of the ridge.

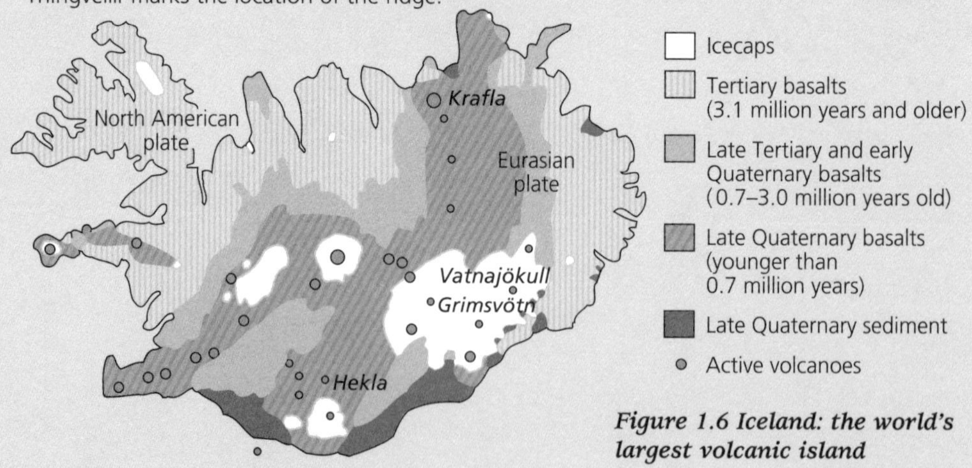

Figure 1.6 Iceland: the world's largest volcanic island

Volcanism in Iceland is exactly the same as that found at constructive plate boundaries on the ocean floor. Iceland is one the most active areas of volcanism in the world. Much of the country consists of a lava plateau up to 2,000 metres above sea level. None of the rocks is more than 3 million years old. Eldfjell, Hekla and Grimsvötn volcanoes have all erupted in the last 30 years. In 1963 an eruption off the south-west coast of Iceland created the island of Surtsey.

3.2 Destructive plate boundaries

At destructive (convergent) plate boundaries or **subduction zones**, oceanic crust is destroyed (Figure 1.5). The process of subduction involves:

- the descent of the subducted plate into the mantle;
- melting of the subducted plate 100 kilometres or so below the surface;
- the melt (or magma), which is less dense than the surrounding rocks, rising through lines of weakness and fissures to the surface;
- the eruption of lava, gases and ash at the surface through volcanoes and fissures.

Extensive areas of volcanic rocks in the UK indicate the location of a former plate margin.

- 60 million years ago, Greenland split from Scotland along a constructive plate margin and opened up the North Atlantic.
- Vast outpourings of lava in Antrim (Northern Ireland) and Inner Hebrides (Skye, Mull) accompanied this event.

Subduction occurs when two plates converge. The older, denser plate is subducted. If two oceanic plates converge, subduction may give rise to an island arc such as the Kuril Islands in the north Pacific.

The subduction of an oceanic plate beneath a continental plate often produces fold mountain chains. The Andes and Western Cordillera along the Pacific coast of the Americas have been formed in this way.

Destructive plate boundaries are also the location of volcanoes, earthquakes and ocean trenches.

Fold mountain chains

The world's highest mountain ranges, including the Himalayas, Andes, Western Cordillera and Alps, are located along subduction zones.

Where an oceanic plate and continental plate converge, an island arc may collide with the continent and contribute to mountain building. Meanwhile, sedimentary rocks formed on the continental shelf and continental slope, squeezed between the island arc and the continent, crumple to form mountain ranges. Subduction of the oceanic plate may produce huge intrusions of magma beneath the mountains, which creates further uplift. This sequence of events explains the formation of the Andes mountains in South America.

The Himalayas have been formed by the convergence of two continental plates – the Australo-Indian plate and the Eurasian plate. As the two plates converged, the Tethys Sea narrowed until its sea floor sediments were thrust upwards into fold mountain ranges. In South Asia two continental landmasses (Eurasia and India) have collided. The collision has welded the continents together. And because there is no subduction, there is no volcanic activity in the Himalayas.

Ocean trenches

Narrow trenches, hundreds of kilometres long and up to 11 kilometres deep, occur on the ocean floor parallel to island arcs and fold mountain ranges. Ocean trenches are areas of subduction where oceanic crust descends into the mantle. As it does so, the edge of the overriding plate is buckled to form a trench.

3.3 Conservative plate boundaries

At conservative plate boundaries, two plates slide past each other with a shearing movement. This movement can be violent, giving rise to severe earthquakes. However, volcanism is usually absent. In southern and central California, the boundary of the Pacific and North American plates forms a conservative plate margin known as the San Andreas fault. Earthquakes occur frequently along this fault line and threaten major metropolitan areas such as San Francisco and Los Angeles.

INSET 3

Volcanism: definition of terms

aa: lava with a rough clinkery surface.
caldera: a circular or oval volcanic depression at least 1.5 kilometres in diameter.
cinder cone: a conical hill made of ash and cinders thrown out by a volcanic explosion around a volcanic vent.
crater: a small circular depression caused by collapse.
fissure: a fracture in the Earth's crust where volcanic material reaches the Earth's surface.
lava: hot liquid rock extruded on to the Earth's surface.
magma: hot liquid rock beneath the Earth's surface.
pahoehoe: lava with a smooth or ropy surface.
spatter cone: a low, steep-sided hill built up by fragments of lava from a volcanic vent.
vent: an opening where volcanic material reaches the Earth's surface.
volcanic bomb: a large dense chunk of molten material thrown out of a volcano.

4 Volcanoes and volcanic activity

4.1 Volcanoes

A volcano is an opening in the Earth's crust where molten rock and gases reach the surface. The **ejecta** or fragments thrown out by an eruption include lava, pumice, cinders, ash and gases. The nature of these materials is very variable, and explains differences in the shape of volcanoes and the nature of volcanic eruptions.

Many volcanoes, such as Mount Fuji, have a classic conical shape as shown in Figure 1.7. These **strato-volcanoes** comprise layers of lava, ash and other ejecta erupted by the volcano. The **vent** occupies a collapsed hollow which, depending on its size, is known as a **crater** or **caldera**. Feeding the volcano and located 3 or 4 kilometres underground is the **magma chamber**. Magma from the mantle fills this chamber before an eruption. The build-up of magma is detectable at the surface because the ground swells or inflates. Inflation can tear the crust apart to form rifts or fissures at the surface. Fissure eruptions are common in Iceland and Hawaii.

Craters and calderas commonly form from subsidence. Following an eruption the magma chamber collapses, causing the area around the vent to sink. Small circular hollows formed in this way are called craters. Much larger ones, up to 20 kilometres or more in diameter, are called calderas.

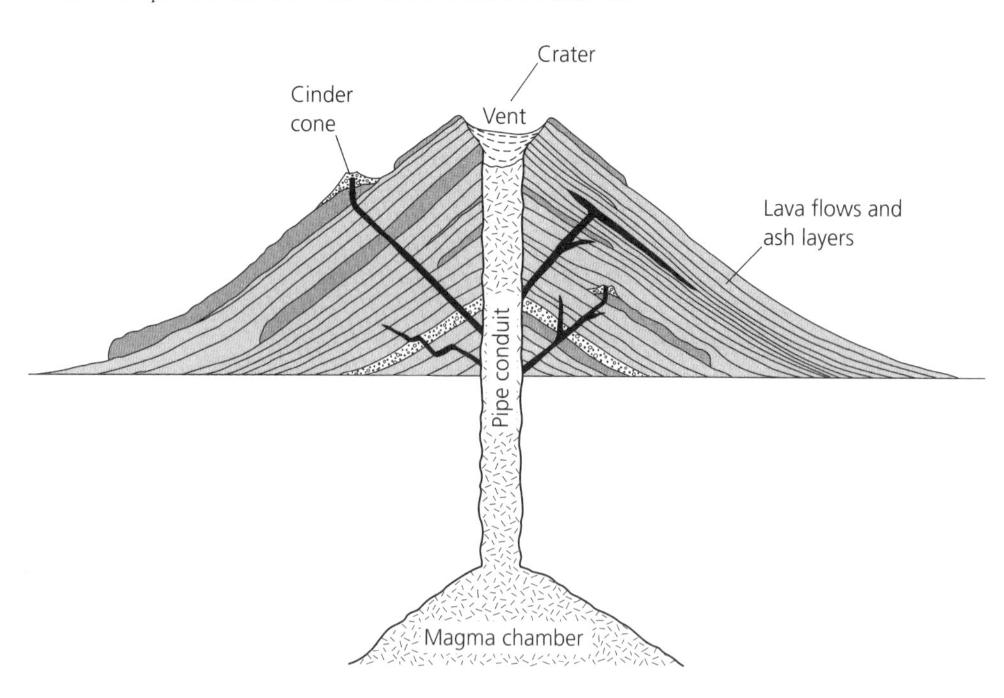

Figure 1.7 A strato-volcano

4.2 Types of volcano

Hawaiian-type volcanoes

The Hawaiian Islands in the Pacific Ocean are one of the most active volcanic areas in the world. Here volcanism is not caused by subduction or a spreading ridge. Located at the centre of the Pacific plate, the cause of volcanism in the Hawaiian Islands is a **hot spot**: a rising plume of magma that has punched a hole through the crust.

This hot spot has had a fixed position for over 70 million years. However, during this time the Pacific plate has moved (at a speed of just 3 or 4 centimetres a year) in a north-westerly direction over the hot spot. Today the Hawaiian hot spot is over the Big Island and it is here that most active volcanism is found. The Big Island was formed in the last 1 million years by eruptions from its five volcanoes. The largest – Mauna Kea and Mauna Loa – reach over 4,000 metres above sea level, and rise 9,000 metres from the ocean floor. Kilauea is the most active volcano: it has erupted continuously since 1983.

In profile the Big Island's volcanoes have the shape of a flattened dome. They are known as **shield volcanoes**. They are giants – at its base Mauna Loa is 120 kilometres in diameter. However, its slopes never exceed a gentle 12 degrees. Hawaii's shield volcanoes form for the following reasons:

- Most eruptions on Hawaii consist of lava rather than ash and gas.
- The basalt lava has only a relatively small proportion of silica. It is non-viscous and has a low gas content, flowing for long distances before cooling and solidifying.
- Eruptions are relatively gentle with little explosive activity.

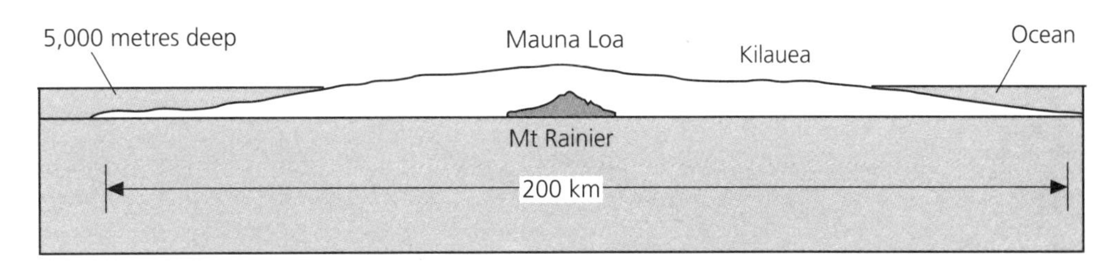

Figure 1.8 Scale comparison: a shield volcano (Mauna Loa) and a strato-(composite) volcano (Mount Rainier)

Strato-(composite) volcanoes

Strato-(composite) volcanoes consist of layers of ash and lava. They have steeper slopes than shield volcanoes and a more conical shape. A scale comparison of shield and strato-volcanoes is shown in Figure 1.8. The magma that forms strato-volcanoes is viscous and has a high silica content. Volcanoes with viscous magmas produce explosive products, such as cinder and ash, and fewer lava flows. In viscous magma, the trapped gas cannot escape easily. In these circumstances, the pressure caused by the build-up of gases can blow a volcano apart.

The chemical composition and gaseous content of magma exert a strong influence on (a) the shape of volcanoes, and (b) the hazards volcanoes present to people.

This is precisely what happened at Mount St Helens in the Cascade range of the north-west USA in 1980. A cataclysmic explosion blew away the top 400 metres of the mountain. Ash and other pyroclastic material combined with hot gases to form **pyroclastic flows** that destroyed everything in their path. Melting snow mixed with ash caused massive debris flows and lahars. The result was total devastation within a 15-kilometre radius of the mountain.

5 Volcanic hazards

5.1 The variable impact of eruptions

Volcanic eruptions produce a range of hazards. Their impact on people depends on three factors.

- The nature of the volcanic ejecta (i.e. lava, tephra, gas) and their violence. Gentle, effusive eruptions of lava, such as those found in Hawaii, pose little threat to human life. Even so, lava flows destroy farmland, buildings and infrastructure. Explosive eruptions of superheated gas and tephra cause total devastation.
- The density of population living in the vicinity of the volcano.
- Warning and evacuation procedures for the population at risk. Compared to less economically developed countries (LEDCs), more economically developed countries (MEDCs) have more sophisticated monitoring, early warning and evacuation procedures. As a result, loss of life in developed countries is greatly reduced.

5.2 Types of volcanic hazard

The main types of volcanic hazard are shown in Figure 1.9.

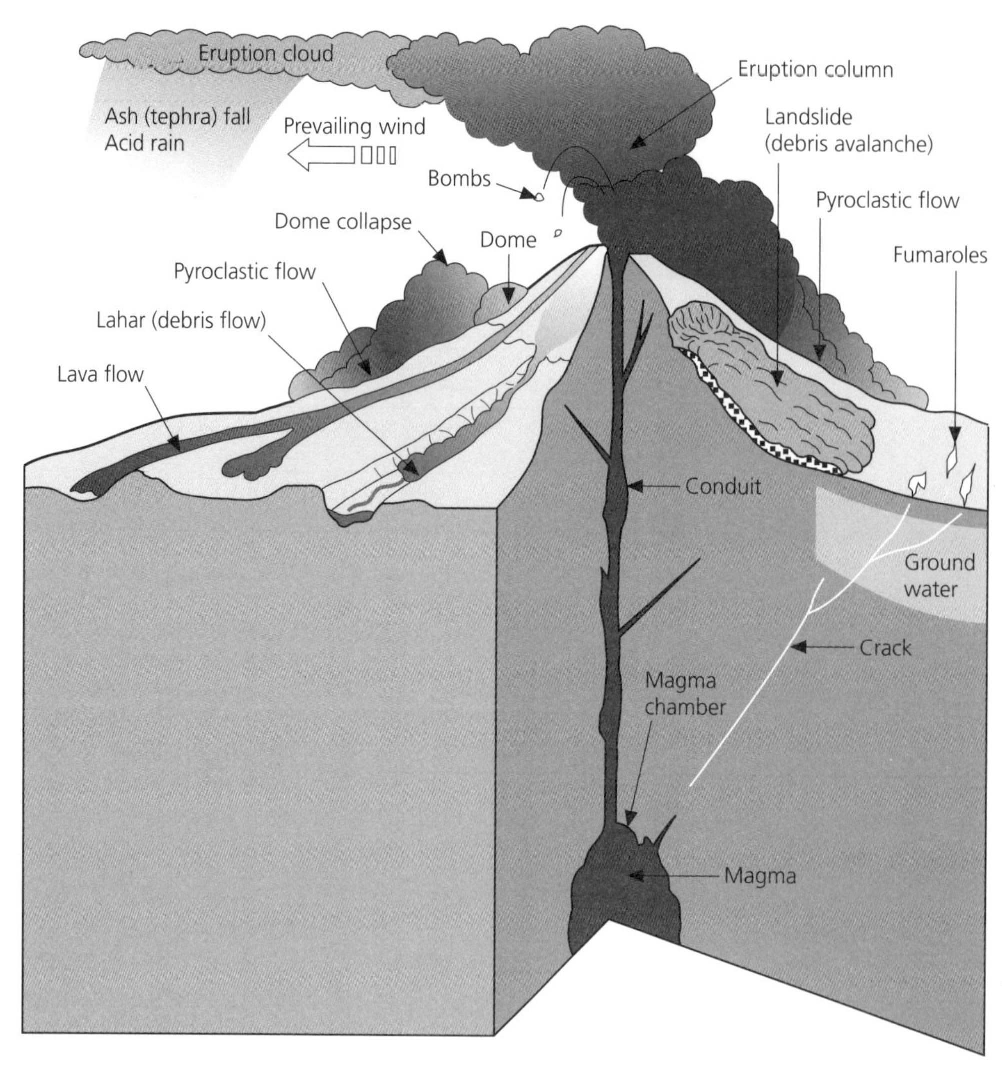

Figure 1.9 Volcanic hazards

Lava flows

The flow of lava is almost irresistible, although lava flows have occasionally been halted by cooling them with water. Lava flows are rarely a threat to life, but cause enormous damage to property. In 1990 a lava flow from Puu Oo crater in Hawaii buried the village of Kalapana. Further eruptions between 1992 and 1993 destroyed 181 homes, buried large areas of farmland and severed the main coastal road.

Most volcanic eruptions cannot be predicted with accuracy. Predictions are made by monitoring earthquakes, inflation and gravity. Despite the sophisticated monitoring of Mount St Helens in 1980, the timing and power of the eruption took geologists by surprise. Sixty-three people died in the eruption.

Pyroclastic flows

Pyroclastic flows are high-speed avalanches of hot ash, rock fragments and gas. They can reach speeds of 200 kph and temperatures of over 1,000 °C, and can destroy everything in their path. Soufriere Hills volcano on the Caribbean island of Montserrat, which erupted between 1995 and 1998, produced many pyroclastic flows. These flows destroyed much of the island's farmland and led to the evacuation of most of Montserrat's 11,000 inhabitants.

Lahars

Lahars are mixtures of water, rock, sand and mud that rush down valleys leading away from a volcano. They can be caused by:

- an eruption melting icefields around a volcano's summit;
- the rapid release of water following the breakout of a summit crater lake;
- flooding following heavy rainfall.

The impact of natural disasters owes as much to human as to physical factors. Population distribution, population density and levels of development have a major influence on loss of life, injury and damage to property.

Lahars are fast-moving and can travel long distances. They are particularly destructive because they follow river valleys where most settlement and population are concentrated. One of the largest lahar events occurred on Mount Rainier in the north-west USA about 5,700 years ago. Rocks and mud moved down the White Valley to their present position near Tacoma – a distance of 120 kilometres.

Jökulhlaups

Equally catastrophic hazards arise when a volcano erupts beneath an icefield or glacier. Rapid melting of ice releases enormous volumes of water and generates massive floods. In Iceland these floods are known as **jökulhlaups**. Iceland's most recent jokulhlaup occurred in 1996 following the eruption of the Grimsvötn volcano beneath the Vatnajökull icefield (see Figure 1.6). A peak flow of 45,000 cumecs was recorded. The flood, which lasted for a week, destroyed several bridges and 10 kilometres of Iceland's ring road. However, because the flood was expected, dykes were strengthened and people were evacuated. Thus there was no loss of life or damage to settlements.

Climate change

Large-scale explosive eruptions may affect the global climate. Droplets of sulphuric acid and dust may remain suspended in the atmosphere for several years. These particles reflect and absorb insolation, lowering temperatures at the surface. The eruption at Mount Pinatubo (Philippines) in 1991 caused a significant cooling of the global climate in the following year. The eruption of Mount Tambora (Indonesia) in 1815 was responsible for one of the coldest summers on record. Crops failed worldwide and famine caused millions of deaths.

INSET 4

Benefits of volcanoes

Although volcanic eruptions often cause death and destruction, they can also benefit people.

- Volcanic ash and lava are rich in minerals, and they weather to form fertile volcanic soils. The high-density rural populations in Java, Indonesia, are largely supported by intensive farming of rich volcanic soils.
- Lava flows may create new areas of land. The lava flows generated by the eruption of Kilauea volcano in Hawaii since 1983 have added 200 hectares to the area of the Big Island.
- Volcanoes often attract visitors and thus help local economies. The Volcanoes National Park in Hawaii attracts nearly 2 million visitors a year; Yellowstone National Park, with its famous geysers, has over 4 million visitors a year. The world's two most climbed mountains are both volcanoes: Mount Fuji in Japan and Mount St Helens in the USA.
- In Iceland and New Zealand volcanic activity is an important source of geothermal energy. Hot water from volcanism provides central heating for Iceland's capital, Reykjavik. Elsewhere, pumice and ash deposits are used by the construction industry.

6 Earthquakes

6.1 Causes of earthquakes

Earthquakes are vibrations in the Earth's crust caused by the fracturing of rocks and their movement along fault lines. The world's major earthquake zones correspond to plate boundaries. Here plate movement leads to tension and compression in the crust. Rocks put under pressure may snap, releasing huge amounts of energy as earthquakes and tremors.

The precise location of an earthquake within the crust is known as the **focus**. The point on the surface immediately above the focus is the **epicentre**. The destructive power of an earthquake is greatest at the epicentre. Earthquakes of similar magnitude are more destructive if they occur near the surface.

6.2 Earthquake magnitude and intensity

The Richter scale measures earthquake magnitude. Seismographs record the amplitude of earthquake waves, which radiate in all directions from an earthquake focus. These waves give a measure of the amount of energy released by an earthquake. The Richter scale is logarithmic. This means that a magnitude 6 earthquake is 10 times more powerful than a magnitude 5 quake, 100 times more powerful than a magnitude 4 quake and so on.

The Mercalli scale measures earthquake intensity, i.e. the impact of an earthquake on people and structures. The scale goes from 1 to 12, where 1 is instrumental (i.e. detected only by seismographs) and 12 is catastrophic.

There is little relationship between earthquake magnitude and intensity. For example, a magnitude 6.6 earthquake struck Los Angeles in 1994 and killed 57 people. Four months earlier an earthquake of similar magnitude in central India caused 22,000 deaths.

INSET 5

The San Andreas fault

The San Andreas fault in southern and central California is the boundary between the Pacific and North American plates and is one of the most active earthquake zones in the world. The Pacific plate is sliding north-west at a speed of a few centimetres a year. However, this movement is not smooth. Friction between the plates restricts movement, causing pressure to build up. When movement occurs there is a sudden release of stored energy, which is an earthquake. Major earthquakes occur every 20 or 30 years along the fault line. The 1906 quake (magnitude 8.1), which destroyed San Francisco and killed around 700 people, is the most powerful ever recorded. San Francisco was hit by another large quake in 1989, though damage was less severe. Frequent small quakes and tremors occur, but cause little damage.

More than one-third of the world's largest cities (most of them in LEDCs) are located in active seismic areas.

6.3 Earthquake damage

Earthquakes damage buildings and infrastructure, and cause injuries and death. Large earthquakes can devastate an entire region and kill or injure thousands of people. Collapsed buildings and other structures are the main cause of death and injury. In the aftermath of an earthquake, fire and disease may add significantly to the death toll.

Five factors influence the destructive effects of an earthquake in any region:

- time of day;
- proximity to the epicentre;
- the size of the earthquake;
- density of population in the region;
- building technology.

INSET 6

Mercalli scale of earthquake intensity

Mercalli no.	Mercalli name	Characteristics
1	Instrumental	Detected only by seismographs
2	Feeble	Noticed only by some people at rest
3	Slight	Similar to vibrations from a passing truck
4	Moderate	Felt generally indoors; parked cars rock
5	Rather strong	Felt generally; most sleepers wake
6	Strong	Trees sway; furniture moves; some damage
7	Very strong	General alarm; walls crack
8	Destructive	Weak structures damaged; walls fail
9	Ruinous	Some houses collapse as ground cracks
10	Disastrous	Many buildings destroyed; rails bend
11	Very disastrous	Few buildings survive; landslides
12	Catastrophic	Total destruction; ground forms waves

People who live in earthquake zones can do little about the first three factors. An earthquake that strikes at night, when most people are asleep indoors, will cause more death and injury than a daytime quake. It is also clear that the more densely populated a region is, the more people are at risk from earthquakes.

Earthquakes are more damaging in poor countries, which lack the resources (a) to construct earthquake-proof buildings and other structures, and (b) to put in place effective emergency procedures to deal with disasters quickly and effectively.

Building technology is controllable and is a significant influence on the amount of damage, death and injury caused by earthquakes. In poor countries, few buildings are earthquake-proof. Even in rural areas in LEDCs, traditional houses with heavy roofs, timbers and mud walls collapse easily, trapping their occupants. In urban areas, multi-storey flats, often built cheaply and ignoring safety standards, may collapse with very high death tolls.

6.4 Responses to earthquake hazards

Building design

The main response to earthquake hazards is to minimise their impact. Rich countries such as Japan and the USA, which straddle active earthquake zones, may avoid building high-rise structures in areas most at risk. However, in densely populated urban areas such as Tokyo or San Francisco this may not be an option. In these areas, strict building regulations are enforced to ensure that buildings and other structures are earthquake-proof.

Earthquake-proof buildings include designs with:

- steel frames and braces that twist and sway during an earthquake without collapsing;
- foundations mounted on rubber shock absorbers;
- deep foundations into the bedrock;
- first-storey car parks allowing the upper floors to sink and cushioning the impact;
- concrete counter-weights on the top of buildings, which move in the opposite direction to the force of the quake.

Prediction

Research in MEDCs into predicting earthquakes has so far been only partly successful. Predicting the timing and size of earthquakes is much more difficult than predicting their location. In an active earthquake zone, such as the San Andreas fault in California, the longer the interval without an earthquake, the more likely one is to occur and the bigger its magnitude is likely to be. It is possible, with sophisticated instruments, to measure the strain in rocks along fault lines by monitoring small-scale surface changes, ground tilt, radon gas concentrations, changes in the Earth's magnetic field and so on. In spite of these advances, it is still not possible to give early warning of earthquakes with any accuracy.

INSET 7

Tsunamis

Tsunamis are huge waves at sea, usually caused by earthquakes. In the open ocean, a tsunami may be less than a metre high and pass unnoticed. However, as the wave approaches shallow coastal waters, its height increases dramatically. It may reach heights of 15 metres or more, and overwhelm coastal settlements.

Tsunamis travel at speeds of 800 kilometres an hour. Thus early warning of tsunamis in coastal areas near an earthquake epicentre is impossible. However, tsunamis often form thousands of kilometres away on the opposite sides of an ocean. This gives the authorities time to evacuate areas at risk. In May 1960 a tsunami triggered by an earthquake off the coast of Chile struck the town of Hilo in Hawaii. It killed 61 people and caused damage to property of over $20 million. The wave completely destroyed areas of the town fronting the Pacific Ocean. Instead of being rebuilt, the low-lying coastal strip was turned into parks and the survivors were relocated on higher ground. Other responses to tsunamis include:

- warning systems (e.g. sirens);
- increasing public awareness (e.g. publication of maps showing areas susceptible to tsunamis and safety zones, practising evacuation drills in high-risk areas);
- construction of tsunami shelters.

UNIT 2 Rock types and weathering

1 Rocks

The solid outer layer of the Earth – the crust – is made of rocks. Rocks are a mixture of different minerals. Minerals such as quartz, feldspar and olivine have a fixed chemical composition and clearly defined physical properties.

- **Lithology** is the chemical composition of rocks. It also includes properties such as joints, bedding planes and cleavage.
- **Structure** describes the form in which rocks occur (i.e. the folding and tilting of rocks) as a result of tectonic movements.

There are three main groups of rocks: **igneous**, **sedimentary** and **metamorphic**.

2 Igneous rocks

- Igneous rocks form from molten magma that originates deep in the mantle.
- When magma cools and solidifies below the surface, it forms **intrusive** igneous rocks (e.g. granite, gabbro).
- Mineral material erupted at the surface by volcanoes and fissures (lava, ash, pumice, etc.) forms **extrusive** igneous rocks such as basalt and tuff.

The minerals that make up igneous rocks are known as **silicates**. Examples of silicate minerals are quartz, feldspar, olivine, mica and pyroxene. Each type of igneous rock consists of combinations of silicate minerals that form at roughly the same temperature. Thus it is common to find some rocks consisting of quartz, mica and feldspar, and others containing olivine, pyroxene and amphibole.

- Minerals such as quartz and feldspar form at low temperatures and are resistant to weathering.
- Minerals that form at higher temperatures, such as olivine and pyroxene, weather more easily.

2.1 Classification of igneous rocks

We classify igneous rocks according to their mineral composition and their texture.

- **Acidic** igneous rocks such as granite and rhyolite are rich in quartz.
- **Basic** igneous rocks contain little quartz, but are rich in olivine and other minerals.

Most igneous rocks are highly resistant to weathering and erosion. This is because they consist of minerals that grew together in tight interlocking bonds when they cooled.

Texture refers to the size and shape of the crystals in rocks. Rocks with large crystals, like granite and gabbro, cooled very slowly as part of **major intrusions** such as **batholiths**. Igneous rocks like basalt, which cooled rapidly at the surface, have much smaller crystals. Some igneous rocks form minor intrusions such as sills and dykes. These rocks have an intermediate texture. Various igneous rocks are classified in Table 2.1.

	Coarse	Intermediate	Fine
Acid	Granite	Granodiorite	Rhyolite
Basic	Gabbro	Dolerite	Basalt

Table 2.1 Classification of igneous rocks according to chemical composition and texture

2.2 Igneous rocks and relief

Igneous rocks are often more resistant to weathering and erosion than surrounding rocks. As a result, they tend to form prominent relief features. We divide these relief features into two groups: intrusive and extrusive.

Intrusive igneous features: batholiths

Batholiths are large-scale intrusive features. Originally they were huge masses of magma, which cooled very slowly within the Earth's crust. Subsequent erosion stripped away the overlying rocks and exposed a small part of the batholith at the surface. Because batholiths comprise resistant rocks such as granite and gabbro, they form prominent uplands, such as Dartmoor in south-west England and the Cairngorms in north-east Scotland. **Bosses** are similar to batholiths, but on a much smaller scale. Shap, in Cumbria, is a typical granite boss that crops out over an area of just a few square kilometres.

INSET 1

The Cairngorms

The Cairngorm upland, shown in Figure 2.1, is a batholith that forms a broad plateau rising to over 1,200 metres. This is the highest continuous surface in the British Isles. Most of the Cairngorms consist of a tough, coarse-grained granite that was intruded to within 6 kilometres of the surface 400 million years ago. The granite took several million years to solidify. Weathering and erosion removed the overlying rocks and exposed the granite mass at the surface.

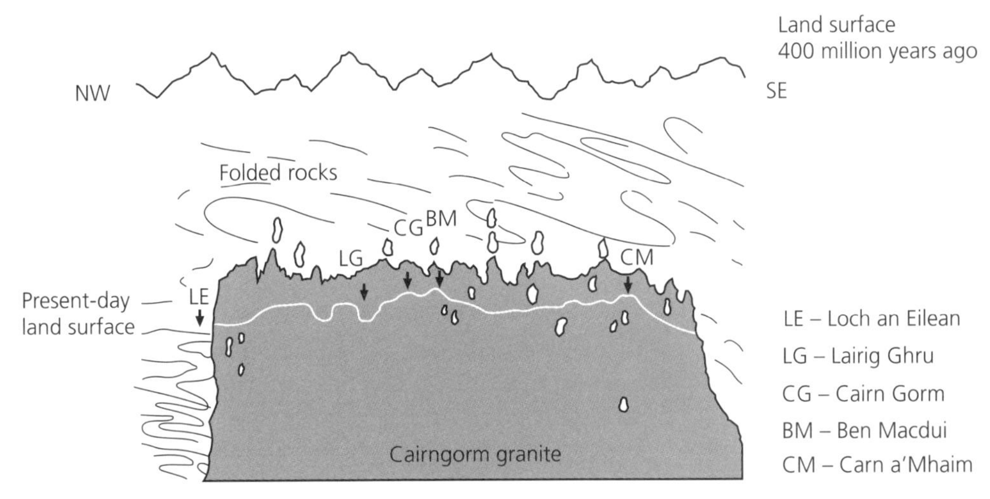

Figure 2.1 Cross-section through the Earth's crust after the emplacement of the Cairngorm granite

Minor igneous intrusions: dykes and sills

Dykes and **sills**, shown in Figure 2.2, are small-scale features that influence relief at a local scale. Dykes are thin sheets of igneous rock at a high angle to the bedding of older rocks, into which they intrude. Because they cut across the bedding, they are also known as **discordant intrusions**. Large numbers of dykes are found in the Inner Hebrides, on the islands of Mull and Skye. They are the result of volcanic activity 60 million years ago, when Greenland split away from Scotland. On Mull, dykes form long, narrow ridges just a few metres high. Some of the dykes extend over long distances. The Cleveland

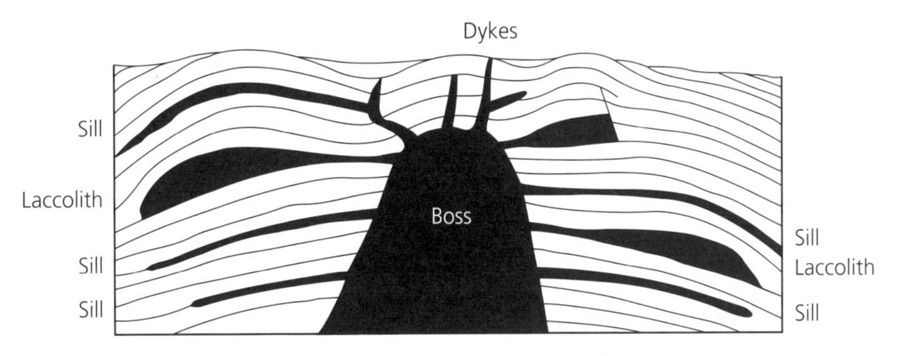

Figure 2.2 Minor igneous intrusions

dyke, for example, runs from Mull to within a few kilometres of the North Sea near Scarborough. Some dykes have a circular form. **Cone sheets** are circular dykes with an inward dip. **Ring dykes** are circular with an outward dip. Both are common on Mull.

Sills are thin, horizontal sheets of magma. Because they follow the bedding of older rocks, they are described as **concordant intrusions**. Where erosion on valley sides has exposed sills, they often form steep cliffs and escarpments.

INSET 2

The Great Whin Sill

The dolerite Great Whin Sill has a strong influence on relief in the northern Pennines. Resistant dolerite was intruded into Carboniferous limestones and sandstones 300 million years ago. Where it crosses the River Tees, the Whin Sill creates a rock step and forms High Force, the highest waterfall in England. Elsewhere in Upper Teesdale, the Whin Sill has altered local rocks by contact metamorphism. Thus limestone has been metamorphosed to form sugar limestone, with the consistency of granulated sugar. At High Cup Nick above the Vale of Eden in Cumbria, the sill crops out on the valley side, forming impressive vertical cliffs. At Housesteads in Northumberland, earth movements have tilted the sill to form a prominent escarpment. Hadrian's Wall follows this scarp for many kilometres. Steep rocky outcrops of the sill along the North Sea coast provide excellent defensive sites for castles such as Bamburgh and Dunstanburgh in Northumberland.

You should remember that the influence of igneous rocks on landscapes varies in scale. Features such as batholiths and lava plateaux have an impact at a regional scale. Sills are widespread, but occur on a smaller scale. Dykes are localised, small- to micro-scale features.

Extrusive igneous features

Lava plateaux are major igneous extrusions. Massive eruptions of lava have occurred in the past, often at constructive plate boundaries or hot spots. Much of Iceland is a lava plateau that has formed in the last 3 million years. Rising to 2,000 metres, the plateau supports one of the largest icefields outside the polar regions. In India the Deccan 'trappes', and in the USA the Snake River Plateau, represent huge outpourings of lava from rising mantle plumes or hot spots. The slopes of lava plateaux have a step-like appearance. This is known as **trap topography** after the Swedish word *trappa*, which means staircase. Each step represents a separate lava flow with its distinctive lithology.

Calderas are large basin-shaped volcanic depressions, more or less circular in shape. They form when a massive eruption empties part of the magma chamber beneath a volcano. As the roof of the magma chamber collapses, the volcano subsides along a series of ring fractures. The Yellowstone caldera in Wyoming is 30 kilometres across. It formed after a massive eruption 650,000 years ago. The Crater Lake caldera in Oregon is shown in Figure 2.3.

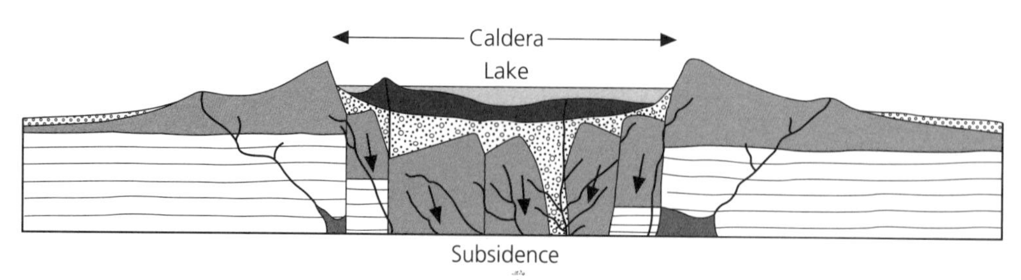

Figure 2.3 Crater Lake caldera, Oregon

Lava flows and **volcanic necks** are small-scale landforms resulting from volcanic eruptions. Runny lavas, such as basalt, may flow many kilometres from fissures and volcanoes, and give rise to low-angled shield volcanoes such as Mauna Loa in Hawaii. Viscous lavas, such as rhyolite, solidify rapidly and produce steep-sided volcanic domes. A volcanic neck is an isolated, vertical plinth of lava that once occupied the vent of an ancient volcano. Erosion has removed the ash and lava that formed the volcanic cone, leaving the resistant neck upstanding. The Devil's Tower in Wyoming is a classic example of a volcanic neck.

3 Sedimentary rocks

In general, sedimentary rocks are less resistant to erosion and weathering than igneous and metamorphic rocks. Many sedimentary rocks consist of weathered particles of sand and mud. The particles may be weakly compressed or weakly cemented together and possess limited internal strength.

Sedimentary rocks form in two ways:

- **Clastic** sedimentary rocks comprise rock particles from pre-existing rocks, broken down by weathering and erosion.
- **Non-clastic** sedimentary rocks form from the accumulation (often on the sea bed) of plant and animal remains (e.g. limestone and coal).

We divide clastic rocks into groups according to the size of particles from which they are made:

- **Rudaceous** rocks consist of very large clasts in a matrix of finer sediments. When the large clasts are angular, the rock is a **breccia**. Where rounded pebbles are cemented into a fine matrix, we call the rock **conglomerate**.
- **Arenaceous** rocks are made from sand-sized particles. Examples include **sandstones** and **gritstones**.
- **Argillaceous** rocks comprise fine, clay-sized particles. **Shale** is an argillaceous rock.

Non-clastic rocks comprise two groups:

- **Calcareous** rocks are various **limestones**, including **chalk**. These rocks derive from the lime-rich shells and skeletons of tiny marine creatures, such as corals and molluscs.
- **Carbonaceous** rocks form from carbon-rich plant remains, and include **coal**, **lignite** and **oil shale**.

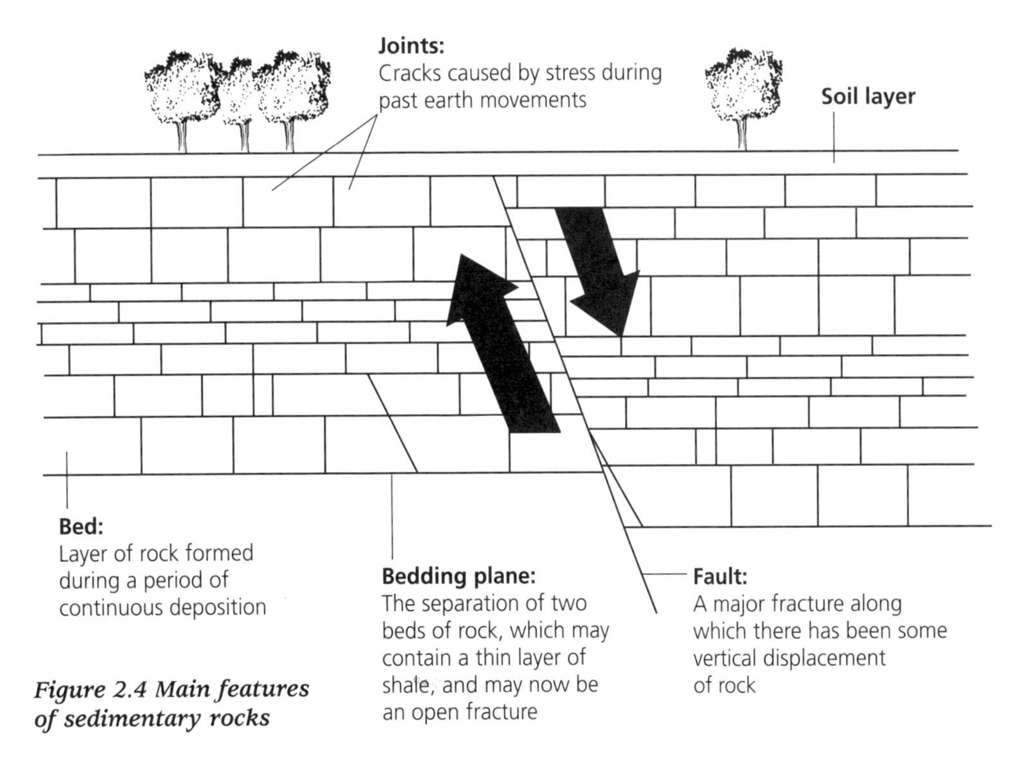

Figure 2.4 Main features of sedimentary rocks

Most sedimentary rocks form in seas and oceans. The rock-forming materials settle on the sea bed in horizontal layers or **strata**, as shown in Figure 2.4. Each stratum represents a particular environment in which the sediments accumulated. The boundaries separating strata are **bedding planes**. Subsequent earth movements may cause the strata to fracture and form **joints**. In some circumstances, sediments were deposited in fast-moving streams and deltas. These sediments show distinctive **cross-bedding**. Not all sedimentary rocks formed in the sea. Some developed as sand dunes and show **dune-bedding**. Others, such as breccia, formed as screes; and conglomerates were originally pebbles on ancient beaches.

4 Metamorphic rocks

Metamorphic rocks have been altered by heat and/or pressure. Often these alterations are so drastic that metamorphic rocks are very different (in terms of minerals and texture) from the original rocks. Many metamorphic rocks are extremely old, and very resistant to erosion and weathering.

Original rock	Metamorphic rock
Sandstone	Quartzite
Shale	Slate
Limestone	Marble
Granite	Gneiss

Table 2.2 Metamorphic rocks

- Rocks in contact with a large igneous intrusion such as a batholith may be altered by heat. Such **contact metamorphism** often produces a rock known as hornfels.
- **Regional metamorphism** affects much larger areas. Heat and pressure may alter great thicknesses of rock. Gneiss and schist are metamorphic rocks associated with regional metamorphism.

Metamorphic rocks subjected to great pressures often develop cleavage planes. Cleavage planes are typical of slate and allow the rock to be split into thin sections and used as roofing material. Other metamorphic rocks affected by high temperature show signs of foliation. Foliated rocks, such as schist, consist of very thin layers of minerals such as mica.

5 Weathering

Do not confuse weathering and erosion. Weathering is the breakdown of rocks by changes in temperature and moisture conditions. Erosion is the wearing away and transport of rock particles and minerals by rivers, glaciers, waves and winds.

Weathering is the *in situ* breakdown of rocks at or near the Earth's surface by chemical, physical and biological processes. Once the rocks have been broken down, the agents of erosion transport the weathered materials to new locations. The type of weathering and its effectiveness depend on lithology and climate.

5.1 Products of weathering

Rock breakdown by weathering produces rock particles and minerals that vary from fine clays to boulders. In the humid tropics, the breakdown of silicate minerals such as feldspar often produces large quantities of clay. Meanwhile, intense chemical weathering below the surface attacks the corners and edges of rocks to form rounded boulders or **corestones**. This is an example of **spheroidal weathering**.

Granular disintegration describes weathered rock particles just a few millimetres in diameter. This is a typical product of weathered sandstone, when weathering has destroyed the cements that normally bind the sand particles together. When rocks break down into boulders, we refer to this as **block disintegration**. Such rocks usually have massive, widely spaced joints.

The weathered rock particles and mineral materials (including soil) form a surface layer of debris known as **regolith**.

Physical weathering merely causes the mechanical breakdown of rocks into smaller particles – there is no chemical alteration. Physical weathering increases the surface area of exposed rock and thus encourages further weathering.

5.2 Physical weathering

Physical or mechanical weathering breaks rocks into smaller particles. During this process, the rocks and their minerals undergo no chemical alteration. The major physical weathering processes are: pressure release or dilatation; insolation weathering; salt weathering; and freeze–thaw.

Pressure release or dilatation

Pressure release breaks up rocks without the intervention of the weather. When prolonged erosion exposes rocks that have been formed at depth, they expand and crack. This expansion occurs parallel to the surface to form **sheet jointing** and **pseudo-bedding planes**. These lines of weakness are easily exploited by weathering.

Pressure release caused by unloading (especially in granite) may produce smooth rounded **exfoliation domes** or **bornhardts**. The outer layers of granite peel away in a process known as **sheeting**. Classic examples of granite exfoliation domes occur in Yosemite, in the Sierra Nevada of California.

You should appreciate that at the global scale the importance of types of physical weathering varies with climate. Thus insolation and salt weathering predominate in hot, dry climates. Freeze–thaw is important in high latitude and high altitude climates.

Insolation weathering

In tropical and sub-tropical climates, surface temperatures in excess of 90 °C have been recorded in summer. Such temperature changes lead to the thermal expansion and contraction of rock minerals. At one time it was thought that such temperature fluctuations could cause rocks to disintegrate. Experiments have since disproved this. Rock breakdown through insolation weathering does take place, but only when moisture (from rain and dew) is present. Insolation weathering often leads to **exfoliation**. This is when thin outer layers of rock peel away to produce smooth, rounded surfaces. Other weathering processes, such as hydration and oxidation, also cause exfoliation.

Salt weathering

Salt weathering is most common in arid and semi-arid environments. In these dryland areas, intermittent streams and rivers transport heavy loads of mineral salts in solution. This run-off often drains to inland basins, where high temperatures and high evaporation rates lead to the formation of salt pans and dry lake beds. The salt is widely dispersed by winds. When it rains, solutions of salt seep into porous rocks. Here the salts precipitate, forming salt crystals. Crystal growth sets up stresses inside the rocks (rather like frost shattering) and causes rock distintegration.

Freeze–thaw weathering

When water freezes, its volume increases by nearly 10%. If freezing occurs in confined spaces, such as joints and rock crevices, the ice exerts enormous pressure on the surrounding rock. The forces involved are sufficient to break apart even the most resistant rocks. This is **frost wedging**.

The main influence on rates of frost wedging is the number of freeze–thaw cycles. Other factors include the presence of water and rock type.

- Ideal climatic conditions for frost wedging are where temperatures fluctuate above and below freezing. We call these temperature changes **freeze–thaw cycles**. Such cycles were most frequent in the British Isles in the cold, periglacial period that followed the last Ice Age. In the British Isles today, severe freeze–thaw weathering is only important in the mountains above 1,000 metres.
- Rocks disintegrate more rapidly by freeze–thaw action where plenty of moisture is available. For this reason, dry tundra areas and cold deserts may experience less freeze–thaw weathering than warmer, more humid environments.

INSET 3

Freeze–thaw weathering

Frost shattering and frost wedging are different processes. Frost shattering occurs when porous rocks absorb water, which freezes and breaks the rock apart. Frost wedging generates forces that have the potential to break up even the hardest rocks. Ice exerts a maximum pressure of around 2,000 kg/cm^2 at –22 °C. Granite, one of the toughest rocks, has a maximum tensile strength of just 70 kg/cm^2. However, most frost wedging occurs in areas of rock weakness (i.e. joints) at pressures well below the theoretical maximum.

- Rocks vary in their susceptibility to freeze–thaw weathering. Tough gritstones and granites are more resistant than soft shales or porous chalk. Jointing is also important. In the mountains of Wester Ross, densely jointed Cambrian quartzite breaks up more rapidly than the more massively jointed Torridonian sandstone.

5.3 Landforms of frost weathering

Talus slopes

Most talus slopes in the British Isles are currently inactive. The evidence for this includes:

- vegetation-covered talus slopes;
- few scree particles with unweathered surfaces, which suggest little recent rockfall.

Coarse, angular rock particles, which accumulate on valley sides below vertical cliffs (free-faces), form **talus** slopes or **screes**. Screes are widespread in Britain's uplands. Most, however, appear to be fossil landforms, no longer forming at the present day.

Screes are best developed on well-jointed rocks such as Carboniferous limestone and basalt.

- Water collects in the joints on the exposed free-face.
- Freezing causes frost wedging, which levers rock particles from the free-face.
- The particles fall and accumulate as a debris slope beneath the free-face. Typically, talus slopes have gradients between 30 and 40 degrees.

Many talus slopes show evidence of sorting by particle size, with larger particles increasing in frequency downslope. Two factors explain this:

- Large particles have more momentum than smaller ones, and therefore roll further down the slope.
- Larger particles are less likely to by trapped in the voids between the scree on the talus slope.

Statham proposed a simple model, shown in Figure 2.5, to explain the sorting of particles on talus slopes.

- In the early stages of development the free-face is high, and all particles have sufficient energy to reach the foot of the slope. This means that sorting is poor.
- In the final stages, where the free-face is almost submerged by talus, particles have insufficient energy to roll far. Again sorting is poor.
- In the middle stage, sorting is most likely. A free-face of moderate size allows large particles to reach the bottom of the slope, but small particles, with little momentum, roll only short distances from the free face.

Blockfields

On level plateau surfaces at high altitude, frost wedging breaks massive jointed rocks into large, angular boulders. This is an example of block disintegration. Without gravity, mass movement of the blocks cannot occur. Thus they remain *in situ* and form a sea of boulders or a **blockfield** (also known as felsenmeer). One of the best examples in the British Isles is the summit plateau of the Glyders in North Wales.

5.4 Chemical weathering

Chemical weathering breaks down rocks into their chemical consitituents, or alters the chemical and mineral composition of rocks.

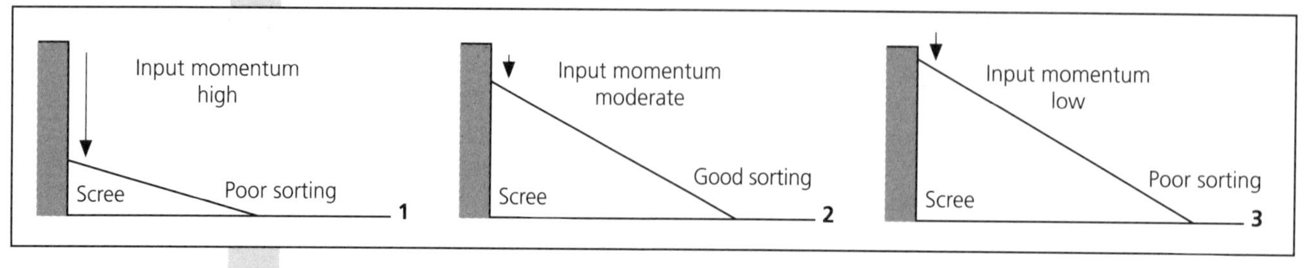

Figure 2.5 Statham's model of scree slope development

- Most chemical weathering processes involve water.
- Temperature controls chemical weathering: rates of chemical reaction double for every 10 °C rise in temperature.

Chemical weathering is most rapid in humid tropical environments. Here, temperatures are high throughout the year. Also the moisture needed for most chemical weathering processes is available in abundance. Rates of chemical weathering are slow in tropical arid and semi-arid environments, where the supply of moisture is limited. Chemical weathering has little effect in cold climates, because low temperatures slow chemical reactions, and water is frozen for most of the year.

Chemical weathering is generally more important than physical weathering, because chemical weathering can occur wherever water is present. In contrast, physical weathering usually requires very specific temperature conditions.

The four main types of chemical weathering are: solution; oxidation; hydrolysis; and hydration.

Solution

Rainwater, containing CO_2 from the atmosphere and the soil, is a weak carbonic acid, which attacks and dissolves rocks such as limestone. This is the process of **carbonation**.

$$\underset{\text{Calcium carbonate}}{CaCO_3} + \underset{\text{Carbonic acid}}{H_2CO_3} \rightarrow \underset{\text{Calcium bicarbonate}}{Ca(HCO_3)_2}$$

Carbonic acid combines with calcium carbonate to form calcium bicarbonate, which is soluble in water. The process of carbonation is reversible. Precipitation of calcite (a deposit also known as dripstone or tufa) happens in water saturated with $CaCO_3$.

Oxidation

Oxidation occurs when minerals combine with oxygen. The process usually involves water in which oxygen is dissolved. Minerals may also take up oxygen directly from the air. Iron minerals are especially prone to oxidation. Oxidation destroys the structure of original minerals, weakening rocks and causing breakdown. It often attacks the iron-rich cements that bind sand grains together in sandstones.

Hydrolysis

Hydrolysis is a chemical reaction between rock minerals and water. Rock minerals known as silicates combine with water (rather than simply dissolving). The process is particularly active in the weathering of feldspar in granite. Secondary minerals or clays, such as kaolinite, illite and montmorillonite, are the products of the hydrolysis of silicates such as feldspar.

Hydration

Water molecules added to minerals form new minerals. For example, water added to anhydrite forms gypsum. The effect of hydration is to increase the volume of minerals. This sets up physical stresses in the rock. Hydration commonly causes surface flaking in rocks.

5.5 Landforms of chemical weathering: karst scenery

The solution of Carboniferous limestone gives rise to unique landscapes known as **karst**. In the British Isles the most spectacular karst scenery is found in the Yorkshire Dales and in The Burren in western Ireland.

Surface water is scarce in limestone areas. Rainwater quickly disappears underground through limestone's many joints.

Exposed rock surfaces and steep slopes are typical karst features. There are three reasons for this. First, limestone has only a thin mantle of soil. Owing to limestone's solubility, mineral material is washed away in solution rather than contributing to soil formation. Second, the lack of surface water means that normal slope processes (e.g. surface wash,

landslides, slumping) which lower slope angles are largely absent. And third, limestone has great mechanical strength and can support cliffs and other steep slopes.

Classic karst landforms include: caves, caverns and swallets; speleothems; dolines; limestone pavements; and dry valleys.

Caves, caverns and swallets

Because limestone is permeable, most drainage is underground. Solution of bedding planes and joints by underground streams forms **caves** and **caverns**. Caves that are roughly tube-like and circular in cross-section are called **phreatic caves**. They have formed below the water table; filled with water, solution is equal in all parts of the cave. **Vadose caves** are found above the water table. They are only partly filled with water and are therefore more incised and less regular in cross-section. **Swallets** (or swallow holes) are found where impermeable rocks crop out alongside limestone. Surface streams developed on impermeable rocks disappear down enlarged joints or swallets when they flow on to the limestone.

Speleothems

Speleothems, such as **stalactites** and **stalagmites**, form in caves and caverns. Stalactites are vertically hanging fingers of calcite on cave ceilings. Stalagmites are upward-growing deposits of calcite on cave floors. CO_2 diffuses into the atmosphere from water droplets in caves, saturating the water with calcium carbonate and precipitating tiny amounts of calcite. Over thousands of years these deposits may produce stalactites half a metre or more in length.

Dolines

Dolines are enclosed surface depressions and can form in three different ways:

- by collapse of an underground cave or cavern, forming a relatively narrow, steep-sided depression;
- by solution of a master joint, producing a funnel-shaped depression;
- by subsidence, where overlying clay and peat slump into a joint widened by solution.

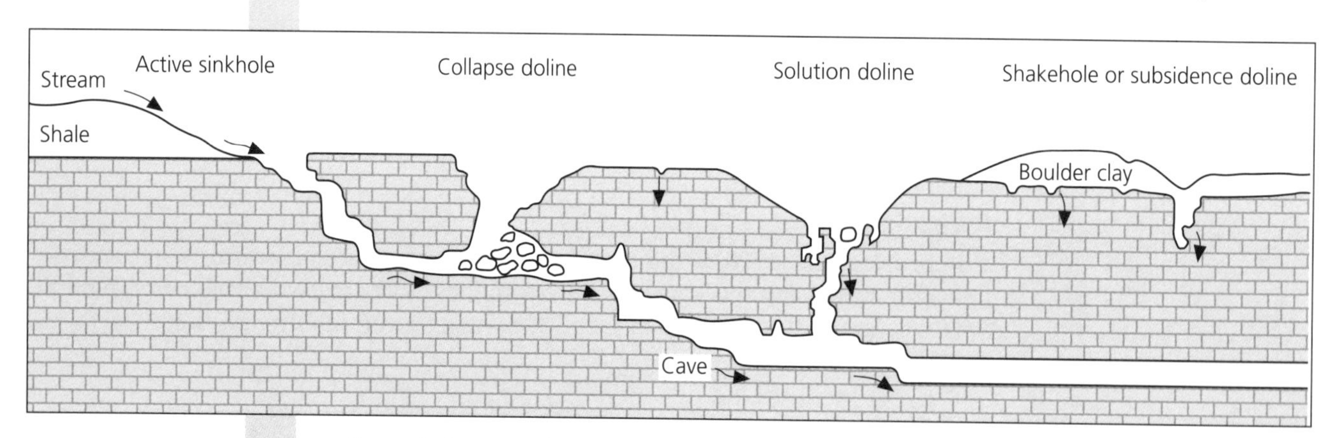

Figure 2.6 Types of doline

Limestone pavements

Limestone pavements are found in karst areas that have been glaciated (e.g. the Yorkshire Dales and The Burren). Ice sheets and glaciers scoured the limestone, leaving large areas of abraded rock when the ice retreated. For the last 10,000 years, solution has modified these limestone surfaces. Joints have been enlarged to form **grikes**. Between the grikes, rectangular blocks of limestone are known as **clints**. Often the surface of the clints is criss-crossed with **karren** (i.e. solution grooves, channels and flutings). Solution has been most rapid where pavements have had a cover of glacial moraine or soil.

Dry valleys

Dry valleys were eroded by streams and rivers that flowed on the limestone surface in the past. This happened in cold periglacial periods, when the ground, although not covered by ice, was permanently frozen. Dry valleys have evolved in two stages.

- During the brief arctic summers, snow and ice would melt. Meltwater streams and rivers flowed across the frozen surface and cut the dry valleys we see today.
- As the climate warmed, and the permafrost thawed, the surface streams disappeared underground, dewatering the valleys.

INSET 4

Tropical karst

In some humid tropical and sub-tropical climates (e.g. eastern China), tower-like hills or **mogotes** dominate limestone landscapes. Up to 100 metres high, these isolated towers are separated by flat, alluvial valley floors. It is thought that tower karst forms when acid water in alluvial valleys undercuts rock faces, causing lateral planation. Tower karst could represent the final stages in karst landscape development, the mogotes being all that is left of a once continuous limestone cover.

Elsewhere in the humid tropics (e.g. Jamaica), another type of karst landscape – **cockpit karst** – is found. Intersecting star-shaped dolines form enclosed depressions or cockpits. Rounded cone-shaped hills or **kegel** separate the depressions. Cockpit karst probably develops when rapid carbonation (caused by high temperatures, high rainfall and rainforest vegetation) produces a dense pattern of solution dolines.

5.6 Landforms of chemical weathering: tors, bornhardts and castle kopjes

Tors

Tors are small rock outcrops often found on exposed hill tops and valley sides. They are formed by a combination of physical and chemical weathering processes, and they have prominent vertical and horizontal joints. The most famous tors in the British Isles result from the weathering of granite (e.g. on Dartmoor and in the Cairngorms). Granite tors are part of larger masses of intruded granite known as batholiths. One explanation for the formation of tors is given in Inset 5 and illustrated in Figure 2.7(a).

INSET 5

The formation of tors

- As the granite cooled and contracted, vertical joints formed. Over millions of years, the removal of overlying rocks by erosion caused expansion of the granite by pressure release. This produced horizontal joints or **pseudo-bedding planes**.
- Water penetrated the vertical joints; hydrolysis rotted the feldspar, forming the clay mineral kaolinite and causing the granite to disintegrate. This weathering occurred deep below the surface.
- Owing to the uneven joint pattern in granite, intense chemical weathering occurred where the joints were densest. Erosion then removed the areas of rotted granite (or saprolite). Where the joints were widely spaced, weathering was less effective. These areas of coherent granite survived to form the tors we see today.
- During colder climatic phases, frost wedging along joints levered angular blocks of granite from the tors. These accumulated at the base of the tors, forming clitter.

Bornhardts and castle kopjes

Other isolated rock outcrops caused by weathering are **bornhardts** and **castle kopjes**. Bornhardts are found in tropical climates (e.g. Namibia, southern Nigeria), where massively jointed granite undergoes deep, sub-surface chemical weathering. On removal of the rotted granite, smooth, dome-shaped rocks rise abruptly from level surfaces, as shown in Figure 2.7(b). Castle kopjes are smaller-scale rock outcrops, with closer jointing, but largely submerged by weathered materials.

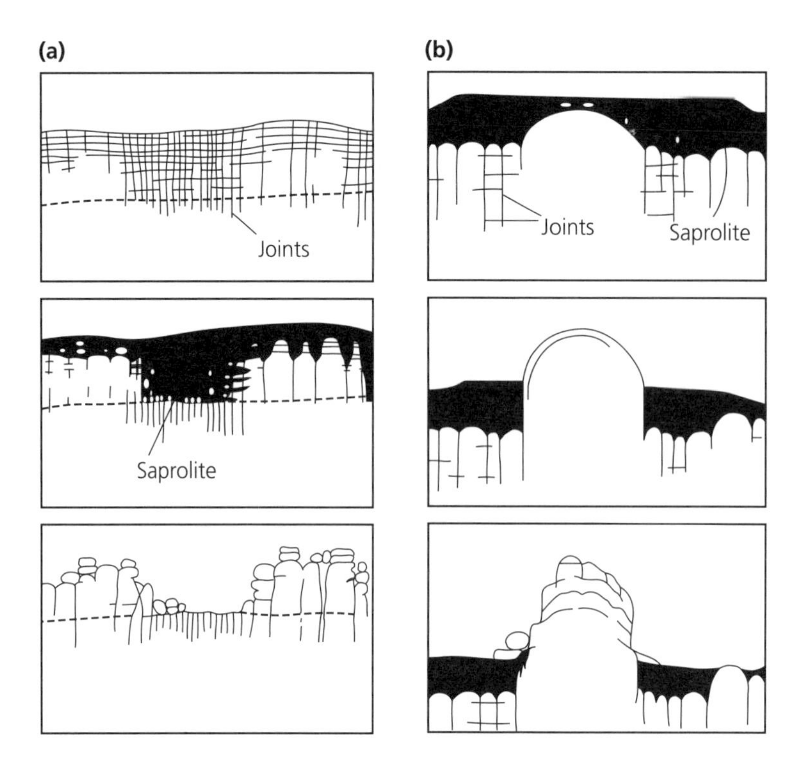

Figure 2.7 Formation of (a) tors and (b) bornhardts

The importance of weathering is that it breaks down and weakens rocks at or near the Earth's surface. The subsequent erosion of weathered surfaces, and the transport of weathered material and its deposition elsewhere, give rise to many varied landscapes.

5.7 Biological weathering

Plants and animals play a key part in weathering. This **biological weathering** includes both physical and chemical processes.

- Physical processes include animals burrowing and tree root penetration. Animals may break up rock fragments by burrowing, and cause weathering by exposing fresh material to the atmosphere. More important are tree roots penetrating rock joints. As they grow and thicken, they prise rocks apart, causing block disintegration. Also when trees topple over, they exert leverage which brings to the surface large masses of rock and soil.
- Dead organic material (particularly leaf litter) mixes with rainwater to form humic acids. These acids attack some rock minerals in a process called **chelation**. Where there is a dense vegetation cover (e.g. tropical rainforest), chelation is likely to be an important process and will contribute to rapid rates of weathering. Biological weathering even occurs in hot deserts. Desert varnish, a shiny film of iron and manganese oxides on rocks, is produced by the weathering activity of blue-green algae.

Small-scale weathering features

Chemical and biological weathering gives rise to a variety of small rock hollows. Most are known as **weathering pits**. Weathering pits are common on granite and sandstone. An initial depression on a rock surface collects rainwater. Within the water-filled hollow, processes such as hydrolysis and solution take place. Meanwhile, algae, lichen and moss may accelerate weathering through chelation. In hot deserts, holes just a few centimetres in diameter often develop on inclined rock surfaces. Salt weathering is the most likely cause of these **tafoni**. Rocks in coastal areas often show **honeycomb weathering**, which may also be due to salt weathering from sea spray.

6 Geological structure

Geological structure describes the 'primary' form of rocks resulting from tectonic movements such as faulting and folding, volcanic activity and sedimentation. Geological structure determines the initial form of the landscape. Over time, processes such as weathering and erosion reduce this structural control. Even so, geological structure, particularly at the large scale, leaves a strong imprint on most landscapes.

Four geological structures give rise to distinctive landscapes and landforms: horizontal structures; faulted structures; folding structures; and tilted structures.

6.1 Horizontal structures

Horizontal structures produce simple landforms which reflect the interaction of rock types and erosive processes. Complicating tectonic forces (e.g. folding and faulting) are largely absent.

Horizontal structures are found where:

- level sedimentary strata remain *in situ*;
- volcanic eruptions have produced successive lava flows.

The occurrence of horizontal rock layers in an area indicates great stability in the Earth's crust. Over long periods of time, tectonic movements such as folding and tilting have been minimal. Horizontal strata give rise to distinctive landforms such as structural plateaux, stepped topography, mesas and buttes.

Structural plateaux

A **structural plateau**, shown in Figure 2.8, is an extensive upland with a level surface, bounded by steep slopes. The level surface is formed by horizontally bedded rocks. Often the uppermost stratum is a layer of resistant caprock, which protects the weaker underlying rocks from erosion. Kinder Scout in the Peak District is an example of a structural plateau. Here, resistant millstone grit forms a caprock. Where deep valleys such as Edale dissect the plateau, the millstone grit forms steep edges. Lava plateaux (see p. 18), such as the Antrim Plateau in Northern Ireland, have a similar appearance to structural plateaux. They consist of horizontal layers of lava and ash of variable resistance to weathering and erosion.

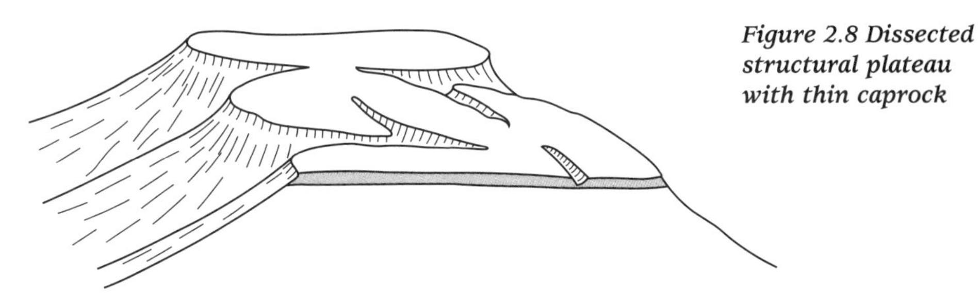

Figure 2.8 Dissected structural plateau with thin caprock

Stepped topography

Often horizontal strata comprise alternate layers of resistant and less resistant rock. Differential weathering and erosion produce distinctive benches that give a step-like appearance to the landscape, as shown in Figure 2.9. In the central Pennines, the Yoredale series of rocks are responsible for the striking profiles of hills such as Ingleborough and Penyghent. A similar type of stepped landscape known as 'trap' scenery (see p. 18) is found along the edges of lava plateaux.

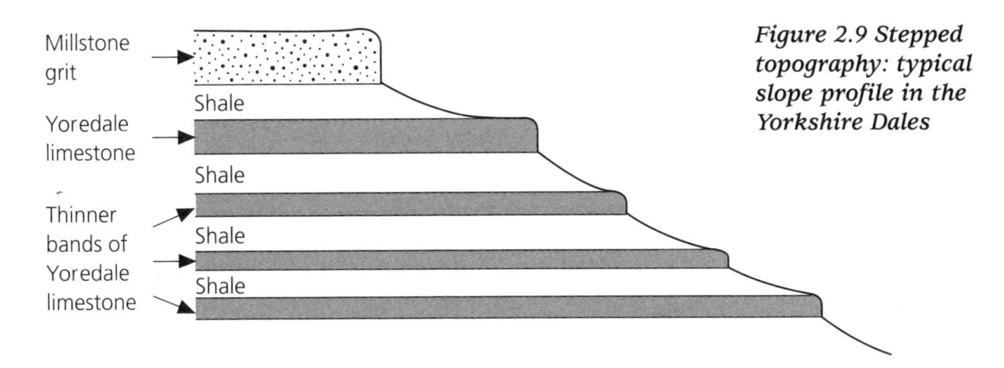

Figure 2.9 Stepped topography: typical slope profile in the Yorkshire Dales

Mesas and buttes

The parallel retreat of slopes around the edges of plateaux may ultimately produce isolated flat-topped hills known as **mesas** and **buttes**. The Colorado Plateau in the south-west USA has many striking examples of mesas and buttes, especially those carved in red sandstone in Monument Valley. In central Sweden, mesas such as Mosseberg and Kinnekulle, protected by a resistant dolerite sill, are dominant relief features. Erosion of lava plateaux can also form flat-topped residual hills such as Macleod's Tables on Skye.

6.2 Faulted structures

Faults are fractures in rocks along which movements have occurred. The **fault plane** is the surface of dislocation and usually has a steep incline or dip.

Landform	Origin	Examples
Fault scarps	Normal and reverse faults often create a 'step' in the landscape. The resulting landform is a fault scarp.	
Fault-line scarps	Scarps coincide with fault lines only if they are geologically very recent. More often the scarp has retreated (by weathering and erosion) from the line of the fault. This is a fault-line scarp.	Malham Cove on the Mid-Craven fault in North Yorkshire; the North Pennine fault above the Vale of Eden in Cumbria
Block mountains and graben	Downfaulted blocks between pairs of parallel normal faults create basins or graben. Upfaulted blocks between pairs of parallel reversed faults produce uplands known as block mountains or horsts.	Basin range topography in Nevada and southern California
Rift valleys	Valleys formed between parallel pairs of normal faults, often where the Earth's crust is stretched at constructive plate boundaries.	East African Rift Valley; Thingvellir Valley in Iceland
Fault-guided valleys	Along strike-slip or tear faults, numerous fault planes often shatter the rocks. These easily eroded rocks may be responsible for the formation of fault-guided valleys.	The Great Glen between Inverness and Fort William in Scotland

Table 2.3 Faulting and landforms

Faults result from either tensional or compressional forces in the Earth's crust. As Figure 2.10 shows, movements along faults may be vertical or lateral. A **normal fault** occurs

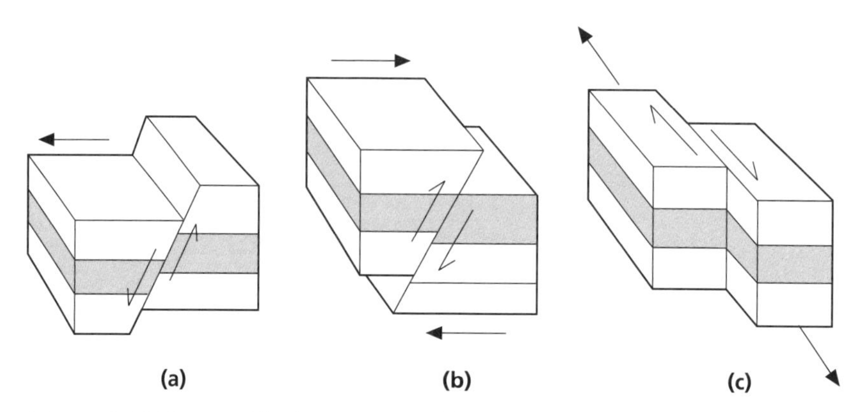

Figure 2.10 Types of fault: (a) normal fault, (b) reverse fault and (c) strike-slip or tear fault

when tension causes a block of strata to slip down. The opposite, when compression lifts up a block of strata, is a **reverse fault**. Lateral movement along a fault plane produces a **strike-slip** or **tear fault**. Where the angle of dip of a fault is very low, the term **thrust fault** is often applied. A thrust fault is a type of reverse fault caused by compression. In north-west Scotland, the Moine Thrust has pushed huge slabs of crust westwards, burying much older Pre-Cambrian and Cambrian rocks.

6.3 Folded structures

The slow application of pressure in the Earth's crust often causes layered rocks to bend rather than fracture. The result is folding. Each **fold** has an **axis**, which is the hinge line where the sides of the fold change their dip. The sides of the fold are called **limbs**. The simplest types of fold are shown in Figure 2.11.

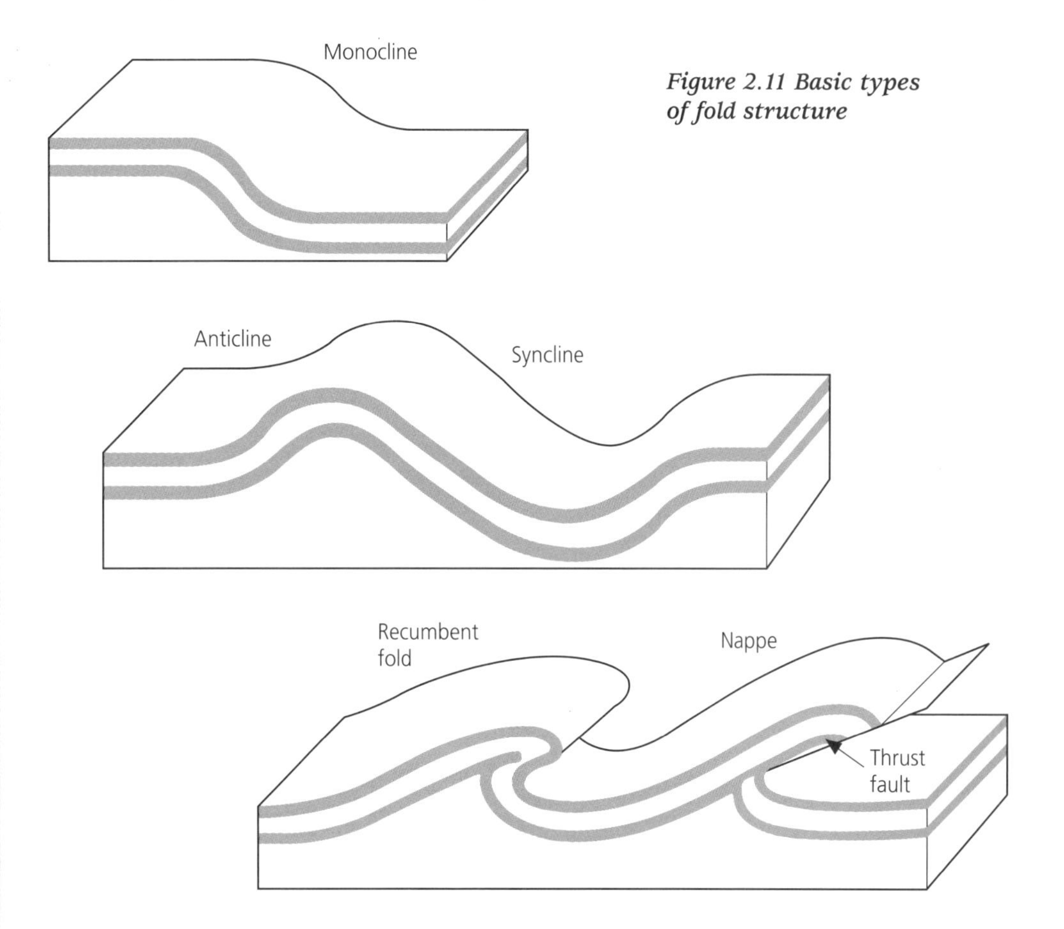

Figure 2.11 Basic types of fold structure

- **Anticlines** (upfolds) and **synclines** (downfolds) are folds that are symmetrical around their axes.
- The stripping of younger strata from an anticline produces an **eroded anticline** (or eroded dome). The Weald is an example of an eroded dome with inward-facing escarpments, and with the rocks increasing in age towards the centre. Most anticlines and domes at a regional scale have experienced significant erosion.
- The axis of an anticline is a point of weakness. Stretching of the strata at this point may lead to joint widening and the formation of an **anticlinal valley** (e.g. the Esk Valley in the North Yorkshire Moors).
- When lateral pressure increases, more complex folds develop. In a **recumbent fold**, the strata are overturned with both limbs of the fold nearly horizontal. Horizontal compression may lead to the shearing of the upper part of the fold along a thrust fault. The strata moved forward over the thrust fault is called a **nappe**. Complex folds of this type are found in intensely folded mountains such as the Alps.

The character of tilted blocks depends on their angle of dip. The gentlest dip produces escarpments. Cuesta ridges form with a more steeply inclined block. A hog's back is formed when the dip is so steep that the scarp and dip slope are at the same angle.

6.4 Tilted structures

Tilted structures develop when gentle earth movements give strata of varying resistance a low-angled regional dip. Tilted blocks are found on the margins of major fold structures, and may form the limbs of large-scale anticlines and synclines.

The effect of tilting is to expose rocks of varying resistance to erosion. Differential erosion reduces weaker rocks such as clay to areas of low relief or **vales**. Harder or more permeable rocks such as chalk and limestone resist erosion to form gently dipping uplands known as **escarpments** or **cuestas**. Escarpments have a steep scarp slope (up to 30 degrees) and a long, low-angled dip slope. A belt of scarp and vale country stretches all the way from Dorset to the north-east coast of Yorkshire, dominating the landscape of eastern and southern England. It includes uplands, such as the Cotswolds and Lincoln Edge, and broad vales, such as the Vale of Oxford and Vale of Belvoir.

1 The global hydrological cycle

Within the narrow range of temperature found on the Earth's surface and within the atmosphere, water exists in its three phases – as a liquid, solid (ice) and gas (vapour). Figure 3.1 shows the phase changes of water. **Evaporation** and **condensation** are probably the two most important phase changes. Both are crucial in the formation of clouds and the hydrological cycle.

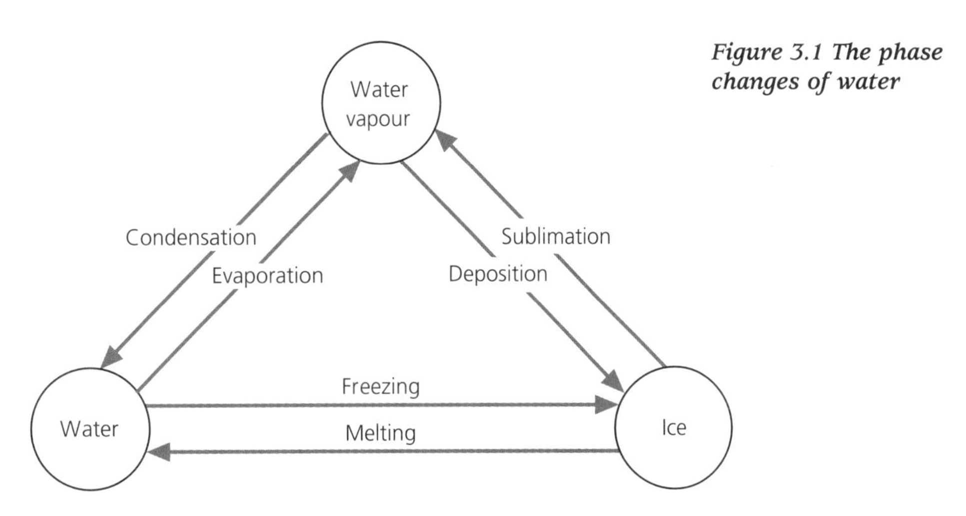

Figure 3.1 The phase changes of water

- Water circulates continually between the Earth's surface and the atmosphere. This is known as the global hydrological cycle and is shown in Figure 3.2.
- The hydrological cycle comprises two components: reservoirs and flows.
- Reservoirs vary in size and in the length of time they store water. The oceans are the largest reservoirs (Table 3.1). They hold 97% of all water on the planet. The remaining 3% is fresh water. Ice sheets and glaciers account for most of the world's fresh water (around 80%). They can store water for thousands of years. During glacials (ice ages), ice sheets and glaciers expand, removing water from the oceans. The result is a worldwide fall in sea level by up to 140 metres. In warmer periods (interglacials), melting causes a similar rise in sea level.
- The amount of water stored in rivers, lakes, permeable rocks, soil, living organisms (biota) and the atmosphere is relatively small. Indeed, the amount of water vapour in the atmosphere is sufficient for just 14 days' rainfall.

Note the balance between precipitation and evaporation at the global scale. However, precipitation and evaporation do not balance for the oceans and land. The relief of the land and the greater extent of the oceans account for this.

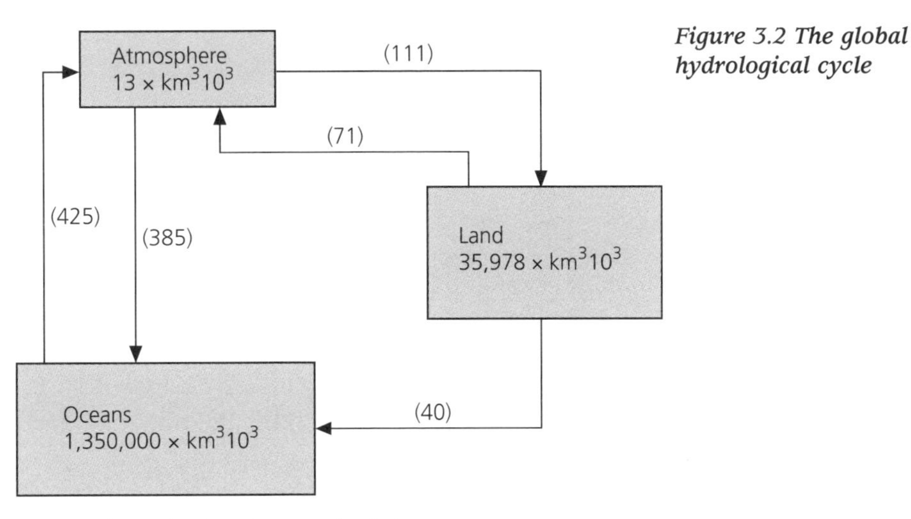

Figure 3.2 The global hydrological cycle

Note: Numbers in brackets denote km^3 10^3 of water.

Reservoir	km³ × 10³	% total
Oceans	1,350,000	97.4
Atmosphere	13	0.0009
Land	35,978	2.596
Rivers	1.7	0.0001
Lakes	100	0.007
Inland seas	105	0.008
Soil water	70	0.005
Groundwater	8,200	0.592
Ice sheets	27,500	1.984
Biota	1.1	0.0001

Table 3.1 Global water reservoirs

2 Precipitation

Precipitation is moisture that falls from clouds. As part of the hydrological cycle, precipitation is the principal input of moisture from the atmosphere to the Earth's surface. The most common types of precipitation are rain, drizzle, snow, sleet and hail (see p. 94).

2.1 Precipitation mechanisms

Precipitation takes place when water vapour cools to its **dew-point temperature** (see Inset 1) and forms tiny droplets of water or particles of ice within clouds. Cooling occurs when air:

- rises through the atmosphere;
- comes into contact with a relatively cool land or sea surface;
- mixes with cold air.

The British Isles experience all three types of precipitation. Cyclonic precipitation is most important, but convectional precipitation makes July and August the wettest months in eastern England. Orographic precipitation dominates in western uplands.

Uplift is the main cause of cooling. Thus we recognise three types of precipitation based on the vertical movement of air: cyclonic, convectional and orographic.

- **Cyclonic precipitation** occurs along **frontal zones** in mid-latitude depressions. Fronts are boundaries where warm and cold **air masses** meet. The lighter, warmer air rises above the colder air, cooling to form extensive cloud and prolonged precipitation (see p. 99).
- **Convectional precipitation** occurs when air in contact with the Earth's surface is warmed. As a result, it becomes less dense than the surrounding air and rises through the atmosphere. We call such a column of rising, warm air a convection current or **thermal**. Eventually, the rising air reaches its dew-point temperature and condenses to form clouds and precipitation. Precipitation is usually in the form of showers or thunderstorms.
- **Orographic precipitation** is a feature of upland areas. Mechanical uplift occurs when an air mass approaches a hilly or mountainous region. The resultant cooling produces cloud and precipitation. Precipitation is usually higher on **windward** than on **leeward** slopes. There is often a **rain shadow** (an area of below average rainfall) on leeward slopes.

INSET 1

Cloud formation and precipitation

Clouds form when water vapour cools to its dew-point temperature. Dew-point is the critical temperature when air becomes saturated, i.e. it has reached 100% humidity and cannot hold any more water vapour (see p. 91, Inset 2). As a result, condensation occurs: the excess water vapour changes to droplets of liquid water (or particles of ice) and clouds form. The dew-point temperature is not constant: it varies from day to day. This is because warm air can hold more vapour than cold air. The water droplets that form clouds are much smaller than rain droplets. Rain (and other types of precipitation) results from a complex process by which water droplets and ice particles grow inside clouds (see p. 95, Inset 5).

Consider the effects of precipitation type, intensity, duration, amount and seasonal distribution on stream and river flow. High-intensity events are likely to result in low rates of **interception** by vegetation, low rates of **infiltration** into the soil, and rapid **overland flow** into streams and rivers.

2.2 Characteristics of precipitation

Precipitation has a number of characteristics that influence the hydrological cycle. These include its: type; intensity; duration; amount; and seasonal distribution.

- When rain reaches the ground, it quickly flows into streams and rivers. Snow, which is the main type of precipitation in high latitudes, may remain on the ground for long periods before melting. Hail is a special case: although solid, it falls at temperatures above freezing, and melts rapidly.
- Precipitation intensity is a measure of the amount of precipitation falling in a given unit of time. Showers and thunderstorms have high intensities (e.g. 10–15 mm an hour).
- Precipitation duration describes the length of time a precipitation event lasts. Cyclonic precipitation typically lasts for several hours. Although the total amounts of precipitation may be high, intensities are often low (e.g. 2–5 mm an hour). This allows more interception and more infiltration, slowing the movement of water into streams and rivers.
- Precipitation amount varies according to the time scale used. A single storm may produce 20 mm. Mean annual precipitation in Britain's western uplands exceeds 1,000 mm, while in eastern lowlands it is less than 700 mm.
- In some parts of the world, there is a strong seasonal pattern to precipitation. Figure 3.3 gives an example. In Africa's tropical savannas there are wet and dry seasons. Here seasons are defined by precipitation rather than by temperature. During the wet season, river discharges are high and flooding is common. In the dry season, many rivers cease to flow altogether.

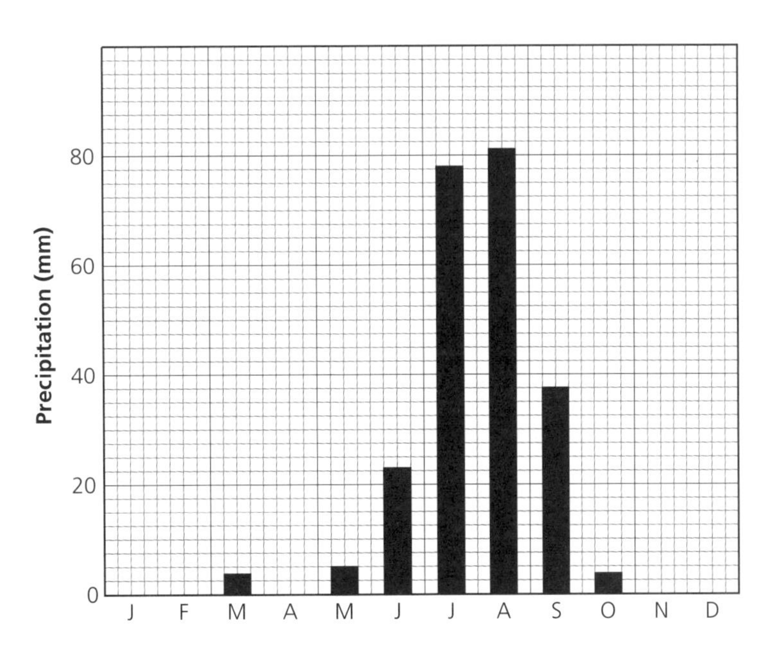

Figure 3.3 Seasonal distribution of precipitation at Timbuktu in the African savannas

Interception of precipitation by vegetation has two effects on run-off:

- It delays the movement of precipitation into streams and rivers.
- As there is some loss of precipitation to evaporation, interception reduces the volume of water reaching streams and rivers.

3 Interception

3.1 Interception mechanisms

Vegetation **intercepts** a proportion of precipitation and stores it temporarily on branch, leaf and stem surfaces. Eventually this moisture either evaporates back into the atmosphere or falls to the ground.

Once precipitation has fallen on to a vegetated surface, it may:

- be retained by plant surfaces and later evaporated – **interception loss**;

- reach the ground directly through spaces in the vegetation canopy, or drip from leaves and branches to the ground – **throughfall**;
- trickle along twigs and branches, and eventually to the ground down the main stem or trunk – **stemflow**.

3.2 Factors affecting interception loss

- The most important factor is the **interception storage capacity** of the vegetation. Before a precipitation event, the vegetation is dry and storage capacity is at a maximum. Initially, the dry vegetation intercepts most of the precipitation. But as the leaves become wetter and reach their storage capacity, water droplets start to fall to the ground.
- Wind speed has an important influence on interception loss. Evaporation increases rapidly at higher wind speeds.
- Interception loss decreases with the duration of precipitation. In short-lived events such as showers, the maximum storage capacity of the vegetation may not be achieved. As a result, most precipitation may be intercepted.
- Interception losses are greater from grasses than from agricultural crops. Trees, which have a large surface area and considerable aerodynamic roughness, have higher interception losses than grasses.
- Interception losses are greater from evergreen conifers than from broad-leaved deciduous trees. Apart from conifers having leaves all year round, water clings to the needle leaves of conifers such as spruce and pine (like water on a comb), from where it evaporates easily.

4 *Surface run-off*

Run-off is the gravity flow of water in channels. We normally measure run-off in units of time, such as cubic metres per second (cumecs).

Under natural conditions, each stream or river receives water only from its own catchment or **drainage basin**. Each drainage basin is a simple system, with inputs of precipitation and outputs of evapotranspiration and streamflow. Allowing for storage in the system (e.g. in permeable rocks, soil and peat), inputs and outputs of water are equal.

4.1 Hydrographs

A hydrograph shows how a stream or river responds to inputs of precipitation. The time scale of such inputs varies from years and months to individual storms. Hydrographs that show average river flow over several years describe a river's **regime**. A hydrograph of the River Wyre in Lancashire is shown in Figure 3.4.

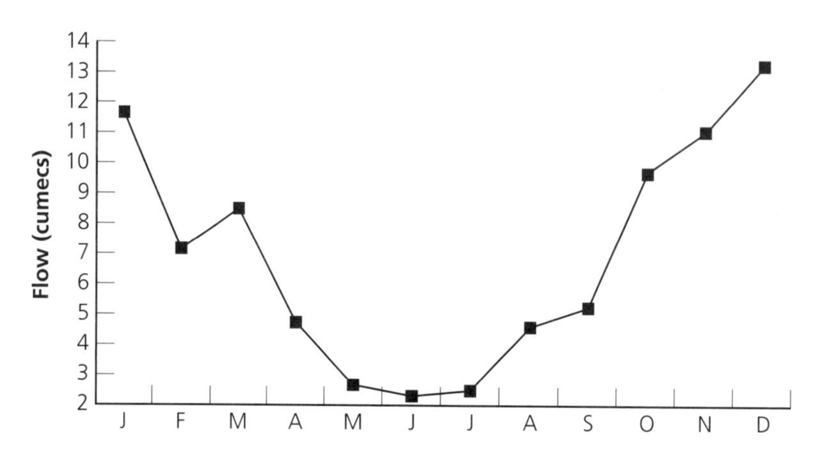

Figure 3.4 Hydrograph of the River Wyre: mean monthly flow, 1976–94

Figure 3.5 is a storm hydrograph of the River Wyre. It shows how the river's discharge responded to a precipitation event on 19 December 1993. The hydrograph comprises a discharge curve and a bar chart to show precipitation at hourly intervals. The main features of hydrographs are:

- a **rising limb** – the increase in discharge in response to precipitation. The more rapid the river's response to precipitation, the steeper the rising limb.
- **peak flow** – the highest point or maximum discharge on the hydrograph.
- a **falling limb** when discharge declines after the peak flow.
- the **lag time**, i.e. the time difference between maximum precipitation and peak flow. This is an important measure of how quickly a river responds to a storm event.
- the **stormflow** or **quickflow**, i.e. the proportion of discharge contributed by the storm.
- the **slowflow** or **baseflow**, i.e. the proportion of discharge from permeable rocks and soil.

'Flashy' rivers have short lag times. They respond quickly to precipitation events and have a high flood risk. Drainage-basin characteristics of flashy rivers include: impermeable rocks; steep slopes; high drainage density; little forest/woodland cover.

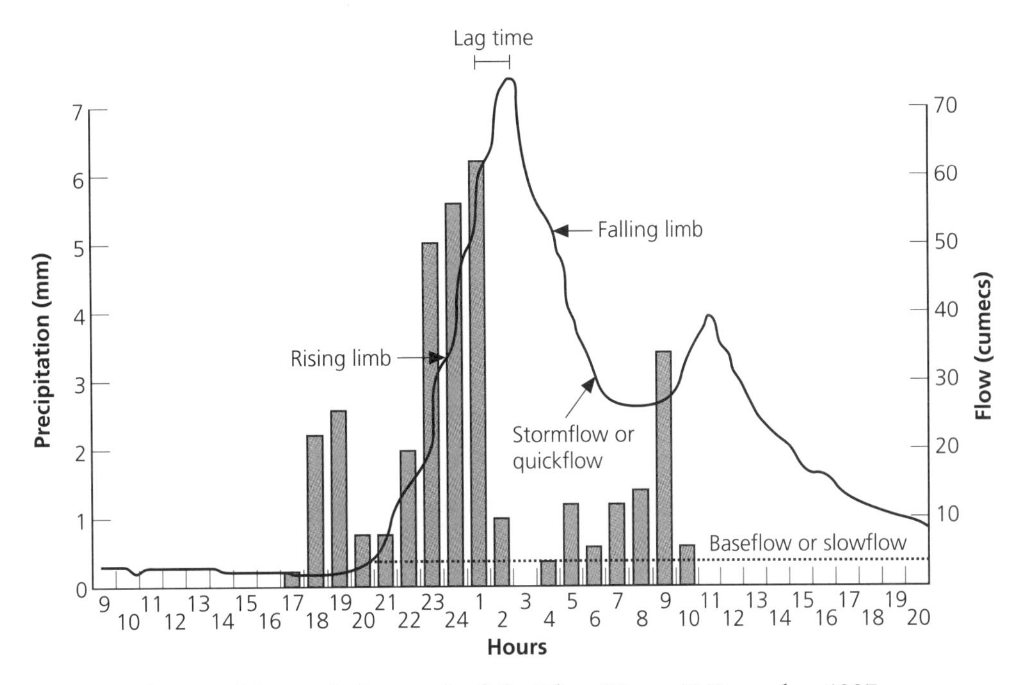

Figure 3.5 Storm hydrograph of the River Wyre, 19 December 1993

The shape of a storm hydrograph is influenced by two groups of factors:

- the nature of the precipitation event (amount, type and duration of precipitation);
- the physical properties of the drainage basin (rock type, soil type and depth, soil moisture status, slopes, drainage density, vegetation cover, land use, etc.).

The principal influences on the shape of storm hydrographs are as follows.

Factor	Effect on peak discharge and lag time
Fixed physical properties of the drainage basin	
Geology	Permeable rocks, such as chalk, store most precipitation and release it gradually as base flow. The result is a low peak discharge and a long lag time. The difference between peak and average flow is usually small. Impermeable catchments (e.g. granite or schist) have high peak discharges and short lag times.
Slopes	Precipitation moves slowly across gentle slopes into streams and rivers. This lengthens the lag time and reduces the peak flow. In upland catchments with steep slopes, rapid surface run-off causes short lag times and high peak discharges.
Soils	Clayey soils cause more rapid run-off, and shorter lag times, than loamy or sandy soils. Clayey soils are impermeable, so their soil moisture capacity is limited (see p.110).
Drainage density	The greater the drainage density (average length of stream channel per square kilometre), the faster surface and sub-surface water flows into streams or rivers. Thus high drainage densities give short lag times and high peak discharges.

Factor	Effect on peak discharge and lag time
Vegetation cover	A dense vegetation cover will intercept a large proportion of precipitation. This will lengthen lag times and reduce peak discharges. The effect of vegetation cover in middle to high latitudes will vary seasonally.
Land use	Crops intercept less precipitation than natural vegetation. Thus farmland normally has shorter lag times and higher peak discharges. Towns and cities have extensive surfaces of impermeable materials (roofing slate, tiles, tarmac, concrete, etc.) and efficient drainage systems (gutters, sewers, etc.). Consequently, short lag times and high peak flows are typical of streams draining large urban areas.
Drainage basin shape	Elongated basins following major river valleys have relatively short lag times, but peak discharges which, although fairly low, may be sustained for several hours. Roughly circular drainage basins have longer lag times, but high peak discharges.
Variable physical properties and storm characteristics	
Antecedent soil moisture	If soils are saturated or frozen, they behave as impermeable surfaces. As a result, precipitation will run off quickly, giving short lag times and high peak discharges.
Precipitation intensity	High-intensity showers and thunderstorms may exceed the soil's infiltration capacity. This leads to rapid surface run-off, short lag times and high peak discharges.
Precipitation type	Snow takes variable lengths of time to thaw and contribute to stream flow. A slow thaw will give long lag times and modest peak flows. Rapid snowmelt will produce exceptionally high peak discharges that may be sustained for several days.

Table 3.2 Influences on the shape of storm hydrographs

INSET 2

Sources and components of run-off

Precipitation may reach the stream channel through several flowpaths, as shown in Figure 3.6.

- **Channel precipitation:** direct precipitation into streams and rivers. The contribution of channel precipitation is small because stream and river channels occupy only a tiny fraction of the area of a drainage basin.
- **Overland flow:** water that flows over the ground either as a sheet or as trickles and rivulets. Overland flow is important where the soil is either saturated or frozen.
- **Throughflow:** water that infiltrates the soil and then moves laterally through the upper part of the soil towards stream channels.
- **Groundwater flow:** precipitation that percolates from the soil into permeable rocks and forms part of the groundwater. Groundwater storage may last for several days, months or even years.

4.2 Quickflow and slowflow

Most streams and rivers respond quickly to precipitation. This suggests that some precipitation takes a fairly direct route to the stream channel. This **quickflow** is mainly overland. Some precipitation takes a much slower route to stream and river channels. This **slowflow** or baseflow occurs through permeable rocks and the soil. Slowflow is what keeps most streams and rivers flowing during periods of drought.

Quickflow is responsible for flooding. The probability of flooding depends on how rapidly rainfall reaches a river. Steep slopes, impermeable rocks, saturated soils, sparse vegetation, etc. promote overland flow and increase the flood risk.

4.3 Flowpaths

Rain falling to the ground will follow one of two paths as it flows to streams and rivers:

- One part infiltrates the soil, and finds its way into streams and rivers via throughflow and groundwater flow.
- The other part moves across the soil surface as overland flow.

These are shown in Figure 3.7.

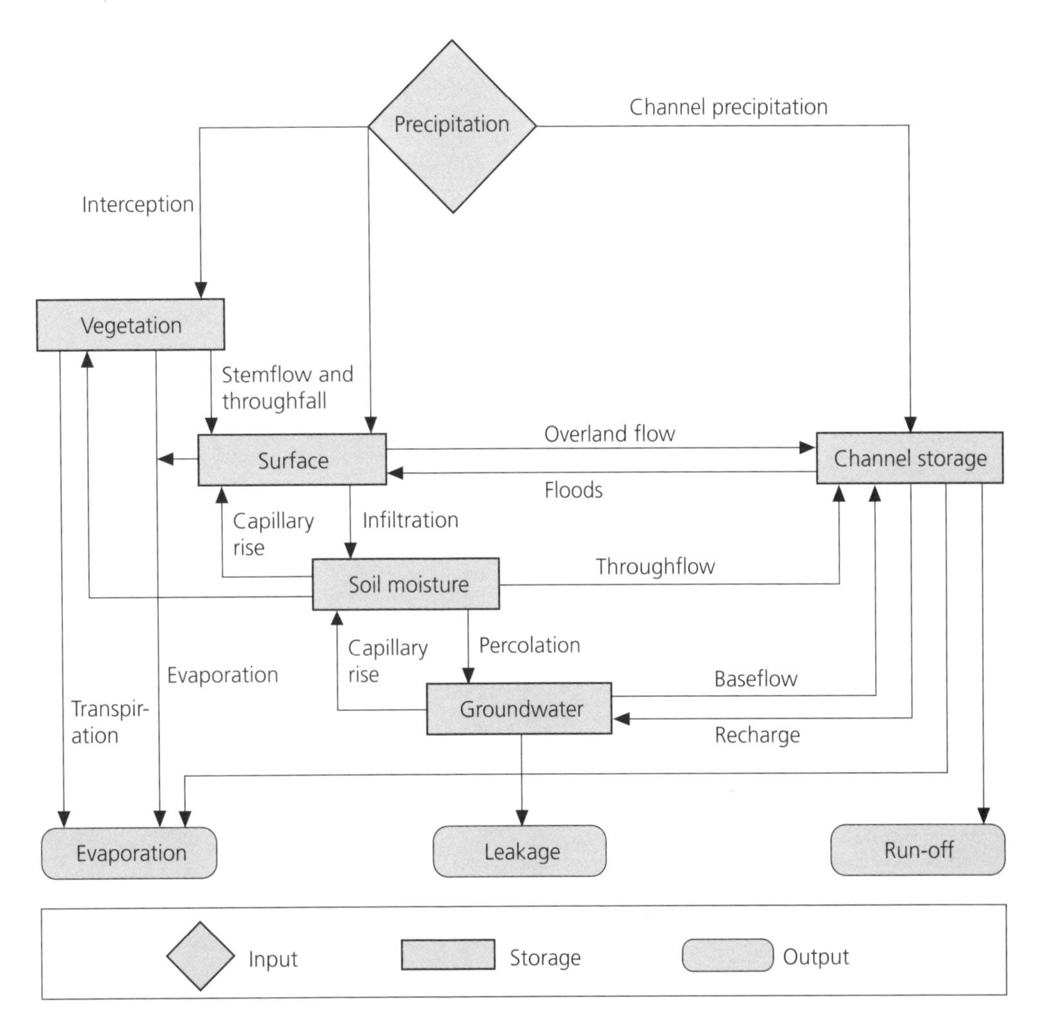

Figure 3.6 The drainage basin hydrological system

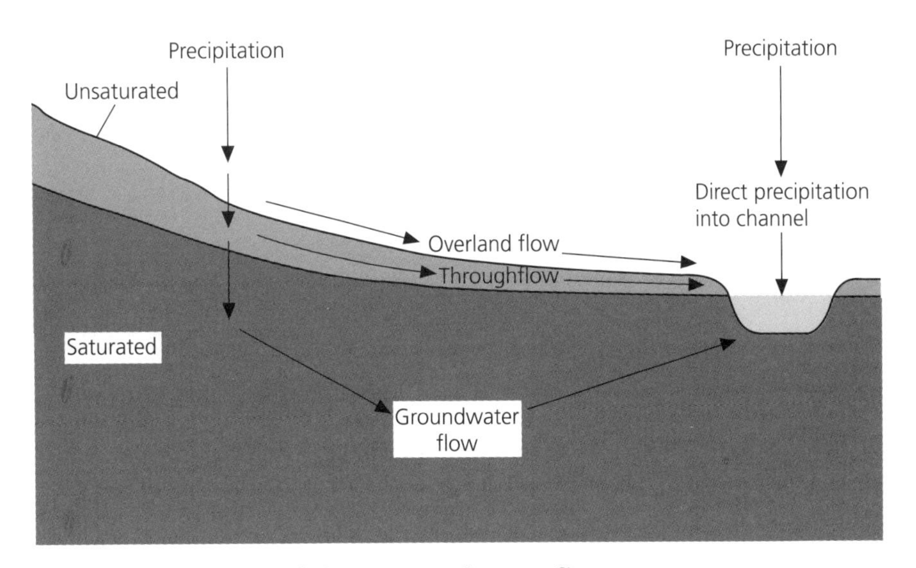

Figure 3.7 Flowpaths of the sources of streamflow

The hydrologist R.E. Horton said that the path followed by rainfall depends on the soil's infiltration capacity (i.e. the maximum rate at which the soil can absorb rain). If the rainfall intensity is less than the infiltration capacity, overland flow will not occur. It has been suggested that the soil's infiltration capacity changes during a storm. Starting with a maximum value, the infiltration capacity gradually decreases. This is because the surface soil becomes compacted; soil particles swell as they absorb water; and the air spaces in the soil become clogged with soil particles. Thus, the longer the duration of a storm, the more important overland flow becomes.

An alternative hypothesis says that *all* precipitation (however intense or prolonged) infiltrates the soil. Eventually, the water table in the soil rises. It first reaches the surface in valleys, close to streams and rivers. Here **saturated overland flow** occurs. The saturated area gradually extends to more distant parts of the catchment. Thus, saturated overland flow (rather than very intensive precipitation) is the only source of quickflow.

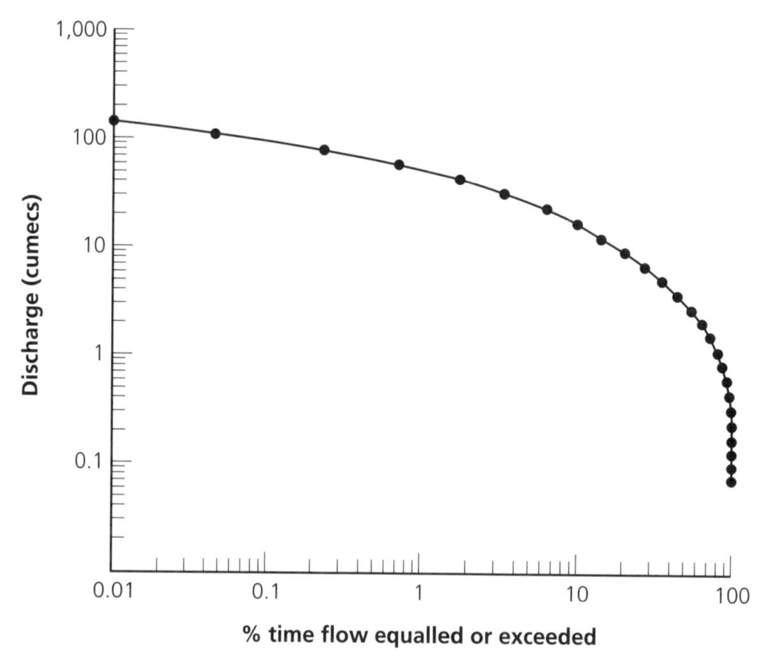

Figure 3.8 Flow duration curve for the River Wyre

INSET 3

Flow duration curves

Flow duration curves show the proportion of time that a given discharge is equalled or exceeded. For instance, in Figure 3.8, the River Wyre has a mean daily flow of 0.34 cumecs or higher, 99% of the time. At the other extreme, a mean daily flow of 110 cumecs or more occurs at a much lower frequency: just 0.046% of the time. Flow duration curves vary from river to river. A steep curve (such as the River Wyre's) indicates extremes of flow, with large differences between high flow and low flow. Such 'flashy' rivers are typical of upland catchments, with steep slopes and impermeable rocks. Flatter curves describe a more regular discharge, with base (or slow) flow from permeable rocks important. Chalk streams in southern England have relatively flat flow duration curves.

5 Drainage basin morphometry

5.1 Morphometric analysis

Surface run-off produces a network of stream channels. Using a technique known as **morphometric analysis**, we can measure some of the properties of these stream networks. Such measurements allow us to compare the differences between drainage basins with precision. There are two common morphometric measurements:

- drainage density – the average length of stream (in kilometres) per square kilometre in a drainage basin;
- stream ordering – the numbering of streams according to their importance.

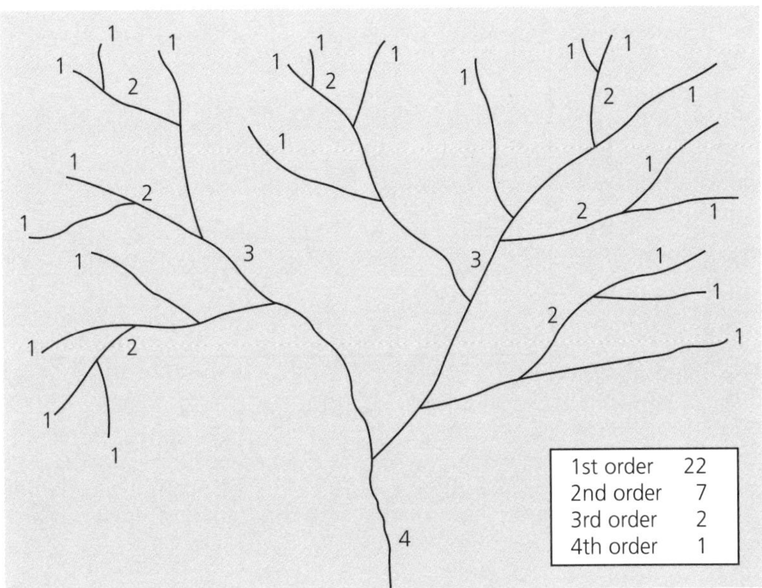

Figure 3.9 Strahler's system of stream ordering

INSET 4

Strahler's stream ordering system and bifurcation ratios

In Strahler's ordering system, the fingertip tributaries are 1st-order streams. When two 1st-order streams meet they form a 2nd-order stream; two 2nd-order streams form a 3rd-order stream, and so on. However, if a 2nd-order stream is joined by a 1st-order stream, it remains a 2nd-order stream.

The ratio of the number of streams of one order to the next highest order is the **bifurcation ratio**. Thus in Figure 3.9, the bifurcation ratio of 1st- to 2nd-order streams is 22/7 or 3.14. This means that on average 3.14 1st-order streams make one 2nd-order stream. The remaining bifurcation ratios are: 2nd to 3rd order, 3.5; and 3rd to 4th order, 2.

Normally, bifurcation ratios vary between 2 and 4. Low values suggest well-developed, mature river basins, with gentle slopes, low precipitation and complete vegetation cover. Higher values are typical of steep, immature, upland catchments.

5.2 The laws of stream morphometry

There are a number of 'laws' or relationships between stream order and drainage basin characteristics. If plotted on log-normal graph paper, each of these relationships follows a straight line, i.e. they are all geometrical.

- The number of streams of each order in a drainage basin, as shown in Figure 3.10.
- The average length of stream of each order in a drainage basin, as shown in Figure 3.11.

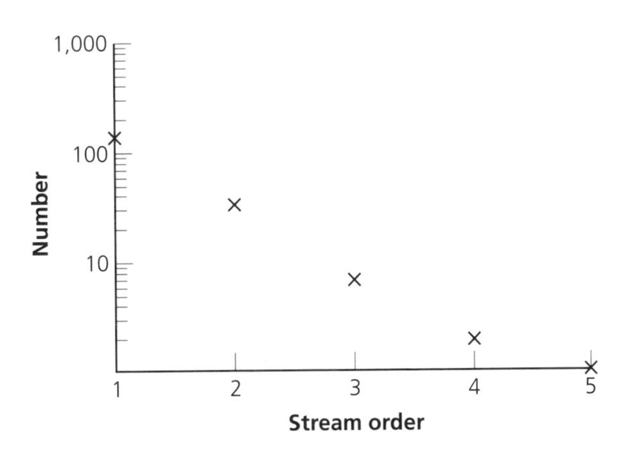

Figure 3.10 Number of streams and stream order: River Wyre

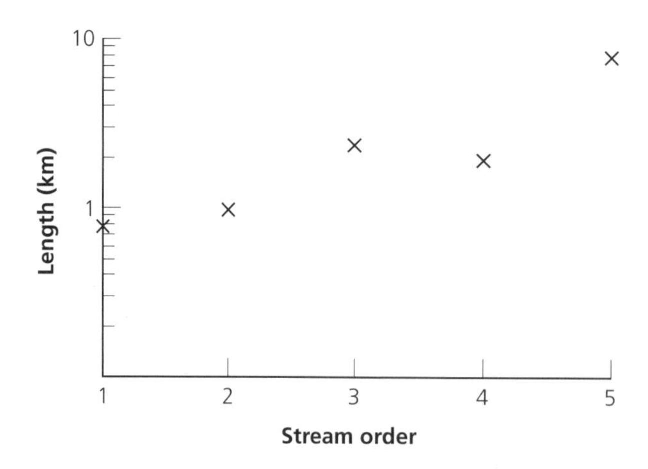

Figure 3.11 Average length of stream of each order: River Wyre

- The average gradient of each stream order in a drainage basin.
- The average area of the drainage basin of each stream order.

6 Groundwater

Groundwater is rainwater that percolates under gravity into permeable rocks or **aquifers**. At depth within permeable rocks, the pores, joints, bedding planes and faults fill with groundwater to form the **zone of saturation**. The uppermost surface of this zone, separating saturated from unsaturated rock, is the **water table**.

Rocks have two types of permeability:

- **primary permeability**, where water passes through the rock pores, as in chalk;
- **secondary permeability**, where water percolates along joints and bedding planes. Carboniferous limestone has secondary permeability. Moreover, owing to solution of joints and bedding planes, its permeability increases over time.

6.1 The shape of the water table

The water table has gentle gradients that follow the shape of the ground surface. Thus the water table is usually most elevated beneath high ground, and lowest in valleys. The surface slope of the water table is known as the **hydraulic gradient**. Groundwater flows along this gradient.

In many aquifers, small reservoirs of groundwater occur above the main water table. These are **perched water tables**. They occur where impermeable strata, such as marl in chalk, impede percolation.

6.2 Fluctuations in the water table

In southern England, where precipitation averages 600–800 mm a year, between 120 and 180 mm percolates down to the water table. However, variations in precipitation from year to year may cause the height of the water table to fluctuate by 40 metres or more. There are also seasonal fluctuations. The average difference in the height of the water table between winter and summer is around 15 metres. During the summer, virtually all rainfall is lost to evapotranspiration, and the water table falls steadily. **Recharge** begins in October, and the water table reaches a maximum in March and April. Between October and April, the water table rises to the surface, causing temporary streams (or **winterbournes**) to flow.

6.3 Geological structure and groundwater

Rock type, angle of dip, and fault and fold structures influence the flow of groundwater.

Absence of surface water in chalk regions limits settlements to wet-point sites. However, water must be available all year round to attract settlement. This explains the concentration of settlement at scarp foot springs, and its absence at dip slope springs.

Rock type

Groundwater supplies are plentiful where there are gently dipping sedimentary rocks, comprising alternate outcrops of permeable and impermeable strata. The dip slopes of permeable escarpments (or cuestas) are extensive catchment areas, as shown in Figure 3.12. The hydraulic gradient towards the foot of the scarp slope results in a line of **scarp foot springs**. These springs are geologically controlled, emerging at the boundary between permeable and impermeable rocks. Because these springs have a fixed position, in the past they have proved reliable wet-point sites for settlement.

Angle of dip

In most escarpments, groundwater flows in the opposite direction to the scarp foot. It forms **dip slope springs** on the floors of dip slope valleys. Dip slope springs have larger catchments than scarp foot springs and therefore flow more strongly. However, because dip slope springs are not controlled geologically, their location on the scarp slope varies seasonally. In winter they migrate up-valley; in summer they move down-valley.

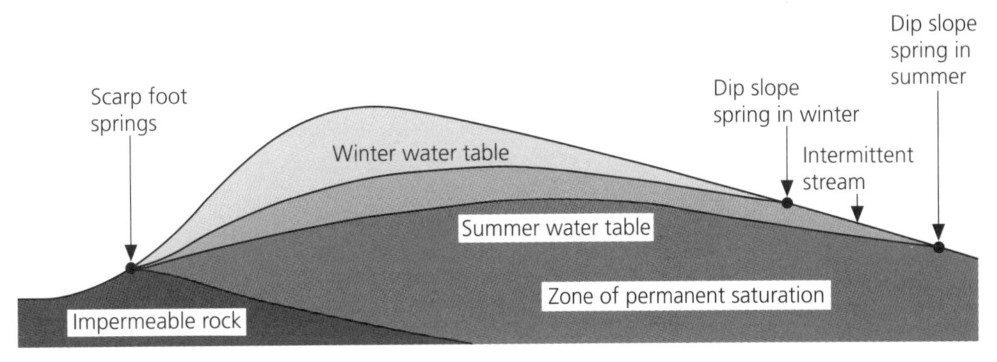

Figure 3.12 Groundwater and springs in escarpments

Fault and fold structures

Some springs are **fault-guided**, i.e. permeable rocks have been faulted against impermeable rocks and water emerges as a line of springs. **Vauclusian springs** mark the resurgence of underground rivers in limestone country.

Artesian basins, such as the London Basin shown in Figure 3.13, are synclines in which an aquifer is sandwiched between two impermeable rock layers. Water sinks into the permeable rock on the higher land around the margins of the basin. It migrates towards the centre of the basin where it accumulates under hydrostatic pressure. If wells are sunk into the aquifer, the water will rise to the surface under its own pressure.

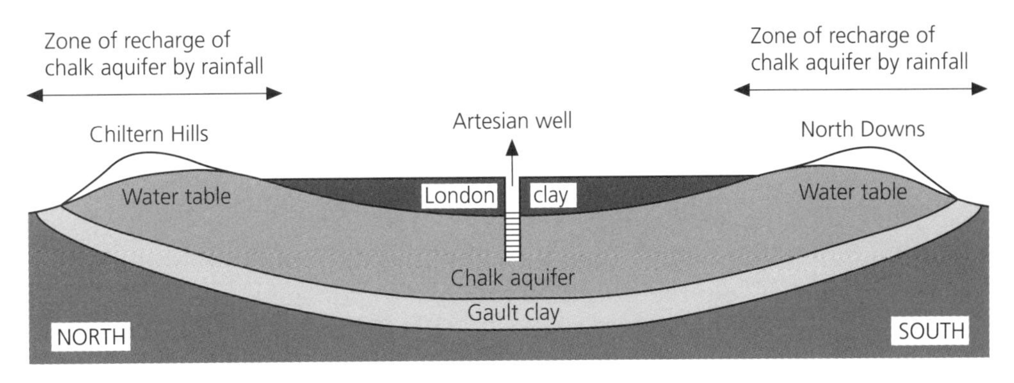

Figure 3.13 The London artesian basin

UNIT 4 Fluvial environments

1 Water flow in river channels

Both laminar and turbulent flow can be found in all parts of a river's course. For example, turbulent flow and laminar flow alternate in pool and riffle sequences in lowland rivers.

Large volumes of water flowing in channels form streams and rivers. The flow of water in channels may be either laminar or turbulent.

- **Laminar flow** is smooth. The water molecules slide past each other in layers. Laminar flow is typical of rivers with roughly semi-circular channels in cross-section, fine sediment loads and gentle gradients.
- **Turbulent flow** is chaotic. In turbulent flow, velocity changes rapidly over short distances, and the water flows in eddies and vortices. Turbulent flow occurs in channels where there is considerable frictional resistance to flow. Thus, turbulent flow is most common on upland streams with steep gradients, boulder-strewn beds and wide, shallow channels.

2 Fluvial processes

2.1 Fluvial erosion

For most of the last 100,000 years in temperate latitudes, glaciers, ice sheets and mass movements have dominated land-forming processes. Only in the last 10,000 years, with the warming of the climate, have rivers become the main agents of landscape change.

Rivers erode, transport and deposit earth materials to produce distinctive landforms. Today, in temperate latitudes, rivers are the dominant landforming agents.

There are three principal fluvial erosional processes: abrasion (or corrasion); hydraulic action; and solution (or corrosion).

- **Abrasion** mainly results from the transport of **bedload**. Like a giant grinding machine, the movement of cobbles and pebbles scours the channel bed and undermines the channel banks. These coarse particles are the 'tools' of erosion. Abrasion is the main cause of the bedload particles themselves becoming smaller and rounder (by attrition) as they move downstream.
- **Hydraulic action** describes the dragging force of flowing water, dislodging particles of sand and silt from the channel. It is important in alluvial channels, but has little effect in channels cut in solid rock.
- **Solution** occurs when rivers flow over carbonate rocks such as limestone.

2.2 Sediment transport

Load is the sediment transported by streams and rivers. We describe the size distribution of the sediment transported by streams and rivers as the **calibre** of the load (see Table 4.1).

Human activities often influence the amount of suspended sediment in streams and rivers. Deforestation and arable farming often lead to soil erosion by surface run-off. The disposal of effluent in streams and rivers also adds to suspended sediment loads.

Sediment transport depends on two factors: flow velocity and particle size. A river's ability to transport particles of a given size is known as its **competence**. Figure 4.1 summarises the relationship between transport, flow velocity and particle size. A critical speed is required to transport particles of a given size; this is the **erosion velocity**.

- Coarse particles (i.e. cobbles and pebbles), and fine particles (i.e. silt and clay) both have high erosion velocities.
- Sand-sized particles have relatively low erosion velocities.

Large particles such as cobbles and pebbles need high flow velocities to get them moving. Fine particles are also entrained at high velocities. This is because they stick together, bonded by tiny electrical charges. In contrast, sand is loose and incoherent. It also has a small mass. For these reasons, it can be entrained at low velocities.

The lower curve in Figure 4.1 shows the velocities needed for particles to stop moving or settle out of suspension.

- Coarse particles come to rest when flow speeds dip just below the erosion velocity.
- Clay particles settle out of suspension only at very low velocities.

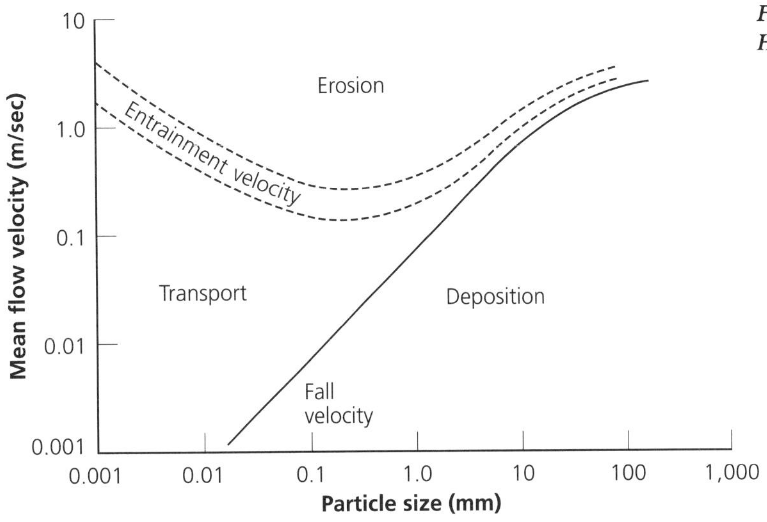

Figure 4.1 Hjulström's curve

Lakes and reservoirs are sediment traps. Thus, rivers leaving lakes and reservoirs often contain no suspended load and bedload. As a result, these rivers have excessive energy that is expended through 'clear water' erosion.

The difference between erosion velocities and depositional velocities of particles has implications for sediment transport.

- Coarse particles will be in transit for relatively brief periods around peak discharge and are therefore likely to travel only short distances.
- Once entrained, fine particles will be transported long distances. The selective removal of fine particles from upland streams is one reason why boulders and cobbles dominate the load of upland streams.

Type of load	Sediments	Transport processes
Bedload	Coarse particles: boulders, cobbles and pebbles	Particles slide and roll along the channel bed at high discharge.
Suspended load	Fine particles such as silt and clay	Particles are entrained at high discharge and transported in suspension in the flow.
Solution load	Dissolved minerals from rocks such as chalk and Carboniferous limestone	Minerals are transported in solution. This type of transport does not depend on high river discharge.

Table 4.1 A river's load

3 River channels

3.1 Bankfull channel shape

- Bankfull discharge is often 100 times (or more) greater than average discharge.
- Velocity at bankfull is often 10 times (or more) greater than at average discharge.

River channels transfer water and sediment. Their shape in cross-section and plan is adjusted to carry the maximum discharge and the sediment transported from upstream. **Bankfull discharge** determines the shape of river channel in cross-section. Bankfull is the maximum capacity of a river channel. On most British rivers, bankfull discharge occurs between 0.5 and two times a year.

3.2 Measuring bankfull channel cross-sections

River channels in cross-section are adjusted to bankfull discharge. Thus, bankfull is the critical shape we need to measure. Where opposite banks of a river are at the same height, this is fairly easy. However, in practice this is often not the case.

There are two commonly used measures of channel cross-section shape: width/depth ratio and hydraulic radius (R).

- The transporting capacity of a river at bankfull is equal to the third or fourth power of the increase in velocity. Thus a tenfold increase in velocity produces a 10^3 or 10^4 increase in transporting power.

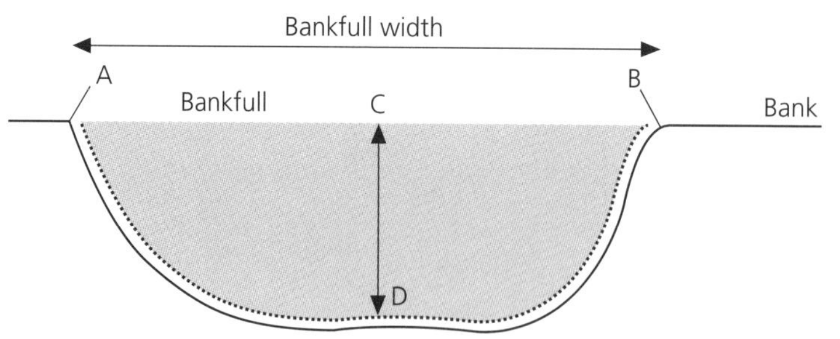

Figure 4.2 Channel parameters for calculating hydraulic radius and width/depth ratio

INSET 1

Bankfull discharge

Stream discharge (Q) is the volume of water passing down the channel in a given time. The units of discharge are usually cubic metres per second (cumecs).

$$\text{Discharge } (Q) = \text{Cross-sectional area } (A) \times \text{Velocity } (V)$$

To estimate bankfull discharge, we need to know the cross-sectional area of the channel and the average speed of flow. As Figure 4.2 shows, a fairly accurate estimate of bankfull cross-sectional area can be obtained by measuring the width of the channel (from the top of each bank) and its depth at regular intervals across the channel. Estimating velocity is more difficult. Velocity varies with depth and across the channel. Crude estimates are obtained by timing a float along a length of channel (e.g. 5 or 10 metres). A current meter gives a more accurate measure. Several velocity readings are taken across the channel and at variable depths, to obtain an average speed.

However, at bankfull such measurements of velocity are impossible and a different approach is used:

- Measure the bankfull cross-section and wetted perimeter and calculate the hydraulic radius.
- Measure the gradient of the channel.
- Estimate channel roughness.
- Subsitute the measurements in Manning's equation.

Manning's equation

Velocity (V) = $(R^{0.66}S^{0.5})/n$

where: R = hydraulic radius
S = slope of channel
n = coefficient of roughness

Channel type	Coefficient range
Mountain stream with pebble and boulder bed	0.04–0.07
Small, clean, straight lowland stream	0.025–0.033
Small, weedy stream with deep pools	0.075–0.150
Flood plain stream on pastureland	0.025–0.035
Flood plain stream in heavy woodland	0.1–0.15
Large streams (>33 metres)	0.025–0.06

Table 4.2 Roughness coefficients

- We calculate the **width/depth ratio** by dividing the width of the channel (from the top of each bank) by its average depth. Large values for width/depth ratio indicate relatively wide, shallow channels. These channels are inefficient for the transfer of water, but effective for transporting coarse bedload. Low width/depth ratios indicate more efficient channels, which are relatively narrow and deep.

- The **hydraulic radius** is the ratio of the bankfull cross-sectional area of a channel to its wetted perimeter. Wetted perimeter is the length of channel bed and banks in cross-section, in contact with the water at bankfull. The higher the value of the hydraulic radius, the more efficient the channel for transporting water.

In practice, channel cross-sections are influenced by bank materials, calibre of load and bank vegetation, as well as bankfull discharge.

3.3 Cross-section channel shape and bankfull discharge

River channels respond to increases in discharge by adjusting their width, depth and velocity. These changes in width, depth and velocity are known as **hydraulic geometry**. An example is given in Figure 4.3.

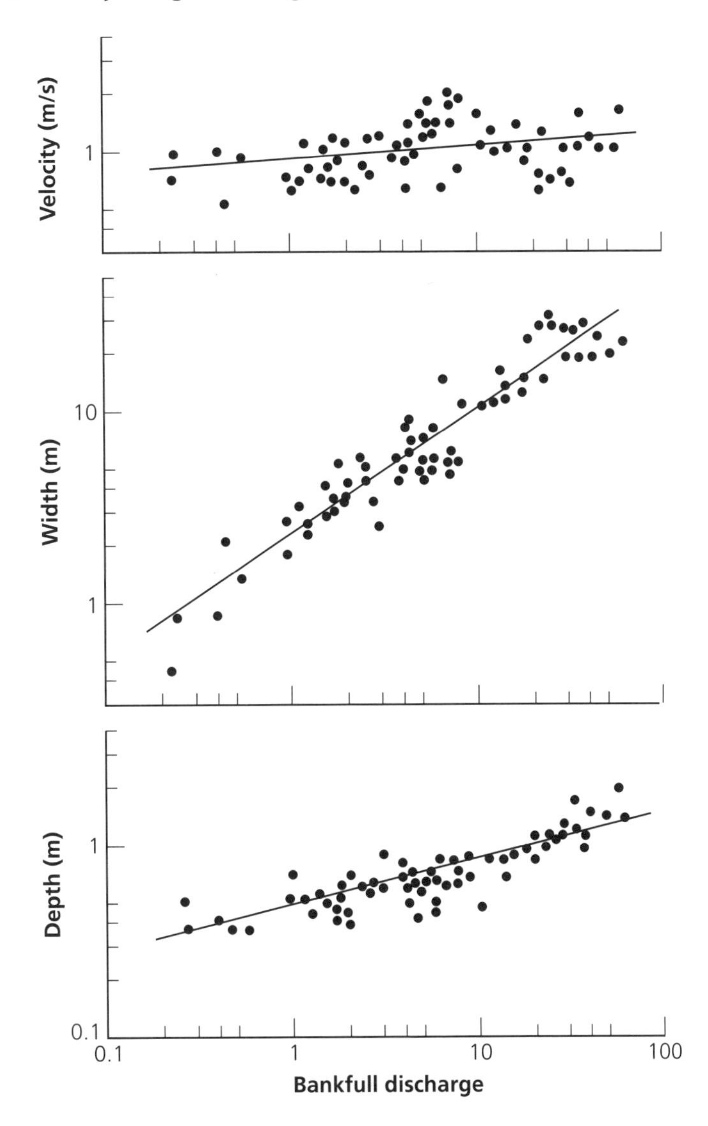

Figure 4.3 Hydraulic geometry: downstream changes of streams on Dartmoor

We can study the hydraulic geometry of a stream either:

- at a station (i.e. at one specific location), or
- at regular intervals downstream.

As discharge rises, width, depth and velocity increase at different rates 'at a station'. Rates of increase depend on channel shape. In deep, narrow channels (often formed in coherent materials such as silt and clay), depth increases most rapidly. In wide, shallow channels (common where banks comprise incoherent gravel), the increase in width is more apparent.

Bankfull discharge also increases downstream and produces corresponding changes in width, depth and velocity. Generally, channel width increases more rapidly downstream than channel depth. Velocity also increases, despite the decrease in channel gradient.

This is because river channels have (a) a more efficient shape downstream, and (b) a smaller-calibre load. As a result, there is less frictional resistance to flow.

INSET 2

Long profiles of alluvial channels

In alluvial channels, gradients decrease downstream. Consequently, the long profile of any stream or river is usually concave.

This downstream decrease in gradient is related to:

- the downstream increase in discharge;
- the downstream increase in channel efficiency;
- the downstream decrease in the calibre of load.

The changes give the river excess energy. The result is an increase in erosion and a reduction in channel gradient. Eventually, a balance is reached: the gradient is such that the river has just sufficient energy to transport its water and sediment, so that no further erosion takes place.

3.4 Pools and riffles

In most reaches of alluvial channels, there is an alternating sequence of shallows and deeps. The shallows that form high points in the stream bed are known as **riffles**. They consist of gravel and have relatively steep gradients. The deeps, with finer bed material, are **pools**. At low flow, the current is faster over the riffles than over the pools.

Pools and riffle sequences develop at high flow. Frictional resistance between the water and the channel bed and banks sets up turbulence, with alternating faster and slower flow. The spacing of these eddies is around six times channel width. The downstream changes in fast and slow flow lead to erosion in the pools (faster flow) and deposition in the riffles (slower flow).

Even in straight channels, water flows in a sinuous path, swinging from bank to bank. In the pool sections, where the flow is fastest, the sinuous path of the water causes bank erosion.

3.5 Channel planform

Channel planform is just one of five ways in which rivers can adjust their channels to increases in discharge and sediment. Apart from planform, rivers can adjust:

- channel depth;
- channel width;
- cross-sectional shape;
- channel gradient.

We have seen that a river responds to changes in discharge and sediment load by adjusting its channel cross-section and channel gradient. A river can also respond by changing its channel planform (see Figure 4.4). There are three types of channel planform: straight; meandering; and braided.

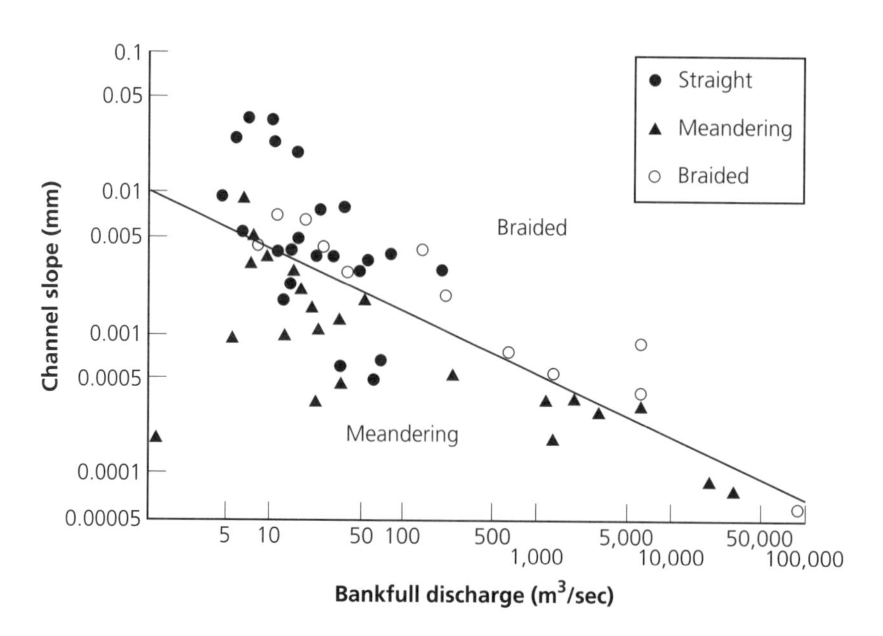

Figure 4.4 Channel planform and stream power

Straight channels

Natural river channels are rarely straight for more than ten times their width. Straight channels occur when streams have low energy levels, small discharges and gentle gradients. There is minimal erosion, minimal sediment transport and little flow deflection.

Meandering channels are one way in which a river can expend surplus energy. The effect of meandering is to reduce average gradient, and therefore potential energy.

Meandering channels

Meandering channels have a sinuous, wave-like form. Around 80% of river channels are classed as meandering. There are many theories of meander development. One of the most easily understood is that friction between flowing water and the channel bed and banks causes the **thalweg** (i.e. path of fastest current) to follow a sinuous path. Where the thalweg hits the channel bank, erosion occurs until eventually the channel takes on a sinuous form, as shown in Figure 4.5.

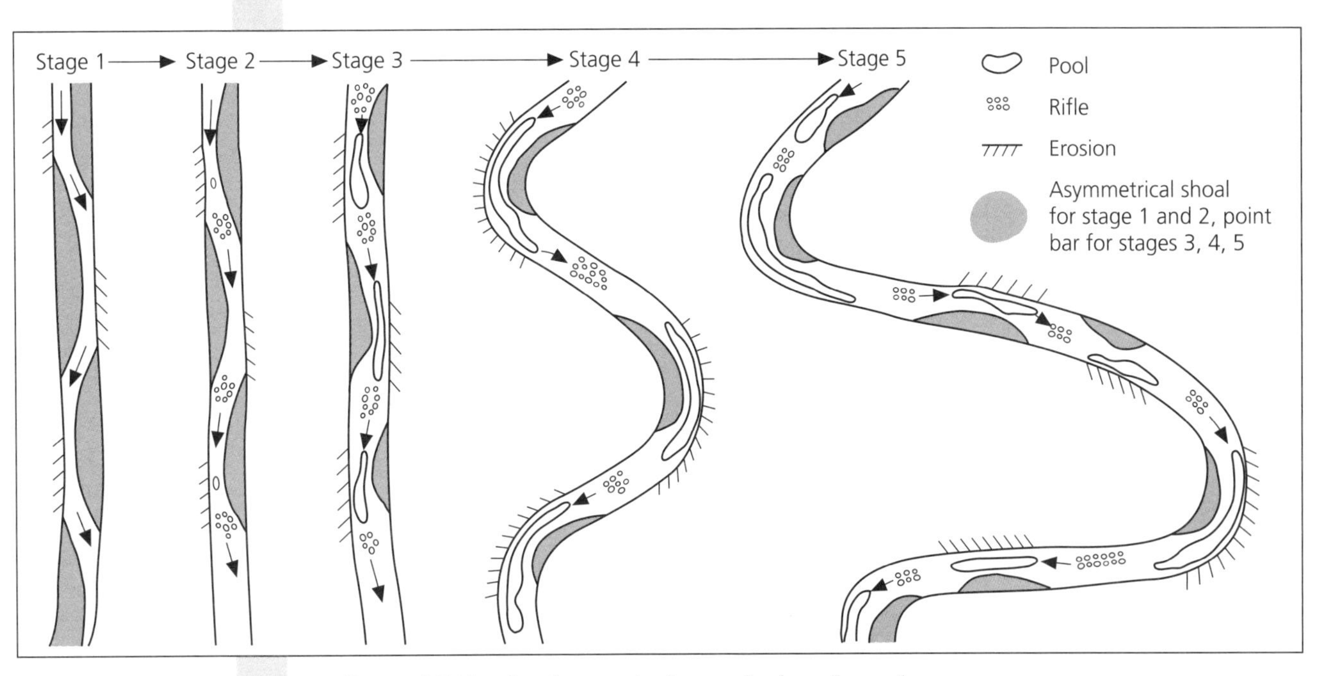

Figure 4.5 The development of meandering channels

INSET 3

Sinuosity and meander characteristics

We measure sinuosity by comparing the straight-line distance between two points in a river channel, with the channel distance. Channels with sinuosities exceeding or equal to 1.5 are classed as meandering. Figure 4.6 shows the main components of meander geometry. Meander wavelength usually varies from 7 to 10 times channel width, radius of curvature varies between 2 and 4 times channel width, and meander wavelength varies between 4 and 5 times the radius of curvature. Channel width is related to discharge, and as discharge increases downstream there will be a corresponding increase in meander dimensions.

Meandering channels most commonly occur where:

- bank material comprises coherent silts and clays (the more coherent the banks, the more sinuous the channel);
- channel gradient is moderately steep so that the river has power to erode its banks.

Within meanders a secondary flow known as **helical flow** occurs, as shown in Figure 4.7. Helical flow is spiral-like motion subsidiary to the main downstream flow. A surface current moves across the river, elevating the water on the outside of the meander. This produces a return current close to the river bed, directed at the inside of the meander. The return current results in lateral accretion and the formation of a point bar.

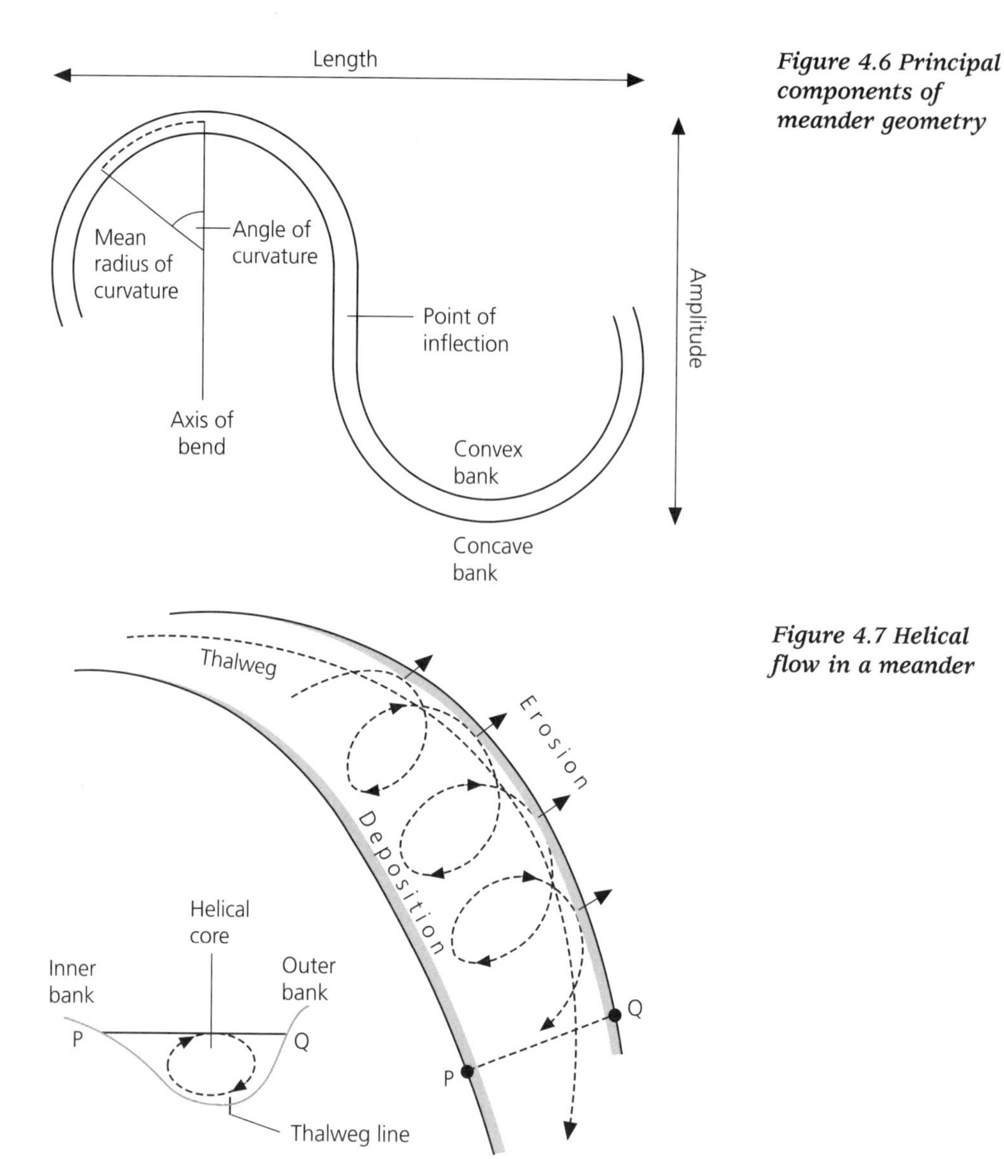

Figure 4.6 Principal components of meander geometry

Figure 4.7 Helical flow in a meander

Pools and riffles are features of meandering as well as straight channels. Pools occur on the outer bend of meanders, with riffles situated at the point of inflection. The spacing of pools and riffles in meanders adds weight to the theory that meanders develop from the sinuous flow found in straight channels.

Braided channels

Braided channels consist of two or more channels divided by bars and islands, as shown in Figure 4.8. The cause of channel division is deposition of sediment within the channel. Braiding results from:

- an abundant bedload owing to poorly vegetated surfaces and coarse debris available from glacial erosion or volcanic activity;
- easily eroded banks – especially banks comprising gravels and sand, which may cause a localised overloading of coarse sediment;
- high and variable discharge, with high peak flows, often associated with meltwater in glaciated regions;
- steep slopes.

Braiding indicates that the river cannot transport its sediment load in a single channel. Deposition (aggradation) in the form of bars steepens the channel gradient and restores the river's competence to transport its bedload. Bars have a coarse upstream (proximal) end and grade to finer particles at the tail (distal end). They gradually migrate downstream.

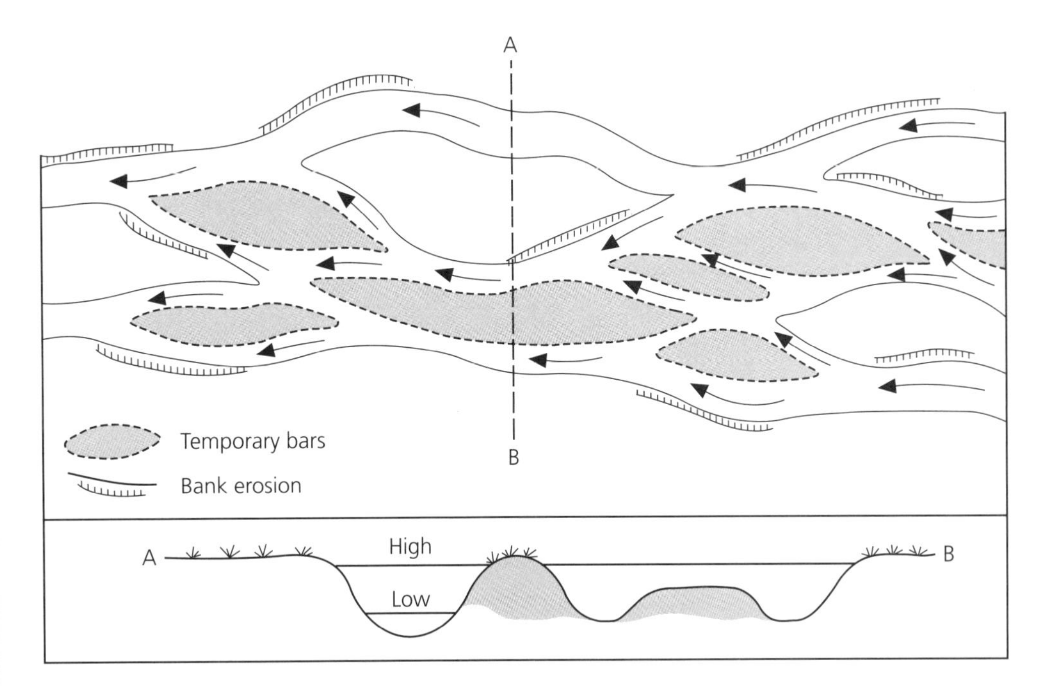

Figure 4.8 Braided channels

INSET 4

Braided rivers in southern Iceland

Many of southern Iceland's rivers have braided channels. Along the coast of southern Iceland, these rivers have built huge outwash plains (sandur) of gravels and sand. The causes of braiding include:

- powerful meltwater rivers (especially in spring), which flow from icefields such as the Vatnajökull, Myrdalsjökull and Eyafjallajökull;
- huge amounts of coarse rock debris, derived from glacial erosion and freeze–thaw weathering;
- catchments dominated by loose volcanic ash, with little soil and vegetation to resist surface wash and mass movement.

Iceland is one of the world's most active volcanic regions. Several active volcanoes lie beneath the icefields of southern Iceland. Occasionally, eruptions occur beneath the icefields. These eruptions (e.g. Grimsvötn in 1997) produce massive amounts of meltwater and devastating floods or jökulhlaups. In just a few hours, these floods transport vast amounts of coarse rock debris to the valleys and coastal plain (see p. 13).

3.6 Stream channels in upland regions

Many upland areas in the British Isles have been modified by glacial erosion. Because deglaciation occurred just 10,000 years ago, rivers have not had time to adjust their channels to discharge and sediment loads.

In upland regions, rock type and structure, and steep slopes usually control the shape of river channels. Unlike lowland river channels, few upland river channels are adjusted to discharge and sediment loads. Upland rivers may take thousands of years to achieve equilibrium. Most have surplus energy that results in rapid rates of erosion. This erosive energy is derived from:

- steep gradients, giving high-velocity flow;
- coarse bedload from weathering, mass movement and fluvial erosion, which causes abrasion;
- steep valley slopes, which give rise to rapid run-off and high peak flows;
- high and intense precipitation events, which also promote high peak flows.

Many upland river channels are formed in solid rock. In cross-section, these channels are often wide and shallow. Such channels, with high width/depth ratios, are effective for transporting coarse bedload. Their width and unevenness causes frictional resistance to flow. This leads to turbulence, giving the localised high velocities needed to transport coarse bedload materials such as boulders and cobbles.

4 Fluvial landforms

4.1 Fluvial landforms in upland regions

Geological structure and past erosional events (e.g. glaciation) have a strong influence on upland streams. The long profiles of upland streams are characteristically uneven. Waterfalls occur where weak rocks are eroded beneath a resistant caprock, or where valleys have been overdeepened by glacial erosion. Rapids also occur where resistant rock bands cross stream channels.

The main fluvial landforms in upland areas are erosional. Upland valleys are often **V-shaped**, with steep valley slopes and narrow floors. Their distinctive shape results from rapid vertical erosion, which exceeds the rate of lowering of valley slopes by mass movement and weathering. Where streams have meandering channels, vertical incision produces **interlocking spurs**.

4.2 Fluvial landforms in lowland regions

Flood plains

Most lowland rivers occupy broad valleys or **flood plains**, like the one in Figure 4.9. Flood plains result from both fluvial erosion and fluvial deposition. Lateral erosion and the downstream migration of meanders widen the valley, which is bordered by a line of steep slopes or **bluffs**. Fluvial deposition infills the valley with alluvium (silt, sand and gravel). This involves two processes: lateral accretion and vertical accretion.

- **Lateral accretion** mainly comprises point bars and channel sediments, abandoned when the river shifts its course through lateral erosion. These deposits are mainly coarse sands and gravels.
- **Vertical accretion** occurs only when the water spills out of the channel and spreads across the flood plain. It consists of fine silts transported as suspended load.

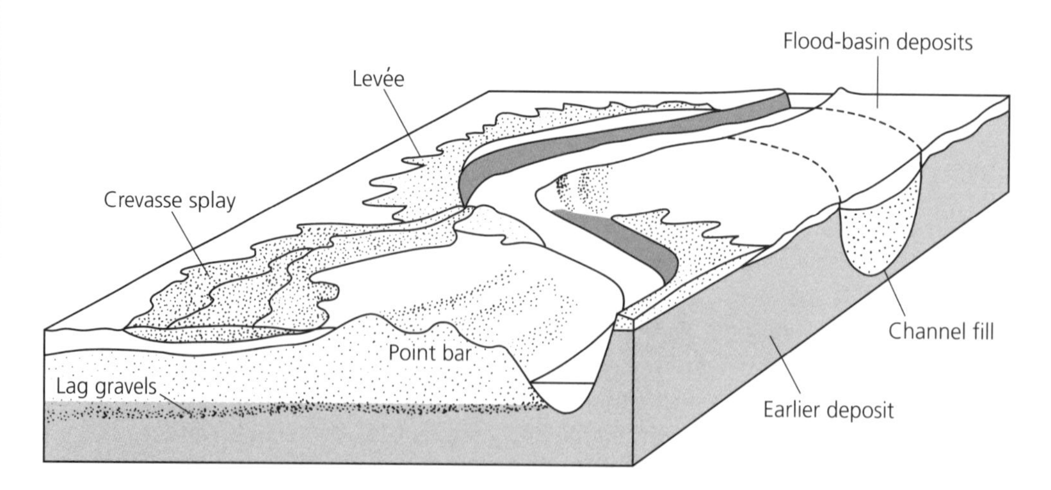

Figure 4.9 Flood plain deposits

INSET 5

Flood plain deposits

Many flood plain deposits in northern Britain comprise two sediment units: a lower unit made up of layers of coarse gravel; and an upper unit of fine silt and clay. One explanation for this sequence is that the coarse sediment represents former point bars and channel bars, deposited by powerful meltwater rivers at the end of the last glacial. Since then, the supply of coarse debris (from glacial deposits) has diminished. The spread of forests and farming has, in the last 5,000 years, resulted in a supply of mainly fine sediment to rivers. Thus vertical accretion has topped off the coarse sediments on flood plains with layers of silt and clay.

Levées are low ridges of alluvium that run parallel to river channels. They form by vertical accretion. When water floods out of the channel at bankfull, it quickly loses energy. Coarse sediment is deposited nearest the channel and builds up to form levées. If flood-water surges through a levée, subsequent deposition may produce a fan-shaped area of alluvium known as a **crevasse splay**.

Channel fill makes a small contribution to flood plain development. Abandoned channels (e.g. cut-off meander loops or ox-bows) are infilled with silt and plant remains.

Alluvial fans

An alluvial fan is a cone-shaped deposit usually found where a river emerges from a mountain course, as shown in Figure 4.10. In its mountainous course, a river may be confined by relief to a narrow channel. Once it emerges from the mountains, its valley widens, causing it to lose energy and deposit its load. A sudden change in gradient on leaving the mountains may also result in deposition. Alluvial fans are concave in profile. The coarseness of the sediment decreases with distance down the fan. Alluvial fans develop where there is abundant sediment supply. In dryland areas they are known as **bajadas**.

Sorting of sediment results from the loss of energy as the river emerges from the uplands. Coarser sediments are deposited near the mountain foot. Finer sediments are carried further.

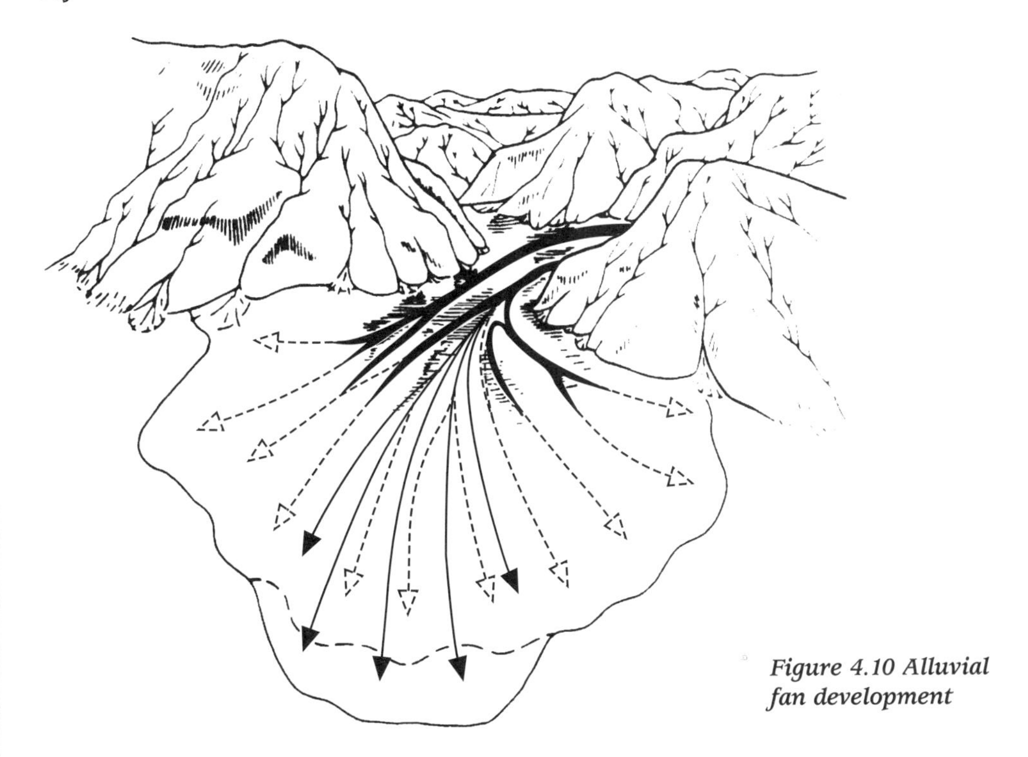

Figure 4.10 Alluvial fan development

4.3 Landforms caused by increased river energy

When rivers gain renewed energy, rates of erosion increase. Renewed energy may occur when rivers undergo:

- an increase in discharge (e.g. climatic change producing higher rainfall, melting glaciers and icefields).
- a fall in base level (e.g. a lowering of sea level, tectonic uplift). This change is known as **rejuvenation**.

The effect of increased discharge or rejuvenation is to create new erosional landforms. These landforms include incised meanders, river terraces and knickpoints.

Incised meanders

Although meandering is mainly associated with alluvial channels, incised meanders are found where a river cuts down into solid bedrock. There are two types of incised meander:

intrenched and ingrown. **Intrenched meanders** occur where downcutting is so rapid that little lateral erosion occurs. **Ingrown meanders** develop where there is a slower rate of downcutting and where lateral erosion is significant. Tectonic uplift may accelerate the process of incision. Uplift of the Colorado Plateau in the last 12 million years is largely responsible for the deep incision of the River Colorado and its tributaries. This incision has produced the Grand Canyon and the classic intrenched meanders of the San Juan River.

River terraces have always been attractive sites for settlement. They are well drained and flood-free and give easy access to water supplies and alluvial soils on the flood plain.

River terraces

Renewed erosion may cause a river to incise into its flood plain. If this occurs rapidly, remnants of the original flood plain may be left as terraces along the edges of the valley, as shown in Figure 4.11. When such terraces occur at the same level, they are known as **paired river terraces**.

Unpaired terraces form where lateral shifting of the river channel is rapid and where some vertical incision occurs. Those parts of the former flood plain that survive form terraces, though not at the same level. Unpaired terraces in the British Isles often form when climatic change leads to variations in river discharge.

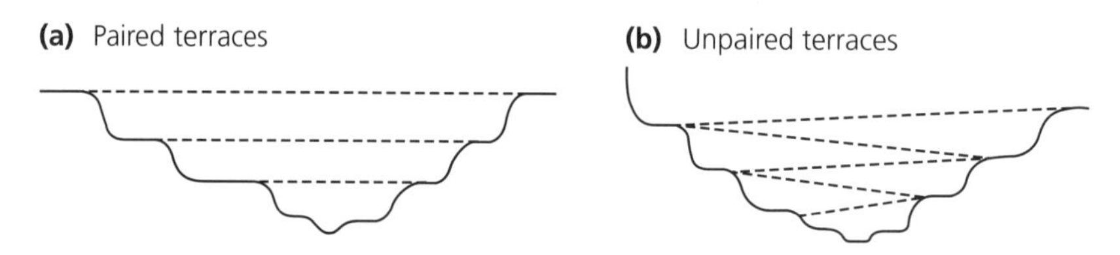

Figure 4.11 River terraces

Knickpoints

Rivers have a long profile that is graded to sea level. If sea level falls, the river will adjust by cutting down to its new base level. This process starts at sea level and progresses upstream. Where the new graded profile intersects the old, an abrupt change of gradient develops. This is called a **knickpoint** and is shown in Figure 4.12.

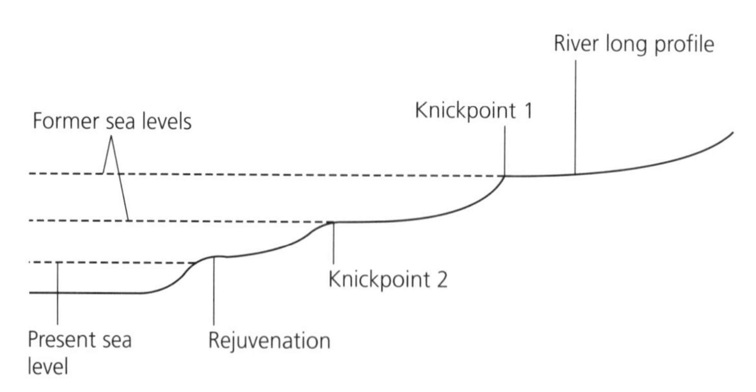

Figure 4.12 Knickpoints

Estuaries

Most river mouths in the British Isles are distinctive funnel-shaped **estuaries**. Estuaries are drowned lowland river valleys. Flooding occurred as sea level rose between 18,000 and 6,000 BP during the melting of Devensian ice sheets. In the last 6,000 years (a period of stable sea level), aggradation has led to the growth of mudflats and salt marshes in estuaries (see p. 77).

Estuaries are areas of low wave energy and sediment sinks. The flood tide sweeps silt and clay into estuaries, where it settles out at high water. Rivers carrying suspended

Incision	Aggradation
Lack of load to deposit	**Too much sediment for river to transport**
Increase in vegetation cover	
Decrease in mass movements	More erosion, weathering and mass movement on slopes
Absence of inputs from wind	
No input of glacial drift	
Decrease in frost weathering	
Change in base level	**Change in base level**
Land rises (tectonics, isostatic change)	Land sinks
Sea level falls	Sea level rises
Increase in velocity of flow	**Decrease in velocity of flow**
Change in slope	
Change in climate	
Change in discharge	**Change in amount of discharge**

Table 4.3 Causes of incision and aggradation

sediment deposit fine particles as a result of **flocculation** (the mixing of fresh water and salt water, which causes the tiny silt and clay particles to stick together and fall out of suspension). A complex network of deep channels or creeks (rather like river channels) criss-cross the mudflats and salt marshes. They reach bankfull twice a day (at high tide) and discharge huge volumes of water.

Deltas

Along some coastlines, the volume of sediment deposited by rivers is too large to be removed by wave and tidal action. Under these conditions, a **delta** of river sediment builds out into the sea.

Deltas show great variation in planform. This reflects the importance of fluvial, wave and tidal controls. Deltas located on lakes and inland seas, where wave energy is

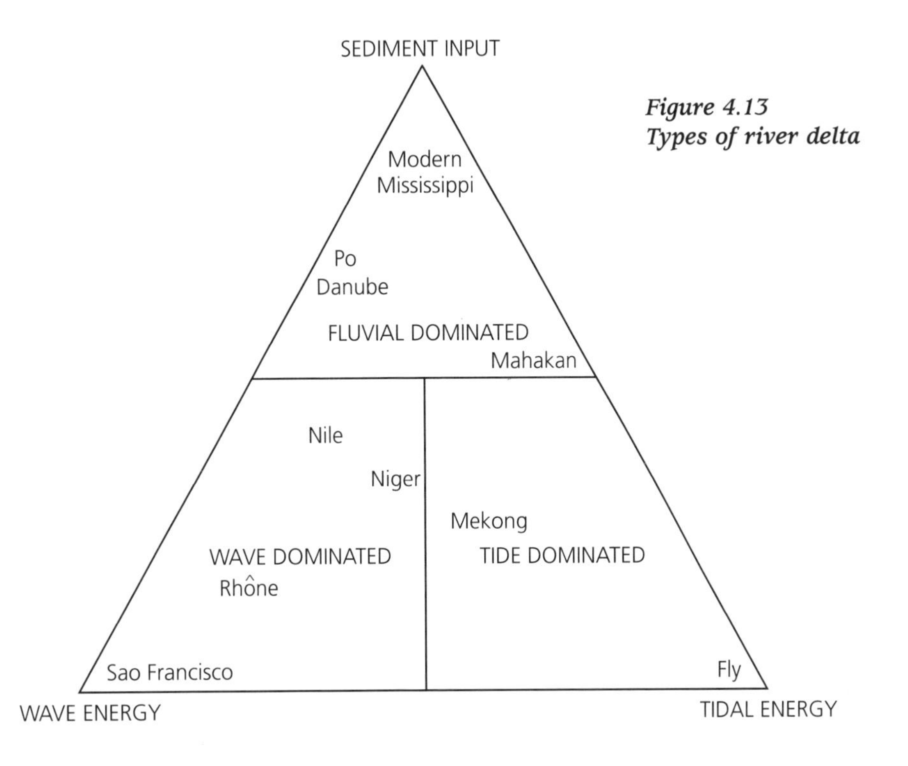

Figure 4.13 Types of river delta

low, are dominated by fluvial processes. In contrast, along coasts with high wave energy or a large tidal range, shoreline processes can disperse the sediment deposited by the river.

Deltas comprise two morphological elements: a delta front (the shoreline and the gently sloping offshore zone); and a delta plain that forms an extensive lowland made up of active and abandoned distributary channels. Delta front morphology is affected by the effectiveness of fluvial, tidal and wave processes, as shown in Figure 4.13. The Mississippi is the only major delta almost solely determined in shape by sediment deposition by distributary channels. It has undergone very little modification by tidal and wave processes. Where wave action is more effective, a smooth arcuate shoreline is developed through the redistribution of river sediment. Along coasts with strong tidal currents, the delta front is dominated by ridges, channels and islands.

5 *River flooding*

Rivers flood when discharge exceeds bankfull channel capacity. The excess water spreads across the flood plain.

5.1 Causes of floods

Most floods result from the rapid transfer of water to river channels by overland flow (see pp. 36–37). Conditions particularly likely to cause flooding include:
- high-intensity rainfall;
- prolonged rainfall on to already saturated soils;
- rapid snowmelt.

You should know that river floods result from both natural processes and human activities. The impact of floods on people (loss of life, damage to property etc.) is largely due to the siting of settlements on vulnerable flood plains.

Human activities often increase the frequency and severity of flooding. Deforestation, land drainage, ploughing on steep slopes and urbanisation all increase the flood risk. Many flood plains are built-up and rivers present a hazard to property and lives in such areas.

INSET 6

Floods in Malton, North Yorkshire

The worst floods for 70 years hit the North Yorkshire town of Malton when the River Derwent burst its banks between 7 and 11 March 1999. During this period, the river was 3 metres above its normal March level. The Malton area is vulnerable to flooding because:
- it is part of the flat Vale of Pickering (a former glacial lake);
- hills, with steep slopes, border the Vale both to the north (North York Moors) and south (Yorkshire Wolds).

Flooding in March 1999 was caused by a combination of factors:
- heavy and prolonged rainfall in the preceding eight days (over 200 mm fell on the North York Moors);
- already saturated soils giving rapid overland flow;
- snow, which fell on the North York Moors during the previous week, melting quickly.

5.2 Flood prevention

There are two approaches to flood prevention: **flood abatement** and **flood protection**.

Flood abatement

Flood abatement aims to slow the movement of water into river channels. Its effect is to lengthen lag times and reduce peak discharge. This can be achieved through land use change and land use management in the upper catchment.
- Afforestation increases interception, evaporation and transpiration, reducing run-off and lengthening lag times.
- Changes in agriculture, from arable to pasture, have a similar effect.

- Land use management in farming, such as terracing and contour ploughing, also helps to reduce the risk of flooding.

Flood abatement policies often run into problems where land is privately owned or in the hands of several owners. In these circumstances, it may be difficult to get agreement on changes in land use and farming practices. Whole-catchment planning may also be hindered where administrative and political boundaries do not coincide with the watersheds of river basins. Flood abatement is a long-term strategy; in the short term, it may do little to reduce flooding.

Flood control

Flood control aims to confine floodwater to the river channel, or to divert it to areas of temporary storage (flood basins). There are a large number of flood control measures, as shown in Figure 4.14 and Table 4.4. Most involve hard engineering and are expensive to implement. Some, such as dam building, may have other benefits, providing water supplies, recreation and leisure opportunities and generating hydro-power.

Measure	Description
Embankments/levées	Embankments on either side of the channel, to increase channel capacity. Potentially hazardous if the water level is above the flood plain.
Channel straightening/ channelisation	Removing meanders increases the average gradient and therefore the velocity of flow.
Flood relief channels	Artificial channels that take some of the floodwater relieve natural channels.
Sluice gates	Sluice gates are raised during times of flood to protect settlements downstream. Water is diverted into flood basins or washlands, where it is stored temporarily.
Dam building	Storage of floodwaters in reservoirs or flood storage basins. Dams and reservoirs offer multipurpose usage, e.g. water supply, HEP, recreation and leisure, as well as flood prevention.

Table 4.4 Flood control measures using hard engineering

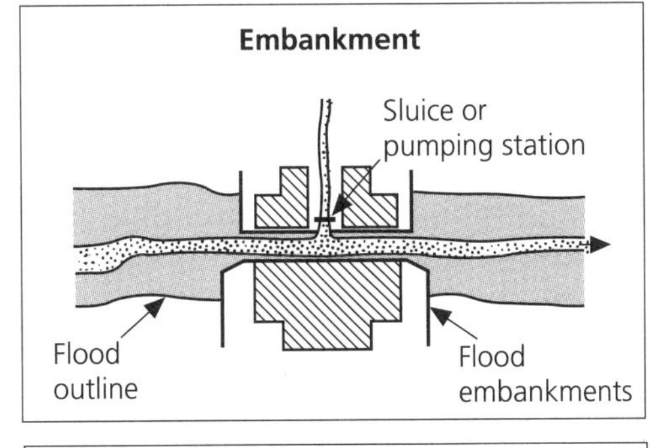

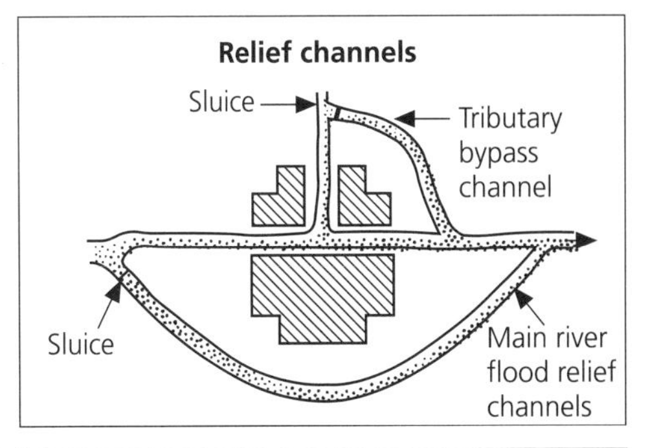

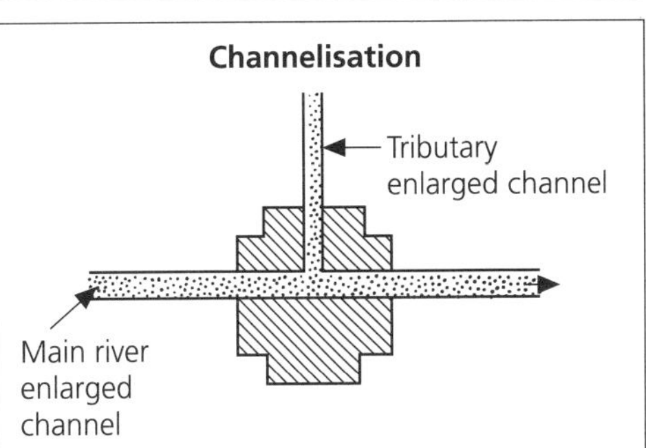

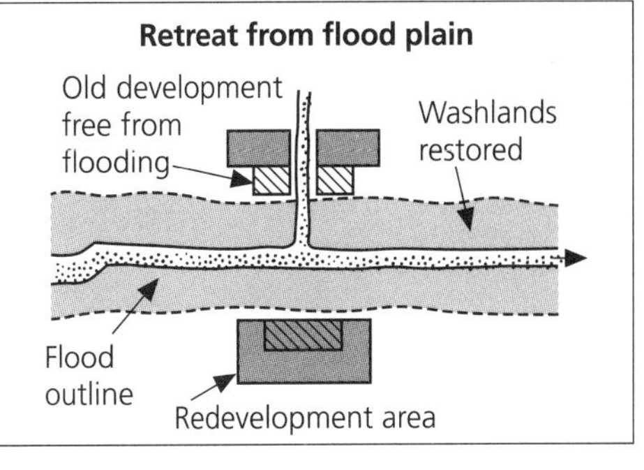

Figure 4.14 Engineering/planning options in urban flood protection

Other responses to flooding include land use zoning and flood insurance.

- Planners may prevent vulnerable developments such as housing and industry from locating in flood-prone areas. Instead they may encourage land uses such as parks, sports fields and pasture land, which are relatively unaffected by floods.
- Individuals may respond to the flood hazard by insuring their properties against flood damage.

6 Droughts and river flow

Droughts in humid, temperate climates are episodic and are the result of unusually dry spells of weather. Whereas floods are usually short-duration events, droughts may last for several months. Moreover, while the impact of flooding is usually local, with the direct effects felt only in flood plain areas, droughts often affect whole regions and even countries.

Responses to drought include the following:

- The construction of dams in headwaters to store a larger proportion of winter flow. This is costly, and flooding valleys raises environmental objections.
- Inter-basin water transfer schemes, such as those in north-east England where water from Kielder is transferred to the Wear, Tees and Swale basins. Ecological problems arise when there are differences in water temperatures and water chemistry (i.e. dissolved load) between two basins.

INSET 7

Drought in West Yorkshire in 1995

In 1995 large parts of northern England were hit by an exceptional drought. Between April and September only 43% of normal rainfall fell in West Yorkshire. This followed a year of below average rainfall. By October 1995, reservoir levels in the Bradford district were between 11 and 18% full. In Halifax reservoirs ran dry: the town's water supply was maintained only by a fleet of tankers bringing water from the River Tees 24 hours a day.

These water shortages had a number of environmental consequences:

- Overpumping of groundwater from chalk aquifers in East Yorkshire led to a fall in the water table, with several chalk streams drying up.
- Increased levels of abstraction from Yorkshire rivers meant greater concentrations of sewage, falling oxygen levels in the water, and higher water temperatures (owing to less turbulent flow). These changes had a severe effect on the ecology of rivers.

INSET 8

Water use on the Colorado River

Much of the Colorado Basin in the south-west USA is a desert or semi-desert region. The Colorado River is the main source of water for much of this region. Since 1933 eight dams have been built on the river. The Hoover and Glen Canyon dams are the largest. They are multipurpose schemes, providing water, electricity and recreational opportunities. However, the huge reservoirs (Lake Mead and Lake Powell) created by the dams are controversial. Both have flooded some of the finest canyon lands in the world. The Glen Canyon dam has also altered the flow and sediment load of the Colorado River in the Grand Canyon. Deprived of annual floods, the Grand Canyon is becoming choked with sediment and debris. The Glen Canyon dam, by removing suspended sediment from the Colorado and lowering water temperatures, has also had adverse effects on the river's ecology.

Despite the construction of dams, water supplies are fast running out in the lower Colorado Basin. Rapid population growth in cities such as Las Vegas (see p. 195) and Phoenix has increased the demand for water. Irrigated farmland may soon be abandoned in order to divert water supplies to these urban centres. Farming is the main user of water and much of its use is consumptive. Wasteful spray and furrow irrigation methods result in high evaporative losses, while water returned to the river from irrigation is often high in dissolved salts and unusable.

UNIT 5 Glacial and periglacial environments

1 Distribution of glacial environments

Cold, humid climates that support glaciers and ice sheets occur in high-latitude and high-altitude areas. The largest expanses of snow and ice are in the polar regions, principally in the ice sheets of Antarctica and Greenland. Most of the world's highest mountain ranges – Himalayas, Andes, Alps and Rockies – also support icefields and glaciers.

2 The chronology of glaciation

For 90% of the last 1.6 million years, middle and high latitudes have experienced glacial conditions. During this period (known as the Pleistocene), there have been at least four major **glacials** or ice ages and three warmer spells or **interglacials**. In addition, there

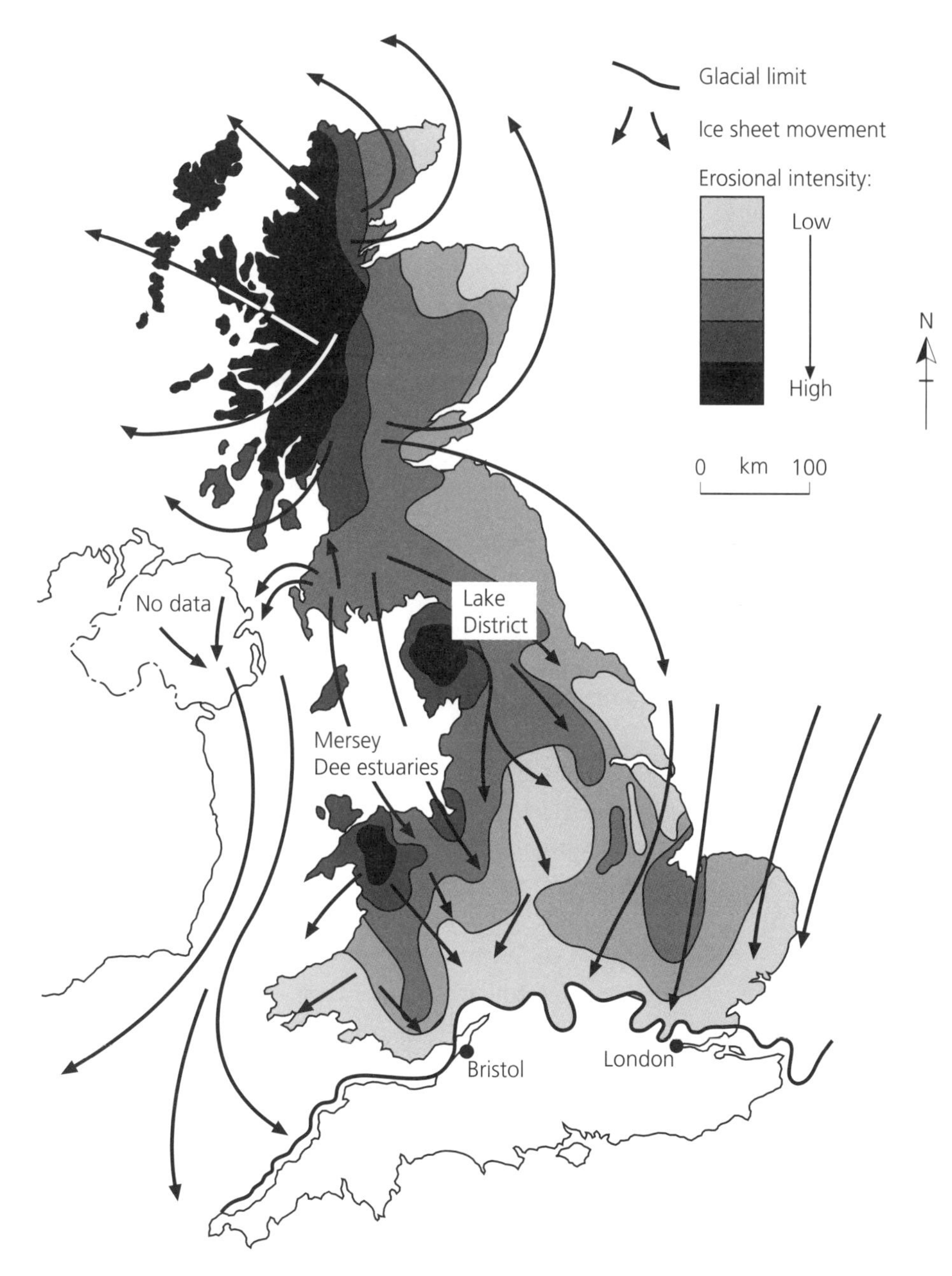

Figure 5.1 Patterns of ice sheet movement and glacial erosion in Britain

Small glaciers survived in Scotland, the Lake District and Snowdonia until just 10,000 years ago. So recent is the last glaciation that the work of ice has left a powerful imprint on the landscapes of northern Britain, especially in upland areas (see Figure 5.1).

have been many cold and warm phases lasting just a few thousand years. These shorter episodes of cold and warmth are called **stadials** and **interstadials** respectively. The last glacial – the Devensian – lasted from approximately 120000 BP to 10000 BP. Following the retreat of the Devensian ice, the world entered a warm interglacial (the Holocene) that has continued to the present day.

INSET 1

The causes of ice ages

A combination of three factors causes ice ages.

- Changes in the output of solar radiation. Glaciations seem to occur when sunspot activity reaches a maximum.
- Changes in the albedo or reflectivity of the Earth's surface. The accumulation of snow and ice increases reflectivity and promotes cooling of the atmosphere. There is a positive feedback effect, as the snow and ice cover lowers temperatures and increases snowfall, which amplifies the initial change.
- Changes in the Earth's orbit and the tilt of the Earth's axis. Over a period of nearly 100,000 years, the Earth's orbit varies from circular to elliptical. Glaciations occur when the orbit is more elliptical. The tilt of the Earth's axis varies from 22 to 25 degrees over a period of 42,000 years. A more extreme tilt gives greater seasonality, with colder winters and an increased likelihood of glacials. Finally, variations in the orientation of the Earth's axis (comparable to the wobble of a spinning top) occur in a cycle of 21,000 years. This determines which hemisphere is closer to the Sun in winter. When the northern hemisphere, with its larger landmasses, is nearer the Sun in winter (the situation today), glacials are less likely to occur.

3 *Types of glacier*

At its maximum 20,000 years ago, the Devensian glacial submerged most of northern Europe in a vast sheet of ice. During such a **continental glaciation**, only the jagged peaks of the highest mountains protrude above the **ice sheet**. These mountains, surrounded by seas of ice, are known as **nunataks**. Today continental-type glaciation is confined to Antarctica and Greenland. The Greenland ice sheet reaches a maximum thickness of 2.5 kilometres.

In plateau-like regions, such as the Vatnajökull in Iceland and the Columbia plateau in Alberta, small ice caps or **icefields** develop. Glaciers nourished by these icefields spill over the edge of the plateaux as **outlet glaciers**. Sometimes outlet glaciers merge in the lowlands to form **piedmont glaciers**.

In steep mountain ranges, such as the Himalayas and Alps, glaciers occupy only the valleys and the flanks of the mountains. Ice accumulates in sheltered circular hollows as **cirque glaciers**. If the mass of ice is sufficient, these glaciers will extend downslope to form **valley glaciers**. Such spatially limited glaciation is known as **Alpine glaciation**. **Niche glaciers** are very small glaciers that cling to gullies and hollows on mountain faces.

In the British Isles a brief cold phase known as the **Loch Lomond stadial** occurred between 11,000 BP and 10,000 BP. Small valley glaciers and cirque glaciers formed in the Scottish Highlands, Lake District and Snowdonia.

4 *Formation of glacier ice*

Glacier ice forms when annual accumulation of snow exceeds melting. Under the weight of successive snowfalls and over many years, low-density snow (density less than 0.1) is compacted. First it forms granular snow (density around 0.3), then **firn** or **nevé** (density 0.5) and finally glacier ice (density 0.9). Unlike snow, glacier ice can flow downhill under its own mass and gravity.

Transverse cracks on the surface of a glacier – crevasses – develop in areas where localised movement of the glacier is more rapid, e.g. where there is a steeper slope to its valley, or where narrowing of the valley confines flow.

5 The movement of glaciers

Glaciers move in two ways: by sliding and by internal deformation.

- In climates of extreme cold, glaciers are frozen permanently to the underlying bedrock. As a result, these cold-based glaciers are incapable of much erosion. This explains how delicate landforms such as tors can survive glaciation. In warm-based glaciers, 90% of movement occurs through basal sliding. A film of water at the base of the glacier (see Inset 2) lubricates the ice and causes sliding. Thus, glaciers in temperate regions can move quite rapidly. For example, the Nisqually Glacier on Mount Rainier in Washington State moves up to 50 centimetres a day. Slope steepness and ice volume also influence rates of glacier flow.
- The mass and gravity of glaciers also cause movement through internal deformation. This is a type of laminar flow within the dense glacier ice.

INSET 2

Pressure melting

Pressure causes ice to melt at temperatures below zero. This explains why water is present at sub-zero temperatures at the base of many glaciers. In temperate glaciers, ice in contact with the bed is often undergoing pressure melting. This allows the glacier to slide on its bed. Constrictions in glacier flow are likely to increase pressure and cause melting. Equally, any reduction in pressure will lead to freezing.

6 Mass balance

Even in a period of global warming, glaciers may advance. This is because the advance and retreat of glaciers depends on precipitation as well as temperature. Future global warming may increase evaporation and snowfall and lead ultimately to the expansion of many glaciers.

Mass balance is the difference between a glacier's annual accumulation and ablation (melting, sublimation) of snow. There are three states of mass balance:

- **positive:** accumulation exceeds ablation and the glacier advances beyond its terminus;
- **negative:** ablation is greater than accumulation and the glacier shrinks and retreats upvalley;
- **neutral:** accumulation and ablation are equal, causing the glacier's terminus to remain static.

In the upper part of a valley, glacier accumulation of ice exceeds ablation. This area is known as the **accumulation zone**, as shown in Figure 5.2. In the lower part or **ablation zone**, ablation is greater than accumulation. The boundary separating the two sections is the equilibrium line or **firn line**. Above the firn line, the glacier surface is snow-covered.

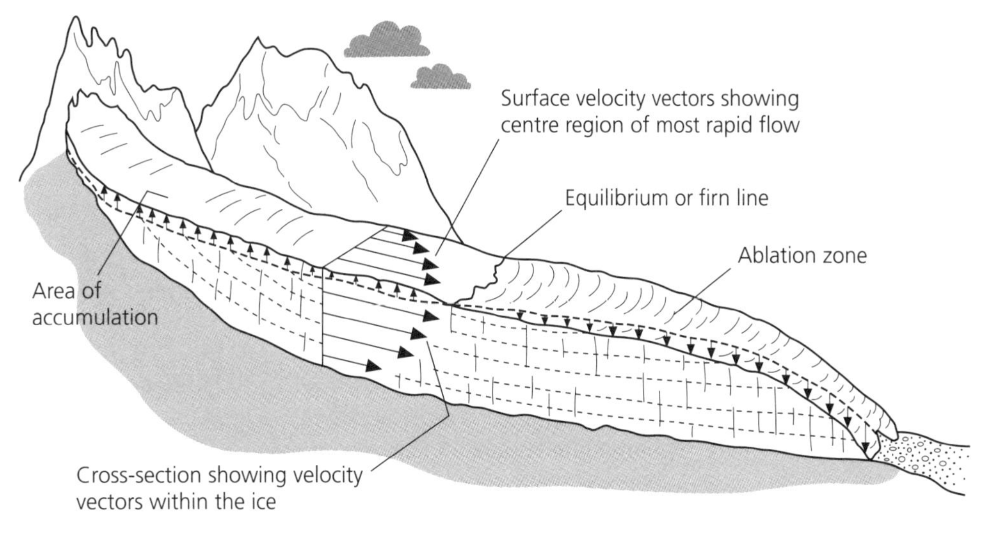

Figure 5.2 Mass balance at a valley glacier

INSET 3

Glacier advance and retreat

An increase in accumulation consequent on a fall in temperature or an increase in precipitation results in glacier expansion and advance. Equally, glaciers will shrink and retreat if there is an increase in temperature or a fall in precipitation. Currently, most valley glaciers are retreating in response to the global warming of climate. However, at a local scale, individual glaciers may respond to winters of heavy snowfall by advancing. The Nisqually Glacier on Mount Rainier retreated steadily from 1840 to 1951. However, following high snow accumulation between 1944 and 1951, the glacier advanced to its present position, where it has remained more or less stationary for the last 20 years.

7 Glacial erosion

7.1 Processes of glacial erosion

Evidence of the direction of ice movement during glacial periods comes from:

- striae;
- erratics;
- orientation of rock particles in glacial moraines;
- orientation of long axes of depositional landforms such as drumlins.

Glaciers erode in two ways: by **abrasion** and by **quarrying**.

- Rock particles frozen into a glacier and particles dragged along at the base of the glacier scour and abrade the bedrock. Often this process of abrasion rounds and smoothes rock outcrops. Fine-grained particles may polish the bedrock, and coarser particles may leave deep scratches called striations or **striae**. Striae provide important clues about the direction of ice flow.
- Quarrying (or plucking) removes bedrock particles along joints and bedding planes. Pressure melting at the base of a glacier causes water to run into rock joints, where it freezes. The process of freeze–thaw weakens the rock, which is then quarried by the ice that flows over it. The moving ice acts like a conveyor belt: it transports rock debris and in doing so provides the conditions for abrasion at the base of the glacier.

Roches moutonnées are small-scale rock outcrops that have been smoothed and steepened by glacial erosion. The upstream side (stoss) is exposed to intense pressure, which causes abrasion and smoothing, as shown in Figure 5.3. Slopes oriented downstream (lee) experience lower pressure. Water freezes in this area. This leads to quarrying and a steep, angular slope.

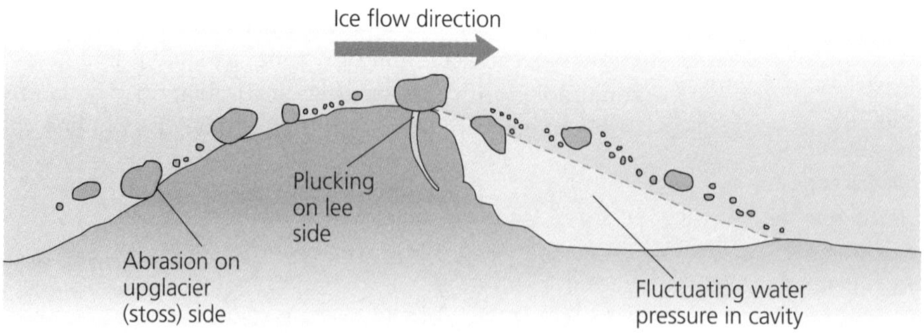

Figure 5.3 The location of plucking or quarrying on the lee side of a roche moutonnée

7.2 Landforms of glacial erosion

Cirques

Cirques (also known as corries, coires and cwms) are deep, amphitheatre-like rock basins cut into mountainsides. Formed by glacial erosion, cirques in the northern hemisphere occur most frequently on north- and east-facing slopes. Cirque glaciers developed on these slopes because of:

- the accumulation of blown snow from prevailing south-westerly winds;
- the colder microclimate (e.g. longer periods of shadow).

Cirques must have formed during glacial periods when ice was confined to upland valleys. Cirque formation is not possible in continental glaciation when the landscape is completely submerged by ice.

The origin of cirques is unclear. However, a possible sequence of events leading to cirque development involves:

- freeze–thaw beneath a snow patch (nivation) and the removal of debris by surface wash and solifluction to create a shallow depression;
- snow turns to firn and glacier ice and slides/flows downslope, overdeepening the depression by abrasion and quarrying;
- the backwall of the overdeepened depression retreats by freeze–thaw weathering, while glacial erosion further deepens the depression.

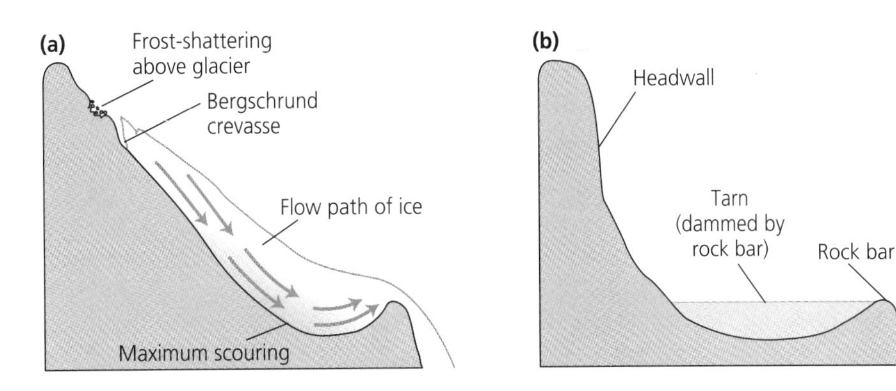

Figure 5.4 Cross-section of a cirque glacier. (a) During the early stages of glaciation, the hollow becomes progressively overdeepened. (b) After glaciation, the overdeepened basin is occupied by a lake or tarn.

In a fully developed cirque glacier, the weight of ice in the upper section of the glacier causes a rotational sliding movement that overdeepens the rock basin by abrasion. However, at the outlet of the basin, where ice movement is directed upwards, erosion is less severe and a rock bar or **lip** forms. A deep crevasse known as a **bergschrund** develops between the glacier and the headwall. Meltwater accumulates here and may assist quarrying on the headwall.

If two adjacent cirque glaciers cut back their headwalls, they may reduce a ridge to a knife-edged feature called an **arête** (e.g. Crib Goch in Snowdonia). When three or more cirque glaciers converge in this way, they form a **pyramidal peak** (e.g. the Matterhorn).

Glacial troughs

Glacial troughs flooded by post-glacial rises of sea level are known as fjords. At the mouth of fjords, a rock bar or **threshold** indicates where glacier movement (and erosion) slowed as the ice began to float on the sea.

Glacial troughs (or glacial valleys) are large-scale landforms, carved through solid rock by valley glaciers and ice streams (areas of more rapid flow within ice sheets). They probably developed along river valleys that existed before glaciation. Glacial troughs are:

- U-shaped in cross-section as a result of glacial erosion of both the valley sides and the valley floor.
- deeper than tributary valleys occupied by smaller glaciers. Because erosion rates of glaciers in major valleys were greater than those of smaller tributary glaciers, on deglaciation these tributary valleys are left hanging above the main glacial trough.
- straighter than river valleys, with projecting spurs planed off or truncated.
- irregular in long profile. The upper part of the trough often has a steep rock wall known as a **trough head**. Trough heads form where glacier ice from extensive icefields converges, increasing its speed and power of erosion. Further downvalley, areas of more intense erosion (e.g. where the valley narrows or tributary glaciers join the main glacier) give rise to rock basins. Following deglaciation, these basins may form **ribbon lakes**.

Diffluent cols

In some circumstances, valley glaciers erode breaches through watersheds. If a valley is blocked by other ice or a constriction restricts ice flow, a valley glacier may overflow

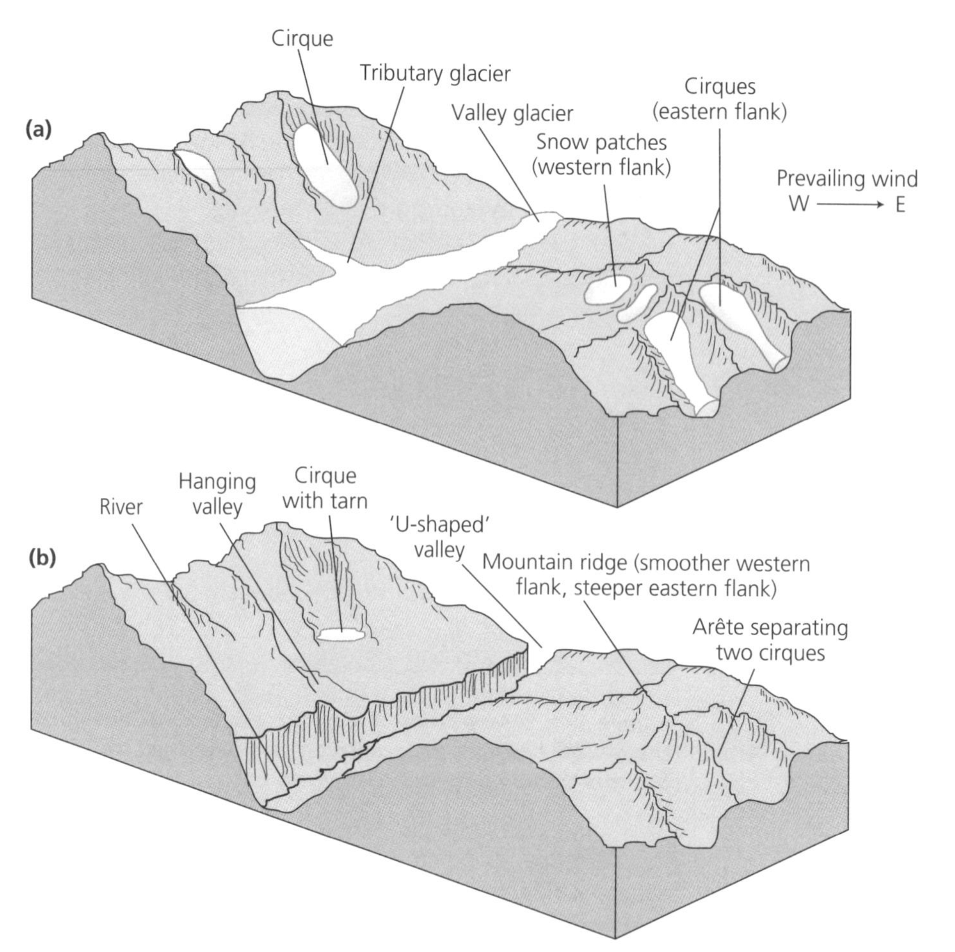

Figure 5.5 Landforms developed by Alpine glaciation: (a) during glaciation; (b) after deglaciation

at the lowest point on a watershed. This process, known as **glacial diffluence**, forms a col or gap in a watershed. The Lairig Ghru is such a col. It forms a spectacular 400-metre breach across the main watershed of the Cairngorms.

Ice sheets and glacially eroded landscapes

Erosion by ice sheets often produces landscapes very different from those eroded by valley glaciers and cirque glaciers. Extensive areas such as the Laurentian Shield in Canada and the Baltic Shield in Scandinavia show the effect of abrasion and quarrying by ice sheets. Typical of these glacially eroded landscapes are streamlined roches moutonnées and interspersed rock basins occupied by small lakes. Such a landscape of rock ridges and shallow lakes is called **knock and lochan topography**.

8 Glacial deposition

Glaciers are like conveyor belts for eroded rock debris. This rock debris derives from:

- glacial erosion of the valley sides and valley floor;
- rockfall due to weathering of valley slopes;
- rock avalanches and other debris flows from valley slopes.

Eventually, this rock debris is deposited:

- at the ice front or terminus of the glacier;
- under the glacier;
- under the ice and beyond the ice front by meltwater flowing within and from the glacier.

Collectively, these deposits are called **glacial drift**. Large particles of rock transported by ice, and which are of different geology to the area in which they are deposited, are known as **erratics**. Erratics provide valuable evidence about the flow of ice during glacial periods. For example, we know from the distribution of erratics of Shap granite (Cumbria) that ice from the Lake District flowed south into Lancashire and Cheshire, and east across the Pennines into the Tees Lowlands.

8.1 Ice-contact depositional landforms

Rock debris deposited in contact with the ice comprises an unsorted mix of particles of all sizes. This material is known as **till** or **boulder clay**. It may be supraglacial, englacial or subglacial. Some till is also bulldozed downvalley ahead of the glacier. **Moraine** is till that has been piled into a variety of hummocky mounds and ridges. The different types of moraine are shown in Figure 5.6.

INSET 4

Types of rock debris transported by glaciers

- Supraglacial: material carried on the surface of the glacier.
- Englacial: material carried within the glacier. This debris may enter the glacier through crevasses or melt its way into the glacier.
- Subglacial: material carried at the base of the glacier and largely responsible for abrasion.

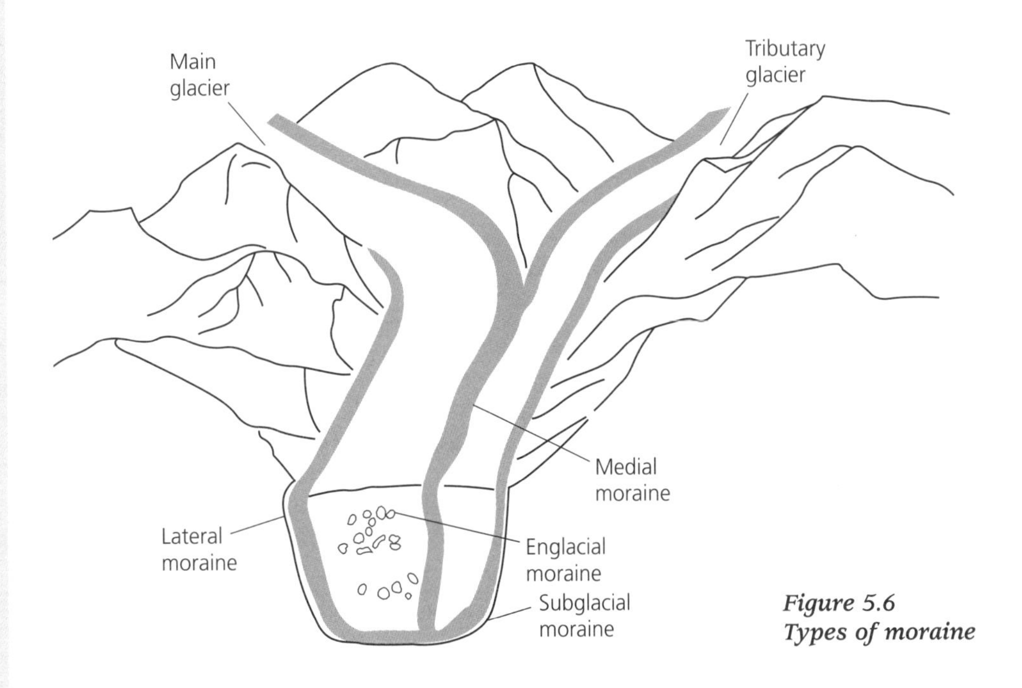

Figure 5.6
Types of moraine

Till deposited by moving ice has a clear 'fabric', with larger rock particles oriented in the direction of flow. Till deposited by the melting of stagnant ice has no discernible fabric.

Lateral moraines

Lateral moraines form along the sides of valley glaciers. They consist of piles of loose rock debris derived from rockfall and avalanching on to the glacier from the adjacent valley slopes. If the glacier recedes or shrinks, this debris forms prominent ridges that run parallel to the valley side. A lateral moraine near the terminus of the Athabasca Glacier in Alberta stands 124 metres high and is 1.5 kilometres long.

Terminal moraines

Terminal moraines form across a valley, at the glacier's downvalley end. Terminal moraines are partly the result of the melt-out of debris-filled ice, and partly the result of debris pushed by an advancing glacier. If a glacier remains stationary for a period of time and then retreats intermittently, it may create a series of **recessional moraines**.

Medial moraines

Medial moraines consist of supraglacial debris that runs down the centre of valley glaciers in a thin ribbon. They form at the confluence of two valley glaciers, where adjacent lateral moraines join together.

Hummocky moraines

Hummocky moraines form chaotic landscapes made up of hundreds of steep-sided mounds (up to 50 metres in height). They have no consistent orientation or linear development. These moraines are associated with wasting ice. The largest area of hummocky moraine in Britain is in Glen Torridon in north-west Scotland.

Drumlins

Drumlins are smooth, oval-shaped hills made of till. They have a streamlined form elongated in the direction of ice flow. Typical dimensions are 5–50 metres in height and 1–2 kilometres in length. In profile, drumlins have a short, steep slope (stoss) which faced up-glacier and a gentle long slope (tail) which faced down-glacier. The typical shape is shown in Figure 5.7. Drumlins occur in swarms often in lowlands (e.g. Vale of Eden) or wide valley systems close to centres of ice dispersal (e.g. Ribblehead).

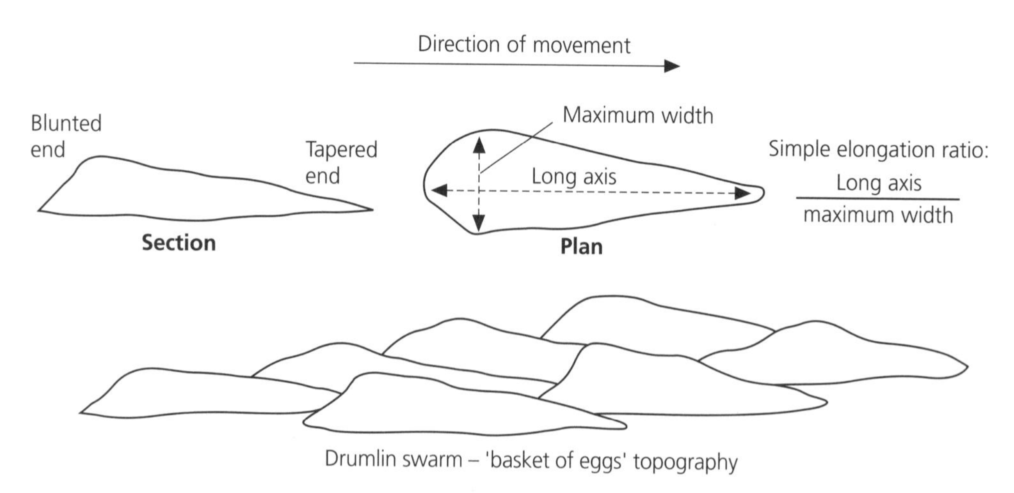

Figure 5.7 Drumlin profiles and plans

There are several theories of drumlin formation. The most widely accepted suggests that till beneath an ice sheet is moulded into streamlined forms by moving ice.

8.2 Glacio-fluvial depositional landforms

- Glacio-fluvial features are prominent landforms of deglaciation.
- Huge amounts of meltwater, abundant rock debris and hydrostatic pressure mean that melt-water streams carry very high sediment loads.

Debris is laid down by meltwater and sorted into layers by particle size – called **glacio-fluvial** deposits. Landforms that result from glacio-fluvial deposition fall into two groups.

- **Pro-glacial features:** deposited by meltwater beyond the ice front (e.g. sandar, valley sandar).
- **Ice contact features:** deposited by meltwater within glaciers (e.g. eskers, kames and kame terraces). These are shown in Figure 5.8.

Sandar

Sandar (or outwash plains) are extensive spreads of sand and gravel laid down by braided meltwater streams beyond the margin of glaciers and ice sheets. In southern Iceland, powerful meltwater streams draining several small icefields have deposited huge amounts of coarse sediment along the coast. In some places, this sandar has extended the coastal plain several kilometres seaward. Proglacial lakes impounded between the ice front and recessional moraines also encourage rapid sedimentation by meltwater streams. Valley sandar develop in steep-sided glacial troughs that limit their lateral expansion.

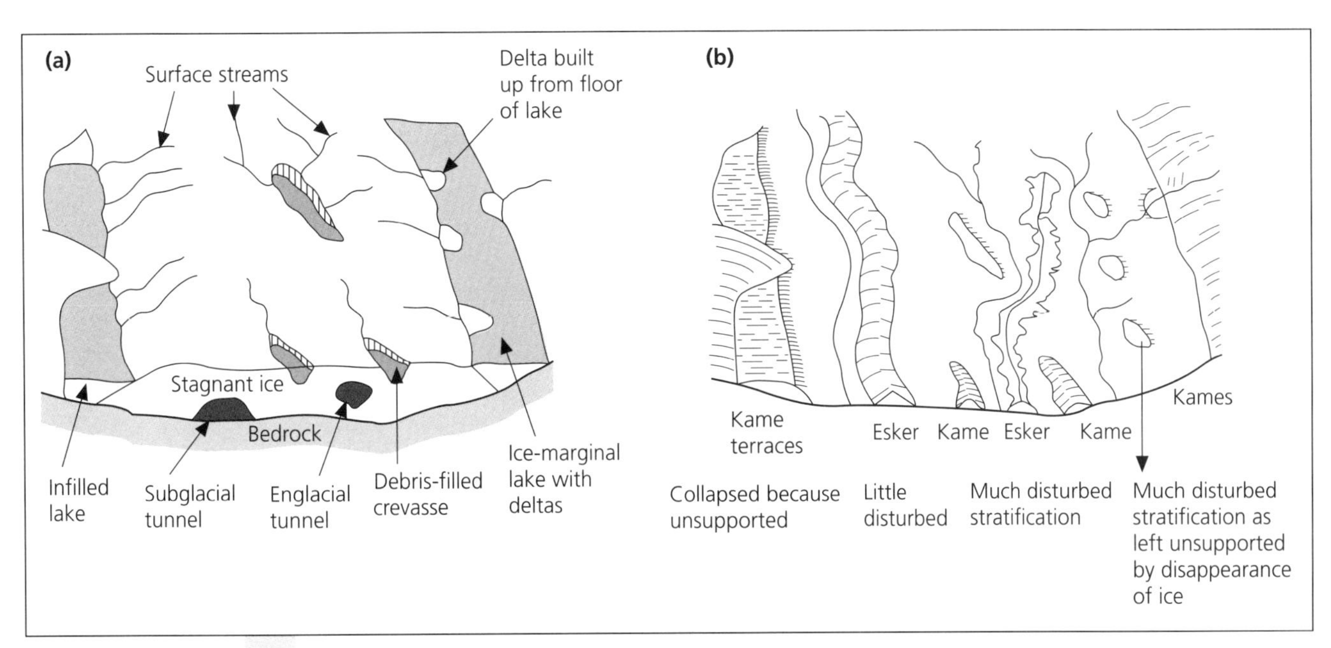

Figure 5.8 Glacio-fluvial ice contact features: (a) during glaciation; (b) after glaciation

Eskers

Eskers are sinuous ridges of sand and gravel that are often several kilometres long. They derive from sediments deposited within the channels of meltwater streams that flowed on, through or at the base of glaciers. Some eskers appear to run up-slope – clear evidence that meltwater, under hydrostatic pressure, can flow uphill.

Kames and kame terraces

Cavities such as crevasses within glaciers may fill with sediment. Subsequent melting of the glacier causes the sediment to collapse to form an isolated mound or **kame**. Where sediment accumulates along an ice margin (e.g. in a marginal lake between a glacier and the valley side), melting leaves a continuous embankment adjacent to the valley side. This is a kame terrace and is a good indicator of the thickness of the former valley glacier. The melting of ice cores trapped beneath glacial deposits may create surface depressions or kettle holes that later form small lakes.

8.3 Meltwater erosional landforms

- The seasonal discharge of meltwater and high sediment loading make braiding a characteristic feature of meltwater channels in proglacial areas.

Meltwater channels are the main glacio-fluvial erosional landform. These channels are subglacial in origin and were cut by meltwater streams with very high discharge. Meltwater channels are usually steep-sided, deep and fairly straight. In long profile, some have up-gradients. Again this shows the influence of hydrostatic pressure, enabling water to flow uphill if there is enough force behind it. The high discharges needed to form large meltwater channels may be related to the formation of temporary lakes beneath glaciers. If a sediment or ice dam holding back such a glacial lake is breached, the sudden release of water would create massive floods or **jökulhlaups** (see p. 13). Such events can cut large meltwater channels.

9 Periglaciation

In high latitude and some high-altitude regions that are not covered by ice, temperatures are so low that the ground is permanently frozen (Table 5.1). In this periglacial environment, processes of freeze–thaw and the growth of ice masses in the ground give rise to distinctive landforms.

The evidence for past periglacial processes is widespread in Britain. In the lowlands there are collapsed pingos, solifluction (head) deposits, block streams, etc. But the most important relict periglaciation landforms are solifluction sheets and lobes that mantle valley sides in the uplands.

As Figure 5.9 shows, today the most extensive periglacial areas are found in northern Canada and northern Siberia. However, periglacial areas were far more widespread in the past. For example, southern Britain, although ice-free, experienced an intensely cold climate throughout the Devensian glacial. Many periglacial landforms in southern Britain are relict features from this period.

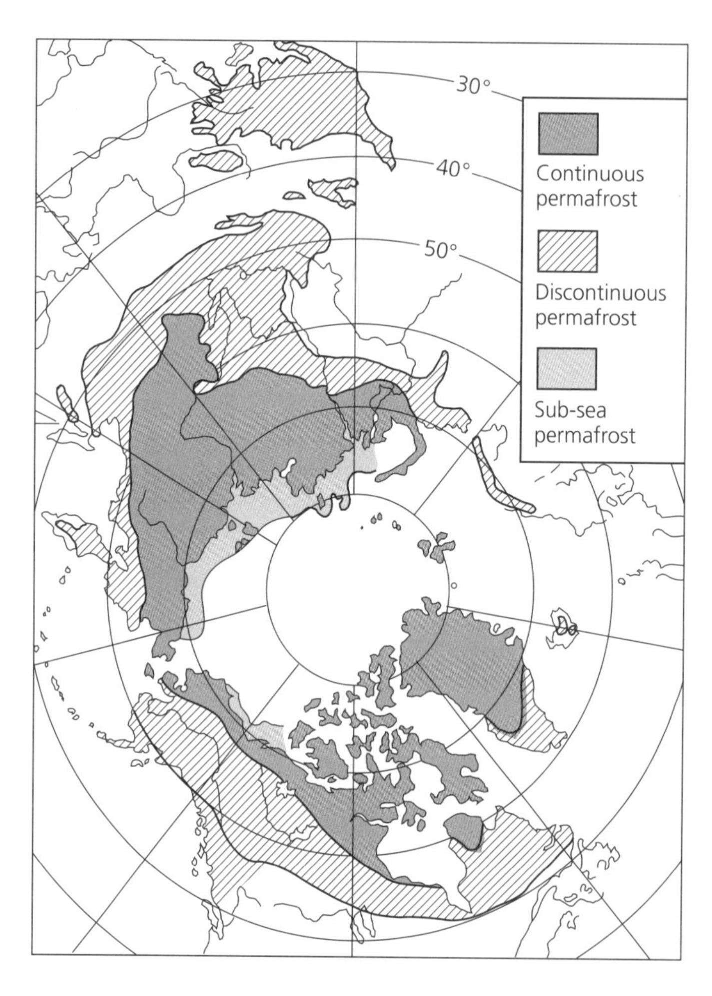

Figure 5.9
The distribution of the main permafrost types in the northern hemisphere

9.1 Periglacial processes

Permafrost

Permafrost is perennially frozen ground. Regions of continuous permafrost usually have a mean annual temperature of –5 °C and below. Permafrost consists of two important layers: the active zone and the frost zone.

- The active zone lies near the surface and above the **frost table**. It is in the active zone that freeze–thaw occurs. The frost melts during the summer before refreezing in the autumn.

The frost table separates the active layer from the permanently frozen layer or **frost zone**. Unfrozen areas within the frost zone are known as **taliks**.

Ground ice

In periglacial areas, ice often exists as large segregated masses in the ground. When water freezes, its volume increases by 9%. If the ground has a high moisture content, the growth of ice crystals will attract remaining liquid water and lead to the development of segregated ice as lenses and veins. The result is local expansion (freezing) and contraction (melting) of the surface – a process that can produce a number of periglacial landforms.

Month	°C	mm
J	−39	5
F	−38	5
M	−32	5
A	−24	3
M	−8	10
J	4	20
J	9	28
A	7	28
S	0	18
O	−14	8
N	−27	8
D	−35	8

Table 5.1 Periglacial climate: Ruskoye Ust'ye (71°N, 149°E)

Frost weathering

Frost weathering (see p. 21) is an important process in periglacial environments. Numerous freeze–thaw cycles and the sparse cover of soil and vegetation favour frost action. Landforms caused by frost weathering include **screes** (talus) and **blockfields** (see p. 22). In upland Britain, most screes and blockfields are relict features formed during cold conditions in the late glacial period.

Frost cracking

Sub-zero temperatures cause the ground to crack by contraction. This process produces polygonal cracks similar to those formed in drying mud. Frost cracking is probably the major cause of **patterned ground**.

Mass movement

Solifluction is one of the most effective processes in periglacial environments. It is defined as 'the slow flowing from higher to lower ground of masses of waste saturated with water'. Solifluction operates on slopes as gentle as 1 or 2 degrees and on fine sand and silt material. Movement is confined to the active layer. Rates of flow vary with climate, slope and vegetation cover, but are usually of the order of 1–10 centimetres a year. In periglacial environments, frost creep (heave) and permafrost (which creates an impermeable zone, causing saturation of the active layer in summer) combine with solifluction. This modified mass movement process is known as **gelifluction**.

9.2 Periglacial landforms

Patterned ground

Some types of patterned ground (e.g. stone stripes) form today in Britain's uplands following periods of very cold weather.

Patterned ground, shown in Figure 5.10, is a characteristic feature of periglacial environments. It describes the distribution of rock particles in systems of polygons, nets, steps, stripes and circles. Each of these features is sub-divided into sorted and unsorted forms.

Circles, nets and polygons normally occur on flat surfaces; steps and stripes form on slopes of between 5 and 30 degrees. Frost cracking and frost heave are important processes in the development of patterned ground. Frost heave pushes larger stones to the surface, and because of the cambering of the surface, stones then move laterally. On steeply sloping ground, this cambering is oriented downslope. Coarser particles raised to the surface by frost heave roll into the depressions between the cambers. The result is alternating stripes of coarse and fine particles.

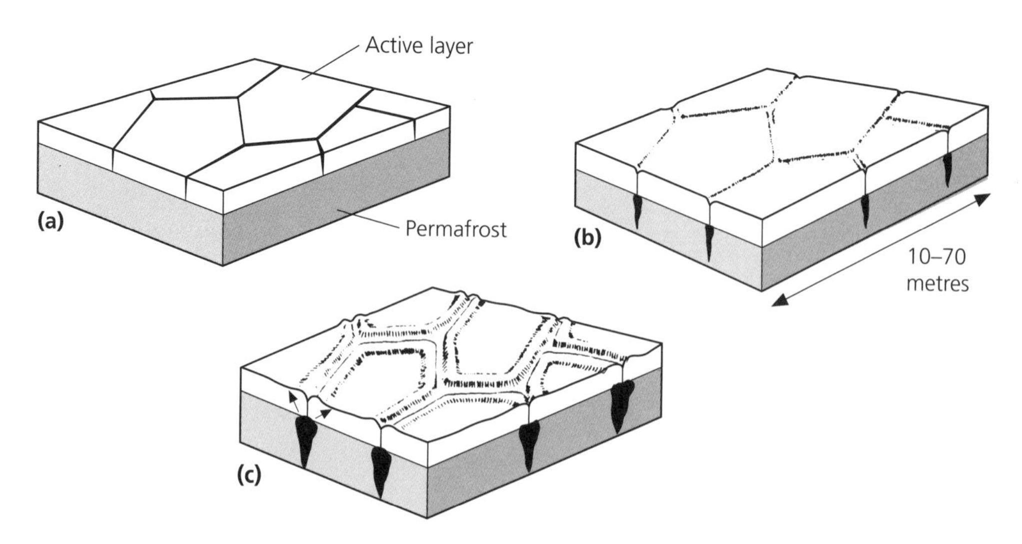

(a) Thermal contraction causes cracks.

(b) Ice wedges develop in fissures, which reopen with each winter freeze.

(c) Wedges expand laterally, pushing the rims up.

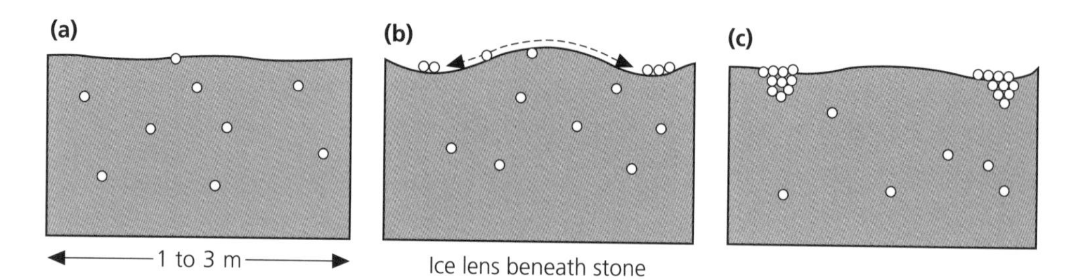

Figure 5.10 Patterned ground

Ground ice phenomena

Ice wedges are downward-tapering bodies of ice up to 10 metres in depth. In plan they form a polygonal pattern at the surface. They appear to result from frost cracking. When an ice wedge melts, it may fill with sediment to form an ice wedge cast.

The formation of ice lenses in the active layer can heave the overlying sediments into small symmetrical mounds (3–70 m high) known as **pingos**. When the ice lens eventually melts, it leaves a circular depression or **ognip**. This process is shown in Figure 5.11.

Two theories describe the formation of pingos:

- Closed-system pingos develop beneath former lakes. Initially, the water in the lake prevents the surrounding regolith from freezing. Eventually, the lake fills with sediment. This reduces its insulating effect and the lake floor freezes. As the permafrost advances, water trapped in sediments beneath the former lake is put under pressure. This pushes the overlying sediments into a dome-shaped hill or pingo.
- Open-system pingos originate when water trapped in a talik or in the active layer migrates under pressure through the frozen regolith. At a point of weakness, the water forces its way to the surface, forming a pingo.

Landscapes affected by thawing ground ice are known as **thermokarst**. Thermokarst contains thousands of shallow depressions which resemble the dolines (see p. 24) of karst scenery. The depressions fill with water to form the most common feature of thermokarst: thaw lakes.

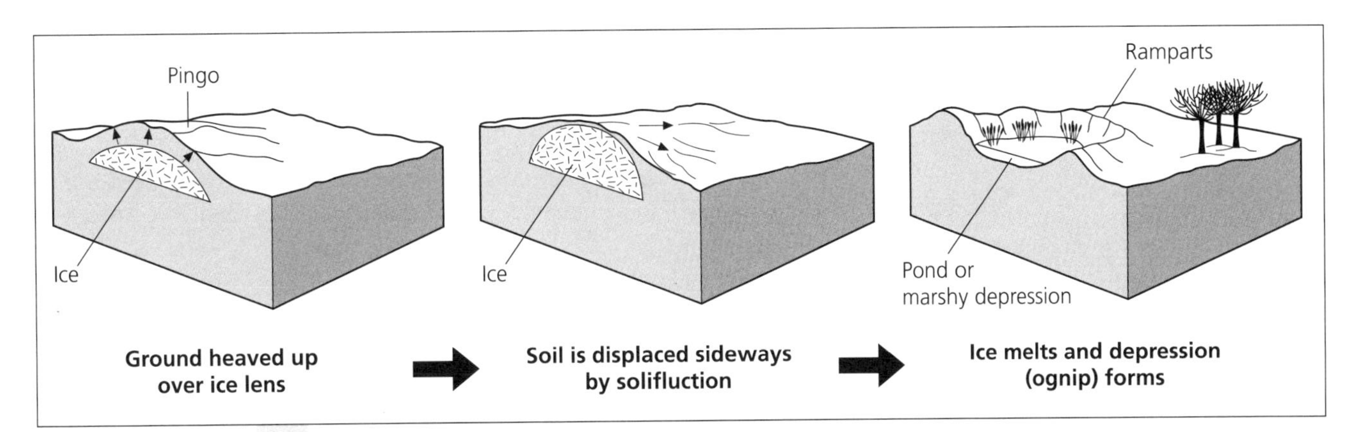

Figure 5.11 Formation of pingos and ognips

Landforms of mass movement

Solifluction or **gelifluction sheets** are the most widespread mass movement landform in periglacial areas. They form vast expanses of smooth terrain, often at uniform angles as low as 1–3 degrees. Large boulders known as **ploughing blocks** may be transported by solifluction/gelifluction sheets. They are 'rafted' downslope, their undersides resting at or near the permafrost table.

Lobes and **terraces** are common solifluction features. They give rise to step-like slopes with steep risers of 2 or 3 metres and low-angled treads. For lobes to develop, solifluction/gelifluction must be concentrated into well-defined linear paths. Where movement is more uniform, terraces develop.

Some lobes and terraces have concentrations of large stones and boulders at their downslope ends. These are sometimes called **stone garlands** or **stone steps**. The stones appear to emerge from the terrace or lobe. This suggests that the sub-surface flow rates exceed those at the surface. **Turf-banked terraces** indicate that surface movement is greater. Angular boulders concentrated in valley bottoms by solifluction/gelifluction are known as **block streams**.

Asymmetric valleys

Asymmetric valleys in cross-section have one slope steeper than the other. They are common in periglacial regions. In the northern hemisphere, north-facing slopes tend to be steepest. The effect of aspect on the microclimate of slopes may explain asymmetry. Sun-facing slopes experience longer periods of thawing, more meltwater and greater solifluction/gelifluction. This causes a lowering of sun-facing valley slopes.

UNIT 6 Coastal environments

1 The coastal system

The coast is an open system. Figure 6.1 shows that inputs of energy from waves, winds and tides interact with geology, sediments, plants and human activities to produce distinctive coastal landforms.

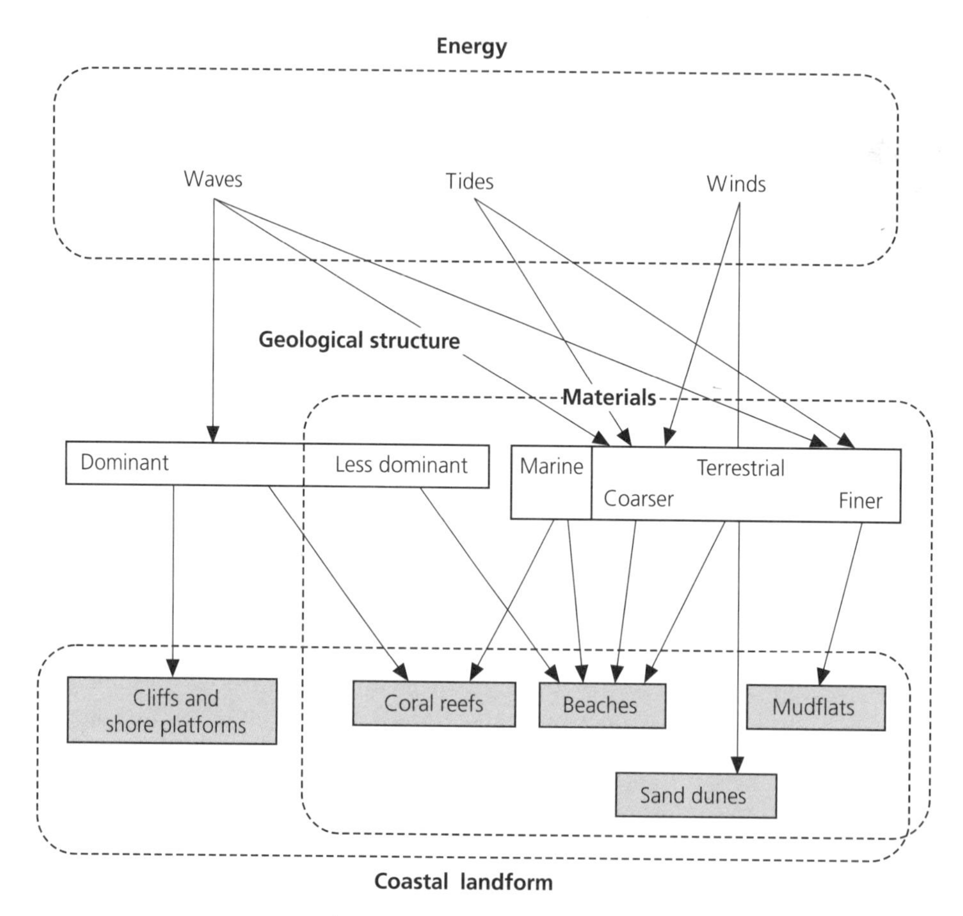

Figure 6.1 The coastal system

The coast is a dynamic place where change (rockfall, landslides, etc.) often occurs rapidly. This suggests that some parts of the coastal system have yet to achieve a steady state. Given that today's coastline is only 6,000 years old (i.e. the rise in sea level which followed the last glacial ended 6,000 years ago), this is not surprising.

INSET 1

Beach profiles and equilibrium

Although coastal landforms such as cliffs and shore platforms may take thousands of years to achieve equilibrium, beaches often have resolution times (i.e. the time needed to achieve an equilibrium form) of just a few hours. This is because the sediments that form beaches can move freely and adjust to changing energy inputs. The following sequence of changes shows how this adjustment is made:

- Low-energy surging breakers approach a coastline.
- These waves cause a net transport of sediment onshore.
- Beach gradients steepen as a result of this net onshore movement of sediment.
- Steeper beach gradients lead to a strengthening of the backwash.
- Eventually, the strength of swash and backwash are equal: the amount of sediment moving up the beach and the amount moving down the beach are the same.
- With no net movement of sediment, the beach assumes an equilibrium profile.

2 Energy inputs

2.1 Waves

Wind waves are the main source of energy driving the coastal system. Waves are superficial undulations of the water surface caused by winds blowing across the sea. They are a means of transmitting energy through water. Waves consist of orbital movements of water molecules that diminish with depth, as Figure 6.2 shows. In fact, water in a wave moves forward only when it approaches the shore and breaks.

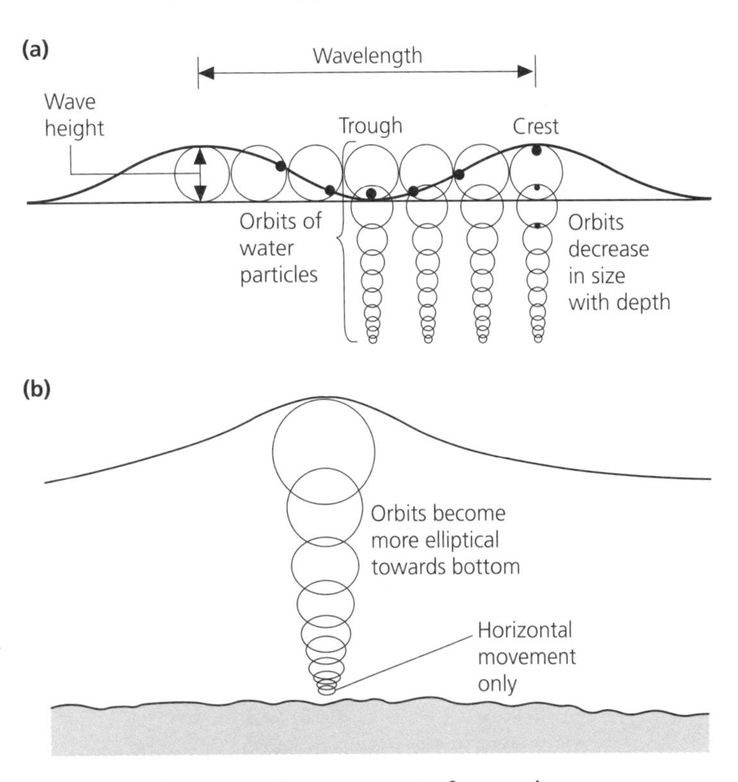

Figure 6.2 The movement of water in waves

The power of waves varies according to the openness of a coastline and the wind's strength and duration.

- Open coastlines in high latitudes are usually high-energy environments dominated by erosional landforms.
- Coastlines sheltered from powerful waves (e.g. estuaries) are low-energy environments where tidal processes and deposition dominate.

INSET 2

Wave characteristics

Wave length: the average distance between successive wave crests.
Wave height: the vertical distance between a wave trough and a wave crest.
Wave steepness: the ratio of wave height to wave length. Powerful waves are steep because they are high and have short wave lengths.

The **energy** in a wave is equal to the square of its height. Thus a wave that is 2 metres high contains four times as much energy as a 1-metre-high wave. **Wave power** takes account of velocity as well as wave height. Thus:

Wave power = $H^2 \times V$ where H is wave height and V is wave velocity.

Phase difference is a measure of wave energy. It is the ratio of swash time to wave period. **Swash time** is the interval (in seconds) between a wave breaking and the swash reaching its highest point on a beach. **Wave period** is the average interval (in seconds) between waves. Surging breakers have phase differences of less than 1. Surfing breakers have phase differences of 3 or above.

Wave energy is used to distinguish two types of wave. **Surfing** (or spilling) breakers are high-energy waves. They are steep and have short wavelengths. **Surging** breakers are low-energy waves that are shallow and have long wavelengths. Wave type is an important control on beach profiles.

Waves behave differently as they enter shallow water near the shoreline. Friction between the wave and the seabed causes a decrease in wave velocity and wave length. Because the rate of energy transport is the same in deep water and shallow water, waves in shallow water compensate for the reduction in velocity by increasing their height and steepness.

2.2 Spatial and temporal variations in wave energy

The input of wave energy to a coastline varies in both space and time. Several factors influence wave energy:

- **Fetch:** fetch is the expanse of open water (in any direction) facing a coastline. Basically, the longer the fetch, the more powerful the waves. Along the coast of eastern England, north-easterly waves dominate coastal erosion and transport. In this direction there is the maximum fetch of around 2,000 kilometres.
- **Water depth:** along shallow water coastlines (e.g. the coastline of south Lancashire), waves break some distance offshore and dissipate much of their energy.
- **Wind strength:** the stronger the wind, the more energy transferred to the waves. Gale force winds generate damaging storm waves.
- **Wind duration:** a steady breeze, blowing for several hours or days, transfers huge amounts of energy to the sea surface, and can generate large waves.

2.3 Tides

Tides are caused by the combined gravitational pull of the Moon and the Sun and centrifugal force. The Moon and the Sun pile the ocean water nearest the two bodies into a tidal wave. On the other side of the globe, centrifugal force exceeds the gravitational force and produces a second tidal wave. Because the Moon moves in relation to the Earth (it orbits the Earth in 29 days), the interval between high tides is nearly 12 hours 26 minutes rather than 12 hours.

Twice a month, when the Moon, Sun and Earth are in a straight line, the tide-raising force is strongest. This produces the highest monthly tidal range or **spring tide**. Also twice a month, the Moon and Sun are positioned in relation to the Earth at 90 degrees to each other. This alignment gives the lowest monthly tidal range or **neap tide**. These tides are shown in Figure 6.3.

Tides generate powerful currents that transport enormous amounts of water and fine sediment. Tidal landforms such as mudflats, salt marshes and estuaries dominate coastlines with high tidal ranges (above 4 metres). On coastlines with tidal ranges below 2 metres, wave action dominates, giving rise to beaches, offshore bars and barrier islands.

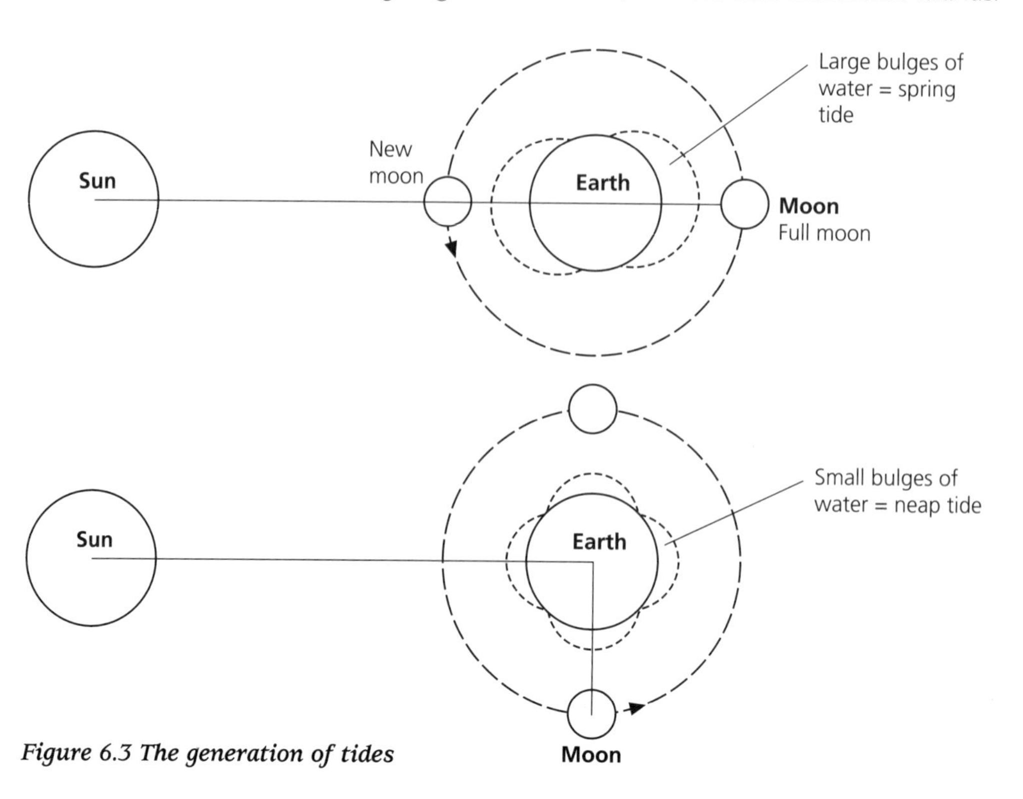

Figure 6.3 The generation of tides

3 Landforms of coastal deposition: beaches

At a local scale, cliff erosion is often a major source of beach sediments. Beaches dominated by rocks which crop out locally include: chalk at Worthing; serpentine at the Lizard; and magnesian limestone in Durham.

Beaches are accumulations of sand and shingle deposited by waves in the shore zone (see Figure 6.4). The sediments that form beaches come from three sources: cliffs, offshore areas and rivers.

- Cliff erosion: on average, cliff erosion provides only a small fraction of beach sediments (around 5%).
- Offshore: some beach sediments have been combed from the shallow seabed. This process occurred at the end of the ice age. Between 18000 and 6000 BP, sea level rose by around 100 metres. Coarse alluvium deposited by rivers on the exposed continental shelf was swept shorewards by wave action, providing sediment for today's beaches.
- Rivers: rivers are the source of around 90% of beach sediments. Sand and shingle are transported into the coastal system through river mouths as bedload.

Coastal sediments are confined to well-defined stretches of coastline known as **sediment cells** or **littoral cells**. The major sediment cells in England and Wales are shown in Figure 6.5.

There is very little transfer of sediment across the boundaries of these cells. This has important implications for the removal of sand and shingle from the coast and littoral zone: if sediments are removed (e.g. for aggregate), they cannot be replaced. Beaches starved of sediment are less effective as natural barriers to wave attack. This increases the risks of coastal flooding and cliff erosion. Today, sediment cells are the basic unit of shoreline management in England and Wales.

3.1 Beach profiles

The cross-section of a beach between the mean high water mark and the mean low water mark is known as the **beach profile**. Two factors influence beach profiles: sediment size and wave type.

Sediment size

Shingle beaches are usually steeper and narrower than sand beaches. Shingle is coarser than sand and has a higher **percolation rate**. The swash pushes shingle up the beach, but with rapid percolation it soon loses power; and there is little or no backwash to drag the

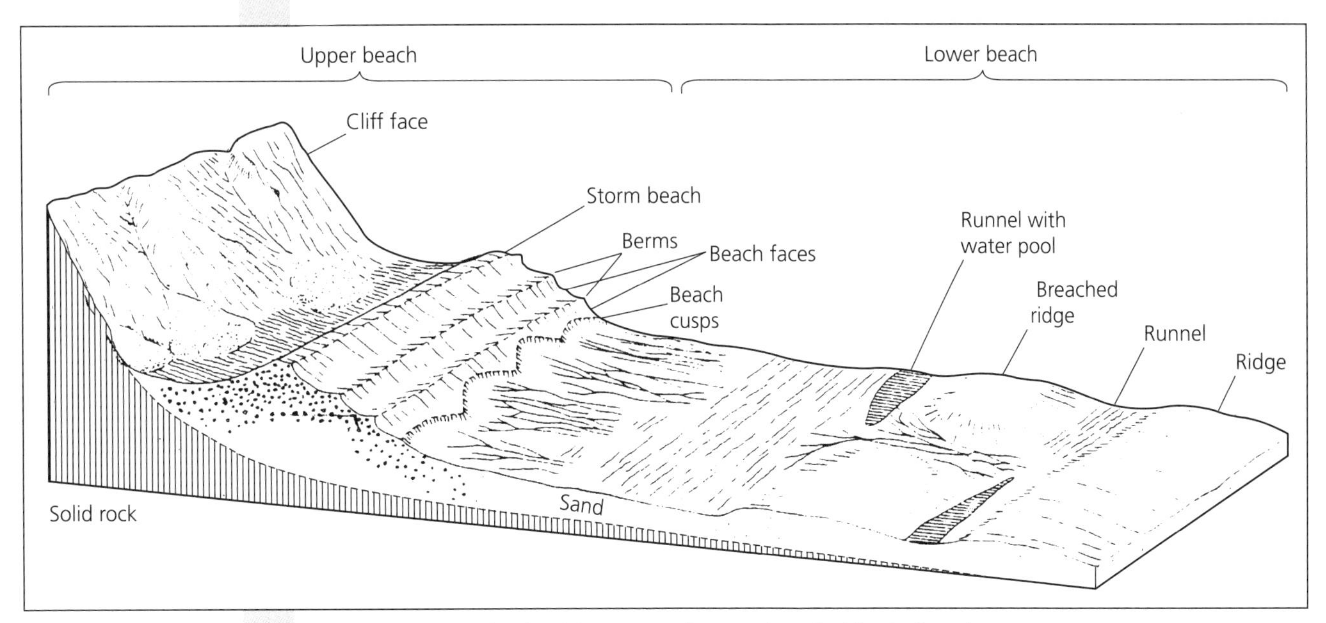

Figure 6.4 Principal features of a sand and shingle beach

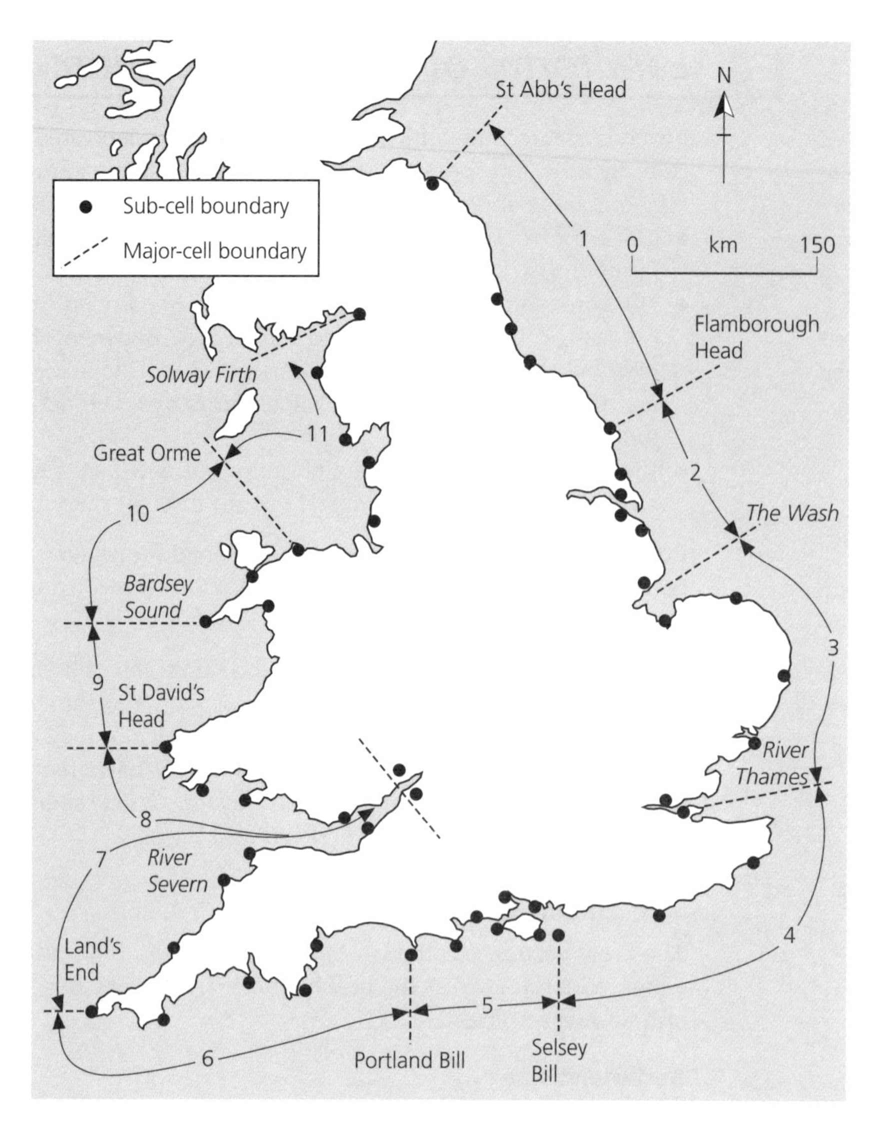

Figure 6.5 Coastal sediment cells in England and Wales

shingle seawards. Thus, the shingle is moved only in one direction and the beach acquires a relatively steep angle. Sand beaches, with lower percolation rates, have a longer swash and more powerful backwash. The result is a beach with a lower average slope angle.

Wave type

Beaches made of similar sediments but with different profiles show the influence of wave type. High-energy surfing breakers produce wide, flat beaches. These waves have a powerful backwash and erode sand and shingle from beaches. The sediments accumulate offshore, where they form a **breakpoint bar**. The wide, flat beach and breakpoint bar absorb wave energy until there is no net sediment transport. Low-energy waves or surging breakers induce a net onshore transfer of sediments. As a result, beaches become steep, with prominent beach faces and **berms** (see Figure 6.4).

3.2 Beach plans

In planform, beaches may be either swash-aligned or drift-aligned.

Swash-aligned beaches

Crescent-shaped bay-head beaches develop on indented coasts where waves are fully refracted (see Inset 3). Swash-aligned beaches are usually straight, without the recurved laterals that indicate longshore drift.

INSET 3

Wave refraction

Wave refraction describes the bending of oblique waves in the nearshore zone until they break almost parallel to the shore. Where the sea is shallow, waves 'feel' the seabed and slow through frictional drag. In deeper water, the wave moves faster. As a result, the wave front bends until it takes on a similar shape to the coastline. When the waves are fully refracted and parallel to the coastline, the swash and backwash follow the same path on the beach. The result is swash-aligned beaches.

Even so, not all waves are fully refracted. Some waves break obliquely and their swash follows a diagonal path across the beach. In these circumstances, a net lateral movement of beach sediment takes place. This movement is known as longshore (or beach) drift, and it produces drift-aligned beaches such as spits.

Wave refraction is also responsible for the uneven distribution of energy on coastlines. Refraction concentrates wave energy (and therefore erosion) on headlands, but disperses energy (favouring deposition) in bays. The process of wave refraction is shown in Figure 6.6.

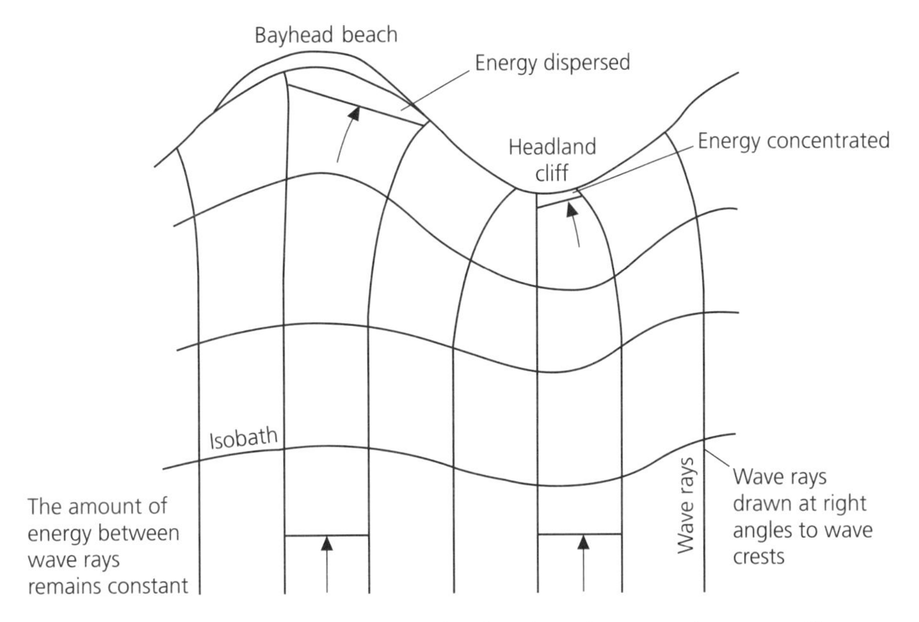

Figure 6.6 Wave refraction and the distribution of energy along coastlines

INSET 4

Chesil Beach

At 30 kilometres long, Chesil Beach (see Figure 6.7) is the longest shingle ridge in the British Isles. It joins mainland Dorset with the Isle of Portland. Such a beach, linking the mainland to an island, is known as a **tombolo**. Because of its straightness, Chesil is thought to be a swash-aligned feature. It originated during the last glacial as a bar of flint and chert in the English Channel. At that time sea level was 100–120 metres lower than today. Rising sea levels followed the end of the glacial, and waves gradually rolled the bar onshore. Chesil reached its present position 6,000 years ago.

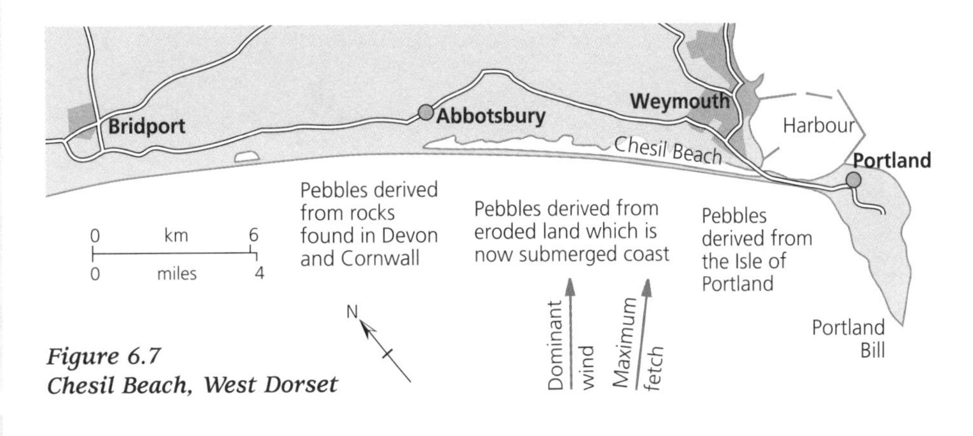

Figure 6.7 Chesil Beach, West Dorset

The names given to types of beach (spits, tombolos, barrier beaches, etc.) are not generic ones. They simply describe the shape/form of beaches and are not an indication of how they were formed. For instance, tombolos may be either drift-aligned or swash-aligned features.

Drift-aligned beaches

Drift-aligned beaches, such as **spits** and **barrier beach islands**, develop on open coastlines. Here waves are rarely fully refracted and **longshore drift** takes place (see Figure 6.8). Spits often form across estuaries (e.g. Spurn Head, Orford Ness) or where there is an abrupt change of direction in the coastline (e.g. Hurst Castle). Growth by longshore drift is shown by the recurved shingle ridges or laterals of spits. The distribution of spits around Britain, shown in Figure 6.9, appears to correlate with coastlines that have a low tidal range (less than 2 metres). A low tidal range concentrates wave action in a narrow vertical band of coast. This seems to be important in shaping the sand and shingle into spits and other drift-aligned beaches.

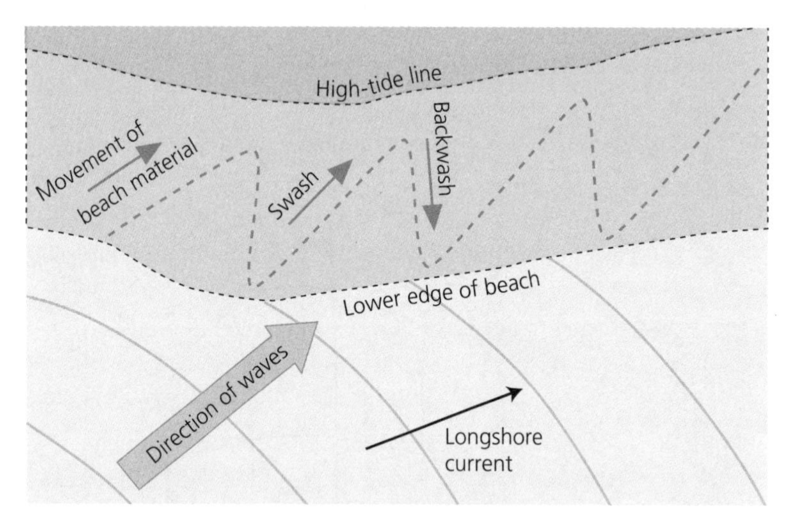

Figure 6.8 Longshore drift: the flow of coastal sediment produced by wave and current action when waves approach at an angle to the coastline

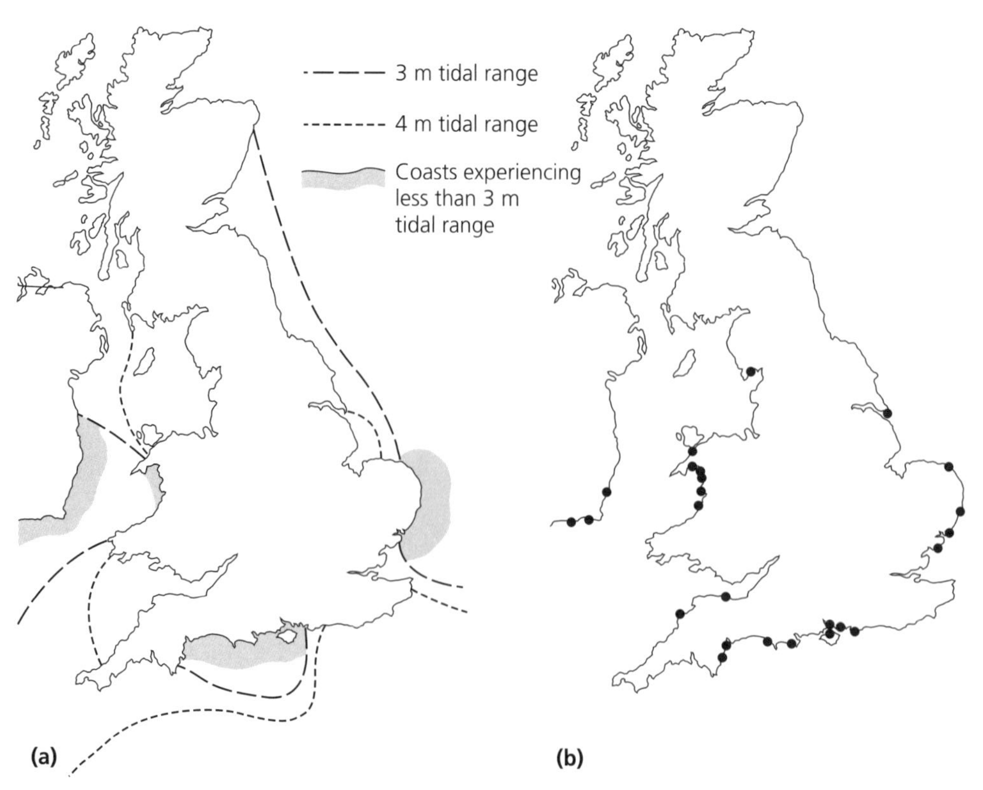

Figure 6.9 Distribution of (a) coasts with low tidal range and (b) major spits around Britain's coast

INSET 5

Blakeney Point and Scolt Head Island

Blakeney Point is a spit 15.5 kilometres long on the north Norfolk coast (see Figure 6.10). Unusually, it is (a) situated on a relatively straight coast and (b) aligned at a steep angle to the coast. It has a series of recurves that form a series of shingle ridges. These mark the westward growth of the feature by longshore drift. However, there is no evidence of longshore drift today. The steep angle that the spit makes with the coast, and the gradual movement of the feature inland, suggest that Blakeney Point may now be swash-aligned.

Scolt Head Island, also on the north Norfolk coast, is similar to Blakeney Point in plan, except that at low tide it is separated from the mainland by a deep narrow channel. This makes Scolt Head a barrier beach island. Like Blakeney, Scolt Head's recurves show that it has formed by longshore drift. As at Blakeney, Scolt Head seems to be gradually moving onshore.

The source of shingle at Blakeney and Scolt Head Island is probably glacial outwash gravel. Deposited offshore by meltwater, it was swept by waves towards the modern coastline as sea level rose in post-glacial times.

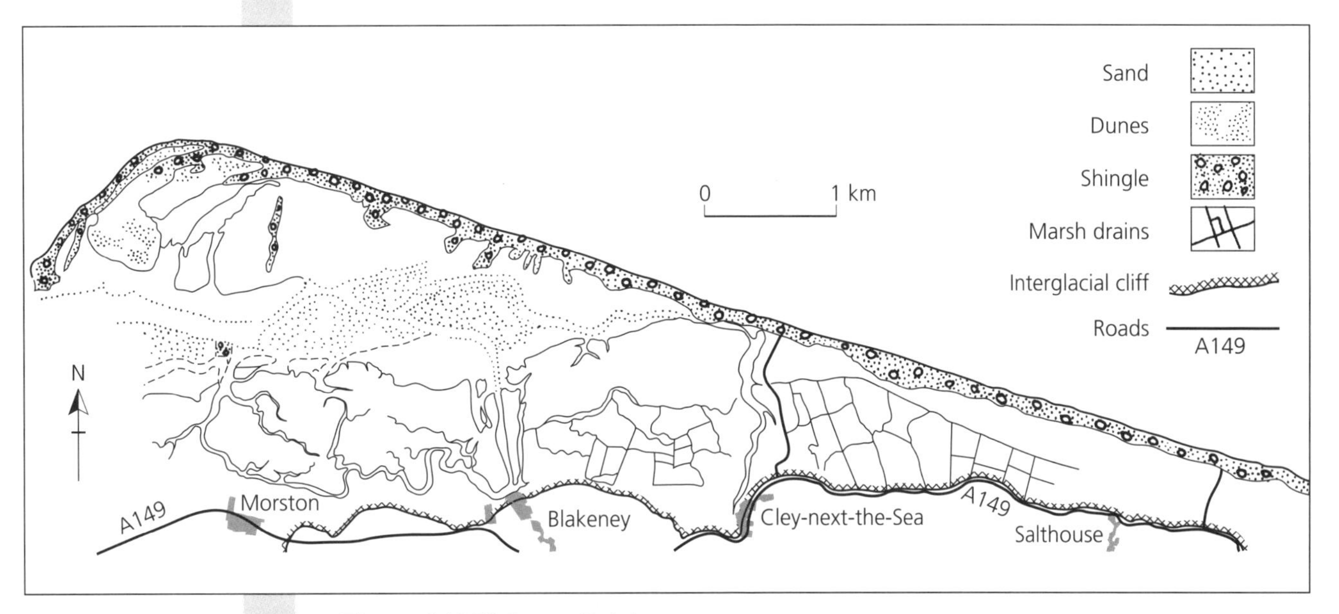

Figure 6.10 Blakeney Point

4 Mudflats and salt marshes

Mudflats and salt marshes are landforms of sheltered coastlines where wave action is weak. In quiet areas such as estuaries, and on the landward side of spits, tidal currents deposit fine sediment in suspension. Accretion leads to the growth of mudflats and salt marshes.

Unlike beaches, mudflats and salt marshes are often associated with large tidal ranges. Large tidal ranges generate powerful tidal currents that can transport large quantities of fine sediment.

Figure 6.11 is a cross-section through a salt marsh in the Aln estuary in Northumberland. It shows a number of typical features:

- There is a low cliff, about half a metre high, which separates the mudflats from the low marsh. Tidal scour maintains this cliff.
- An abrupt break of slope separates the high marsh from the low marsh.
- A dense network of creeks and tributaries drains the marsh and brings water in on the flood tide.
- Small salt pans occur sporadically on the surface of the high marsh.

Vegetation plays a vital role in the development of salt marshes. Many marshes demonstrate a clear zonation of species that is closely related to height above sea level, as shown in Table 6.1. Such a plant succession in a saline, waterlogged environment is known as a **halosere**. This zonation is best seen between the mean low water mark and the strand line on open marshes in estuaries.

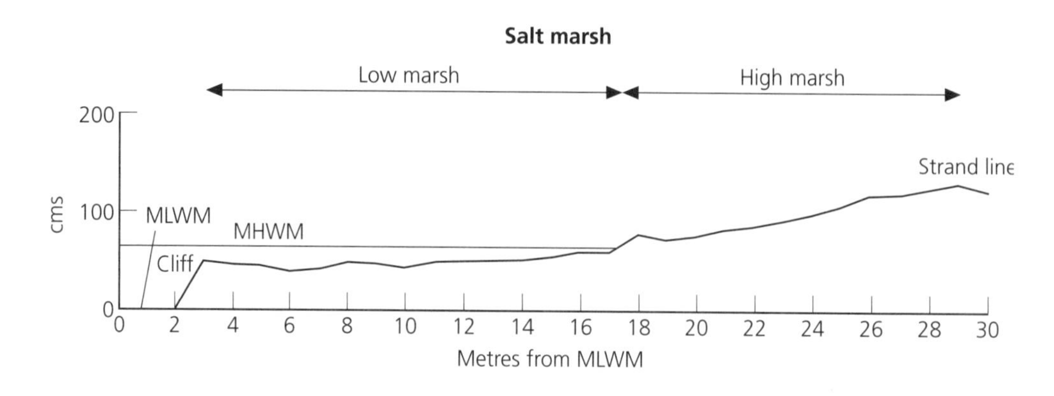

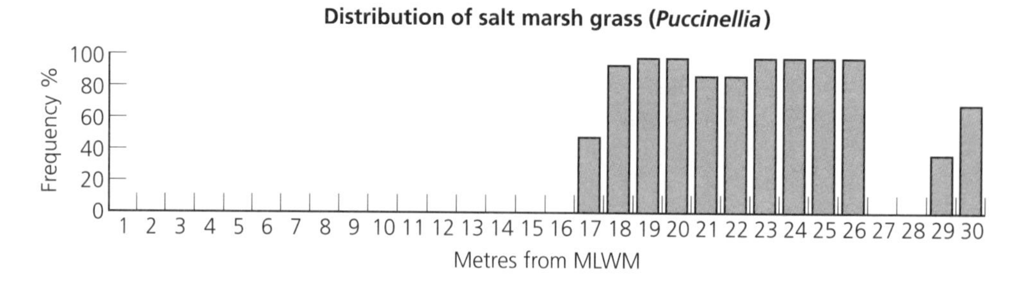

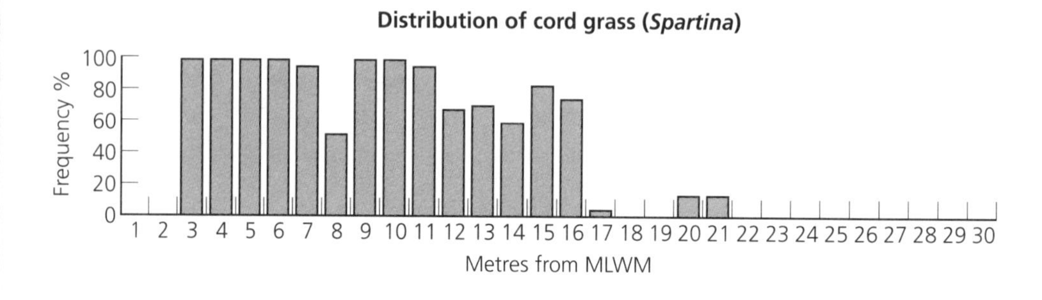

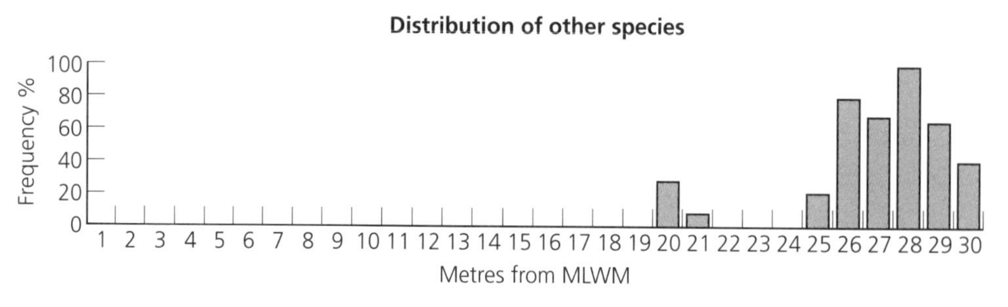

Figure 6.11 Cross-section through a salt marsh at Alnmouth, Northumberland

Ecological succession is responsible for the growth of salt marshes and follows a number of stages.

- Colonisation by pioneer species such as cord grass and glasswort. These plants slow the movement of water and encourage rapid sedimentation (1–2 cm/year). Their roots help to stabilise the mud.
- Through accretion of sediment the marsh increases in height and conditions become more favourable for the invasion of other, less tolerant species. Biodiversity and plant

Environment	Environmental conditions	Plants
Mudflats	High salinity levels; low oxygen levels in mud; high turbidity; long periods of inundation on each tidal cycle.	No plants, only algae.
Low marsh	Less hostile conditions than mudflats. But salinity and turbidity still high and oxygen levels low. Tidal inundation shorter.	*Spartina* (cord grass) and *Salicornia* (glasswort) are the two common pioneer species. Sea blite (*Suaeda*) and sea purslane (*Halimone*) on better-drained areas (e.g. edges of creeks).
High marsh	Flooding only occurs on spring tides. Salinity levels are relatively low and soil develops.	Wide variety of species, including salt marsh grass (*Puccinellia*), sea rush (*Juncus maritimus*), sea lavender (*Limonium*), sea aster (*Aster tripolium*), sea blite (*Suaeda maritima*) and sea purslane (*Halimione*).

Table 6.1 Plant zonation on salt marshes

cover increase. Plants such as sea rush, sea aster, sea lavender, salt marsh grass and common scurvy grass dominate.

- The marsh height stabilises a metre or so above the mean high tide mark. With only occasional inundation on the highest spring tides, vertical accretion ends. Salinity levels are low and soil develops.

5 Sand dunes

- Vegetation is an important land-forming agent in two coastal environments: salt marshes and sand dunes.
- Salt marsh succession is a hydrosere (halosere) and sand dune succession is a xerosere (psammosere). Salt marshes and sand dunes are new environments where primary succession is taking place. Both are harsh environments where conditions for plants are extreme.

Sand dunes are the only important coastal landforms produced by the wind. The wind induces the movement of sand by the collision of particles. Larger particles move by **creep** on the surface of dunes; smaller particles are transported by a skipping process that extends up to a metre or so above the surface. This is **saltation**.

Blown sand accumulates around objects such as logs and bottles. However, once these are buried, sand accumulation ends. Sand dunes can only form when vegetation provides the obstacle to blown sand. This is because some plants, such as marram grass (*Ammophilia arenaria*), thrive when submerged by sand. Burial stimulates rapid growth and encourages further deposition. Deposition also occurs because plants reduce wind speeds near the ground.

Sand dunes develop on lowland coastlines where the following conditions are found:

- a plentiful supply of sand (possibly from nearby river estuaries);
- a shallow offshore zone with gentle gradients, where large exposures of sand dry out at low tide;
- an extensive backshore area where sand can accumulate;
- prevailing on-shore winds.

The primary succession on sand dunes (**psammosere**) often shows a distinct zonation. Nearest the shore, where the youngest (yellow) dunes are found, vegetation cover is patchy and few species survive. With increasing distance inland, the dunes get older (grey dunes) and the environment changes (see Table 6.2). As a result, plant cover, productivity and biodiversity all increase.

Dune systems often form a series of ridges parallel to the coastline, as shown in Figure 6.12. The dunes decrease in height inland, as sand supply diminishes. Troughs or **slacks** separate the dune ridges and here the water table is often at the surface. The dunes usually have a steep windward slope and a less steep leeward slope. Sand eroded from the exposed windward slopes is deposited on the sheltered leeward slopes, so that gradually the dunes migrate inland. For this reason the dunes increase in age with distance from the shoreline.

Dunes	Environmental conditions	Plants
Embryo dunes	Little fresh water for plants. Sand is extremely porous. Blown sand blasts plants. Salt spray and shifting sand are further problems for plants.	Sand twitch or sea couch grass (*Agropyron junceiforme*), which can extract fresh water from salt water, is one of the few species found here.
Foredune ridge	Two or three metres above the beach, conditions are less saline, more exposed and unstable.	Marram grass begins to colonise and compete with sea couch grass. Marram is well adapted to sand dunes: it has deep roots; sand deposition stimulates growth; and moisture loss is reduced by a thick shiny cuticle, sunken pores and leaves that curl in the sun.
First dune ridge	The most prominent relief feature, 10–30 metres high. Sand is more stable and contains some humus.	Almost 100% marram. Marram slows wind speed and reduces sand movement.
Older dune ridges	Dune ridges become progressively lower inland as sand supply diminishes. Dunes become grey as humus builds up in the soil. Soil's moisture retention increases. Soil pH falls.	Environment becomes less harsh. There is shelter, some fresh water and soil. Many new species appear, e.g. creeping willow, sea buckthorn, ragwort, fescue grass. Marram dies out.
Dune slacks	Depressions between the dune ridges. Sheltered and marshy where water table reaches the surface. Often waterlogged after heavy rain.	Wide range of plant species. Some, like flag iris and bog myrtle, are typical wetland species.

Table 6.2 Vegetation succession on sand dunes

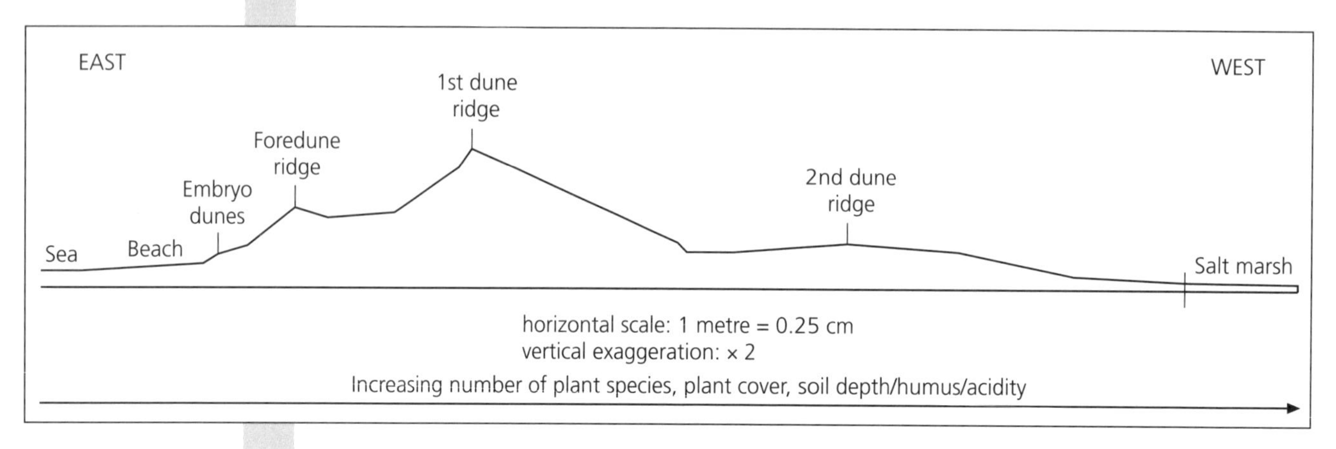

Figure 6.12 Cross-section through the dunes at Alnmouth

Sand dunes are a fragile environment. Destruction of the vegetation cover by grazing (e.g. rabbits) or human activities (e.g. trampling, firing) can lead to massive wind erosion and the formation of **blow-outs**. Frontal erosion of dunes by waves can also occur in storm conditions.

Wave action is concentrated around the high water mark. The result is a wave-cut notch that eventually leads to cliff retreat by rockfall or mass movement.

6 Landforms of coastal erosion

6.1 Marine erosional processes

Wave action on coasts induces three erosional processes: abrasion (or corrasion); hydraulic action; and corrosion (see Table 6.3). These processes are most important when high-energy waves, associated with storm conditions, strike coasts made of weak and incoherent rock.

Type of erosion	Process
Abrasion	High-energy waves pick up shingle and abrade the base of cliffs. The result is a wave-cut notch. The cliff is undermined and retreats through rockfall.
Hydraulic action	Air and water, forced under pressure into joints and bedding planes by storm waves, weaken rocks and cause collapse. The effectiveness of hydraulic action depends on the density of joints etc. in the rock.
Corrosion	Some rock minerals are susceptible to solution. For instance, calcareous cements that bind sandstone particles may be attacked by solution, leading to rock disintegration.

Table 6.3 Marine erosion processes

Most cliff profiles result from the interaction of wave energy, geology and sub-aerial processes. Often the characteristics of a cliff profile will be dominated by one of these processes.

Even mechanically weak rocks, such as boulder clay and sands and gravels, sometimes form steep cliffs. This happens because marine erosion is so rapid that sub-aerial processes do not have enough time to lower slope angles.

6.2 Cliff profiles

Cliff profiles (i.e. cross-sections) reflect the influence of several factors, including rock lithology and structure; sub-aerial processes; relief; wave energy; human activities; and past processes.

Lithology and structure

Mechanically strong rocks, such as basalt and limestone, not only resist erosion but are stable at very steep angles. In contrast, mechanically weak rocks, such as clay and shale, will erode more easily and often form lower-angled slopes.

Rock structure includes the angle of dip of sedimentary rocks. The effect of lithology on cliff profiles is shown in Figure 6.13.

- Horizontally bedded rocks, such as the chalk at Flamborough Head in Yorkshire and at Bat's Head in Dorset, form vertical cliffs. These cliffs, undercut by wave action, retreat parallel to themselves, maintaining their steep slope by rockfall.
- Landward-dipping strata form less steep cliffs. This is because eroded and weathered rock particles are not easily dislodged from the cliff face.
- Seaward-dipping strata have profiles that correspond to the angle of dip of the bedding planes. Blocks weakened by erosion and weathering fail along these planes and slide easily into the sea.

Some cliffs comprise more than one rock type of contrasting lithology and structure. On England's north-east coast, boulder clay caps many hard rock cliffs. Such cliffs have two distinctive slope elements: a steep lower cliff face cut into coherent rock; and a more gentle upper slope of boulder clay.

Sub-aerial processes

Sub-aerial processes such as weathering and mass movement also have a strong influence on cliff profiles. This is particularly evident in weak rocks such as shale and sands, which are susceptible to slides, flows, surface wash and gulleying.

Relief

Relief determines the height of cliffs and the area over which sub-aerial processes operate. In County Clare, the coast rises above 300 metres to form the Cliffs of Moher, the highest in the British Isles. In contrast, at Holderness, the boulder clay cliffs are part of a till plain, with a modest height of between 10 and 20 metres.

Wave energy

- Coastlines with long fetches or exposed to prevailing winds experience high wave energy. As a result, they tend to have relatively high rates of erosion. Moreover, rockfalls, such as the one at Beachy Head in 1999, are easily removed by strong wave action so that erosion can begin anew.

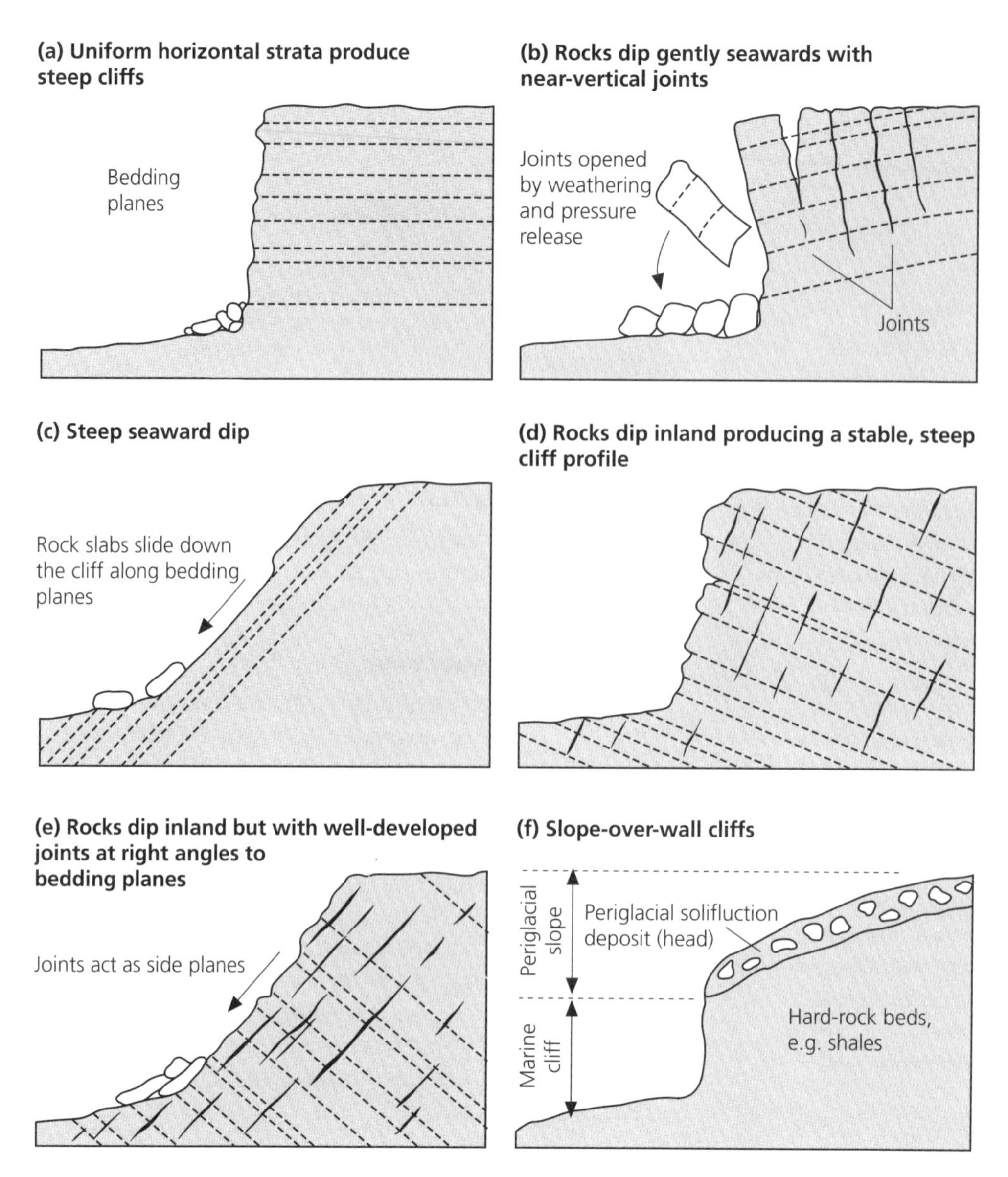

Figure 6.13 Cliff profiles: the influence of lithology

- Low-energy coastlines often experience relatively low rates of erosion. Waves may have low energy owing to the coast's sheltered situation, short fetch and shallow water off-shore (the last dissipates wave energy before it reaches the coastline). In low-energy situations, sub-aerial processes begin to dominate. Rock debris may accumulate at the cliff foot, and cliff slope angles may be lowered by weathering and mass movement.

Human activities

Human activities may either increase or decrease rates of marine erosion.

- As part of coastal management, cliffs may be protected from erosion by coastal defence works (sea walls, armour blocks, etc.). In this situation, marine erosion stops, cliffs become vegetated and sub-aerial processes take over. At Mappleton in Holderness, the boulder cliff angles have been deliberately lowered to reduce the risk of slope failure.
- Human interference in the coastal system has sometimes (inadvertently) accelerated erosion. The removal of beach sand and shingle, which normally protect cliffs from wave attack, may cause accelerated erosion (e.g. the mining of shingle at Hallsands in south Devon or the construction of piers that stopped longshore drift at West Bay in Dorset).

Past processes

Many cliff profiles owe their shape to past processes. Slope-over-wall or bevelled cliffs have a long, convex upper slope and a short, vertical lower section. They are common on many coastlines, especially in parts of south Devon and south Cornwall. The long, convex slope is not related to marine erosion. It formed under cold climatic conditions during the last glacial. At this time, processes such as freeze–thaw and solifluction prevailed, and sea level was 100–120 metres lower than today. Only the basal part of this convex slope has been trimmed back by wave action in the last 6,000 years.

Most of the erosional landforms of hard rock coasts are merely stages in the retreat of cliffs. The development of these features depends on several factors:

- the height of the coast;
- the mechanical strength of the rock;
- the jointing of the rock;
- the dominance of marine erosion over sub-aerial processes.

6.3 Erosional landforms resulting from cliff recession

Landforms of cliff erosion and recession on upland, hard rock coasts include caves, arches, stacks, blowholes, geos and shore platforms.

- **Caves** develop below the mean high water mark, along lines of weakness such as joints, bedding planes and faults. Hydraulic action and abrasion loosen blocks along joints, causing rockfall and hollows that can be further exploited by waves.
- Caves that form on opposite sides of headlands (where wave energy, owing to refraction, is highest) may form **arches** such as Durdle Door and the Green Bridge of Wales.
- The combination of marine and sub-aerial processes leads to arch collapse (as at Marsden in Tyne and Wear in 1996), leaving isolated rock pinnacles or **stacks** (e.g. the Needles on the Isle of Wight).
- If part of the roof of a tunnel-like cave collapses along a master joint, it may form a vertical shaft that reaches the cliff top. This is a **blowhole**.
- When the entire roof of a cave running at right angles to the cliff line collapses, it forms a narrow inlet or **geo**.
- The final stage of cliff recession forms a wide **shore platform**. This, the former base of the cliffs, is abraded by wave action and weathered by biological and chemical processes. Some shore platforms are too wide to have been cut in the last 6,000 years and may have formed in previous inter-glacial periods when sea level was roughly the same as today.

7 Rock structure and the planform of coasts

At a regional scale, rock structure has a strong influence on the shape of coastlines.

- Where the main rock types crop out parallel to the coast, the coast is often straight and uniform. We call such coastlines **accordant** or **Pacific** coasts.
- Where rocks of different types crop out at right angles to the coast, the result is a coastline of headlands and bays. The more resistant rocks form headlands; the less resistant ones form bays. This form of coastline is known as the **discordant** or **Atlantic** type.

The coastline of Purbeck in south-east Dorset, shown in Figure 6.14, illustrates both accordant and discordant types. In south Purbeck, the principal rock types – Portland limestone, Purbeck limestone, Wealden beds and chalk – run parallel to the coast. The Portland limestone is the southernmost outcrop. It forms a barrier to erosion and is responsible for the straightness of the coastline. However, in some places, such as Stair Hole, erosion by waves and rivers has breached the Portland barrier and exposed the weaker Wealden beds. These weaker rocks have been carved into impressive coves and bays. The best examples are Lulworth Cove and Worbarrow Bay.

The east Purbeck coast has the same geology as south Purbeck. The difference is that in east Purbeck the rocks crop out at right angles to the coastline. Thus the resistant Portland and Purbeck limestones and chalk form headlands such as Durlston Head and Peveril Point, while the weaker Wealden beds and Bagshot sands erode to form wide bays such those of Swanage and Studland.

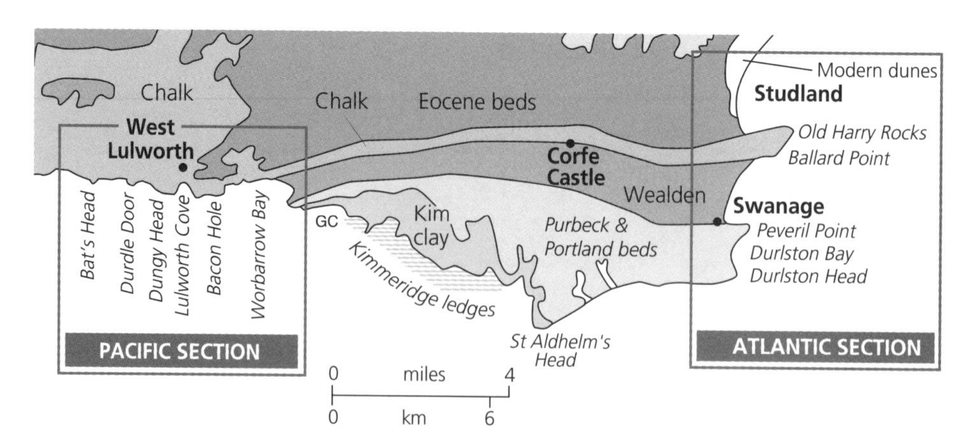

Figure 6.14 The Isle of Purbeck, south-east Dorset

8 Sea level change

Sea level has risen between 100 and 120 metres in the last 20,000 years. Historically, current sea level is high. Thus many coastal landforms (e.g. shore platforms, shingle beaches, slope-over-wall cliffs, etc.) are fossil features, inherited from a time when sea level was lower than today.

Absolute sea level changes result from a worldwide rise or fall in the volume of water in the oceans. This is a **eustatic** change. During the last glacial, sea level was 100–120 metres lower than today, and large areas of the continental shelf around the British Isles were dry land.

Rising sea level, which causes the coastline to retreat, is called a **transgression**. This happens during an inter-glacial period, when ice sheets and glaciers melt. The opposite is a **regression**, which produces an advancing coastline. This occurs during a glacial when huge volumes of water are locked up in ice sheets and glaciers. For example, in the last glacial ice sheets and glaciers in the northern hemisphere occupied an area three times greater than today.

At a local scale, sea level change occurs if the land rises or sinks relative to sea level. This type of sea level change is associated with either **isostatic** or **tectonic** movements. Table 6.4 summarises sea level changes and their effects on coastal landforms.

INSET 6

Isostatic change

During a glacial, the great mass of ice sheets and glaciers loads the continental crust, causing it to sink by several hundred metres. When the ice melts, unloading occurs and the crust slowly rises by a similar amount. This is glacio-isostacy. In the British Isles, the ice was thickest in Scotland and it is here that isostatic recovery has been greatest. This movement, which is ongoing, has taken place faster than the post-glacial rise of the sea level, creating raised beaches and raised shorelines around Scotland's west coast.

9 People and coastlines

Most of the world's population lives on or near the coast. The coast provides a wide variety of opportunities for recreation and leisure, industrial location, trade, wildlife, conservation, land reclamation, farming and waste disposal.

Because of the importance of coasts to human activity, management of the coastal environment to control erosion and flooding is common. A variety of measures are used to stop erosion (see Table 6.5). Low-lying coastal areas vulnerable to flooding are also protected by embankments (dykes) or in some cases by flood barriers (e.g. those on the Thames and the Tees). However, the most important forms of protection against coastal flooding are natural: mudflats, salt marshes and sand dunes.

Glacio-eustacy	
Rising sea level (absolute – submergence)	
Shingle beaches (spits, bars, etc.)	River sediments deposited on the dry continental shelf during the last glacial when the shelf area was above sea level. Rising sea level in the last 20,000 years swept up the sediment and deposited it on present-day coasts.
Estuaries	Drowned, shallow lowland river valleys, e.g. Severn, Thames and Humber estuaries. Transgression flooded low-lying areas around the Wash and Somerset Levels.
Rias	Drowned, incised river valleys on upland coasts, e.g. south-west Ireland, River Dart (Devon), River Fal (Cornwall).
Fjords	Drowned glacial troughs.
Falling sea level (absolute – emergence)	
Ancient shore platforms	Cut by wave action in the last inter-glacial when sea level was 8–10 metres higher than today, e.g. at Start Bay in South Devon.
Glacio-isostacy	
Falling sea levels (relative – emergence)	
Raised beaches	Ancient beaches and cliff lines elevated above sea level following deglaciation and the unloading of ice sheets from northern Britain, e.g. Applecross Peninsula, north-west Scotland (8 m above sea level).
Tectonic movements	
Earthquakes/faulting	Localised tectonic movements leading to submergence or emergence.

Table 6.4 Changing sea levels and coastal landforms in the British Isles

Sea walls	Expensive to build and maintain. Building justified only to defend settlements of some size. Sea walls reflect wave energy. This sets up vertical currents that can undermine and topple sea walls.
Revetments	Wooden barriers parallel to the coast designed to absorb wave energy. Cheaper than sea walls, but unsightly.
Groynes	Wooden or rock barriers at right angles to the shore. They prevent the longshore movement of sand and shingle. By keeping the beach intact, they reduce erosion.
Rock armour	Boulders or concrete blocks placed at the foot of cliffs or in the backshore area of a beach. Unsightly, but cheap and effective.
Beach replenishment	Sand and shingle brought to beaches to replace sediments lost to longshore drift. Beaches are effective absorbers of wave energy, providing the sediment remains *in situ*.

Table 6.5 Coastal protection measures against erosion and their effectiveness

9.1 Shoreline management plans

In the past, human interference in the coastal system to prevent erosion or protect against flooding has been piecemeal. Local defence schemes, such as the construction of revetments or groynes, have protected only those stretches of coastline immediately threatened. Often this has caused serious knock-on effects. For instance, the construction of groynes may starve beaches downdrift of sediment and accelerate erosion in these areas. Protecting cliffs from erosion by building sea walls may reduce inputs of sediment to the coastal system. The effects may be to degrade beaches and mudflats, thus threatening increased erosion and coastal flooding.

Today coastlines are being managed as complete systems. The basic unit of management is the sediment cell. Within these cells there is a self-contained cycle of erosion, transport and deposition of sediment. Shoreline Management Schemes (SMPs) set out a strategy for coastal defence for specified lengths of coast identified as sediment cells. They are funded by the Ministry of Agriculture, Fisheries and Food and promote co-operation between local authorities, the Environment Agency and other organisations involved in coastal defence.

9.2 Managed realignment and retreat

The policy of defending large stretches of Britain's coastline against erosion and flooding is increasingly untenable. Global warming will cause sea level to rise by 1 or 2 metres during the twenty-first century. This will mean committing ever more resources to coastal defences. It is increasingly hard to justify the expense of strengthening sea walls or building higher dykes. Most of the land that is protected is used for agriculture. Yet for the last 40 years there has been a massive food surplus in the EU. Moreover, much of the protected farmland is former salt marsh: an important habitat for wildlife, which has declined significantly. In Essex, for example, 75% of coastal salt marshes have been drained and used for arable production in the last 100 years.

Current ideas are to work with, not against, the natural coastal system. We now know that protection of one stretch of coast often creates an adverse impact elsewhere. Thus we should intervene in the coastal system only where absolutely necessary: for example, where vital installations, such as nuclear power stations, or significant urban areas are threatened. The current policy is known as **managed retreat** or **managed realignment**. This policy means that many coastal areas (especially the lowland coasts of eastern England from Yorkshire to Kent) will no longer be afforded protection. Areas of reclaimed farmland will be allowed to flood, to form new mudflats and salt marshes. This will have three benefits:

- It will reduce the costs of coastal protection.
- It will provide natural defences against flooding and erosion.
- It will create new wetland habitats for wildlife.

As you might expect, managed retreat is highly controversial, especially among farmers, who may not be compensated for their loss of land.

Weather and climate

1 The Earth's atmospheric system

The Earth–atmosphere system is not entirely closed. Small amounts of matter, including meteors and meteorites, enter the atmosphere from space. However, these inputs are minute compared to the mass of the planet.

Unlike most natural systems, the atmosphere is largely a closed system (see Figure 7.1). Essentially it is open only to the transfer of energy.

Energy cascades through the Earth's atmospheric system, where it interacts with the ocean and land surfaces and the gases that make up the atmosphere. The result is weather and climate. **Weather** is the day-to-day changes in temperature, precipitation, winds, cloud, etc. at a place. **Climate** is the average weather expected at a place at a particular time of year.

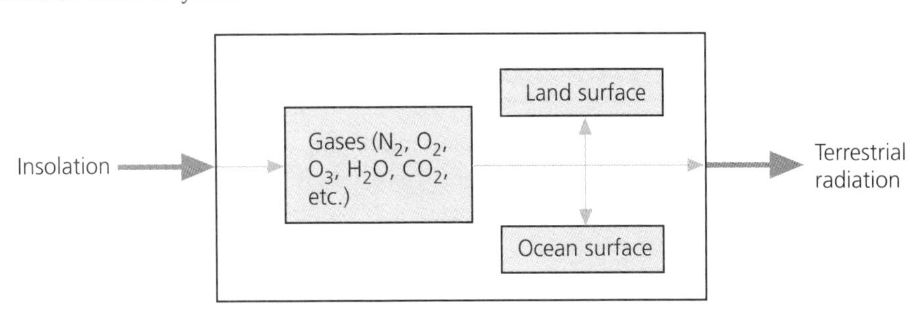

Figure 7.1 The atmospheric system

2 Energy inputs

The Sun's rays are spread over twice the area at latitude 60° than at the equator. Factors other than the Earth's curvature that influence the amount of insolation reaching the Earth's surface are cloudiness, day length and the number of days when the Sun is overhead.

Solar energy powers the atmospheric system. Incoming solar energy (or **insolation**) mainly comprises short-wave radiation in the visible part of the spectrum.

At the top of the atmosphere, the Sun's energy averages 2 calories/cm^2/minute. This is the **solar constant**. While the solar constant is the same everywhere, the amount of insolation reaching the Earth's surface varies with latitude. Because of the Earth's curvature, insolation is much more intense in the tropics than in middle and high latitudes.

Less than half of the energy received at the top of the atmosphere reaches the Earth's surface.

- 30% of all insolation is reflected back into space. The tops of clouds and surfaces such as fresh snow and ice are very reflective. We say they have a high **albedo**.
- Gases in the atmosphere, such as ozone (O_3) and oxygen (O_2), absorb around 15% of the Sun's radiation.
- 10% of insolation is scattered by gas molecules. That part which is scattered towards the Earth's surface is known as **diffuse light**. This is the light we experience on a cloudy day.

Insolation striking the Earth's surface is converted to heat. This heat is then transferred to the overlying air by **radiation**, **convection** and **conduction**. Thus, the atmosphere is heated from below.

3 Energy outputs

The energy emitted by the Earth is mainly long-wave radiation. Gases such as carbon dioxide, water and methane absorb most of this terrestrial radiation. They warm the atmosphere, producing the so-called 'greenhouse effect'. Clouds also absorb the Earth's radiation. They have a blanketing effect, and re-radiate much of the heat back to the surface.

4 Energy transfer

Once converted to heat, energy cascades through the Earth's atmospheric system. About 80% of this energy transfer is **sensible heat**; 20% is **latent heat**.

- Sensible heat describes a body of warm air or warm water, transferred to a cooler environment. Planetary winds account for two-thirds of sensible heat transfer, and ocean currents for the remainder.
- The transfer of latent heat is less obvious. When water evaporates, heat is removed from a surface. When water vapour is cooled, and condensation occurs, the heat removed by evaporation is released and warms the atmosphere.

5 The global energy budget

Many climatologists believe that human activities have upset the delicate global energy balance. They think that the increase in greenhouse gases (especially CO_2), through burning fossil fuels, has increased the atmosphere's absorption of terrestrial radiation. If energy inputs exceed energy outputs, global warming takes place.

For the Earth as a whole, the amount of energy input to the Earth-atmosphere system is equal to output. As a result, the atmosphere is in a state of equilibrium. We know this because there are no long-term shifts in global temperatures.

However, because the amount of energy received at the Earth's surface varies with latitude, an energy balance does not exist everywhere, as shown in Figure 7.2.

- The tropics and sub-tropics (equatorwards of latitudes 35–40°) have an energy surplus. The Earth's surface and atmosphere receive more energy from insolation than they lose from terrestrial radiation.
- The middle and high latitudes (polewards of latitudes 35–40°) have an energy deficit. In these latitudes, more radiation leaves the Earth than arrives from insolation.

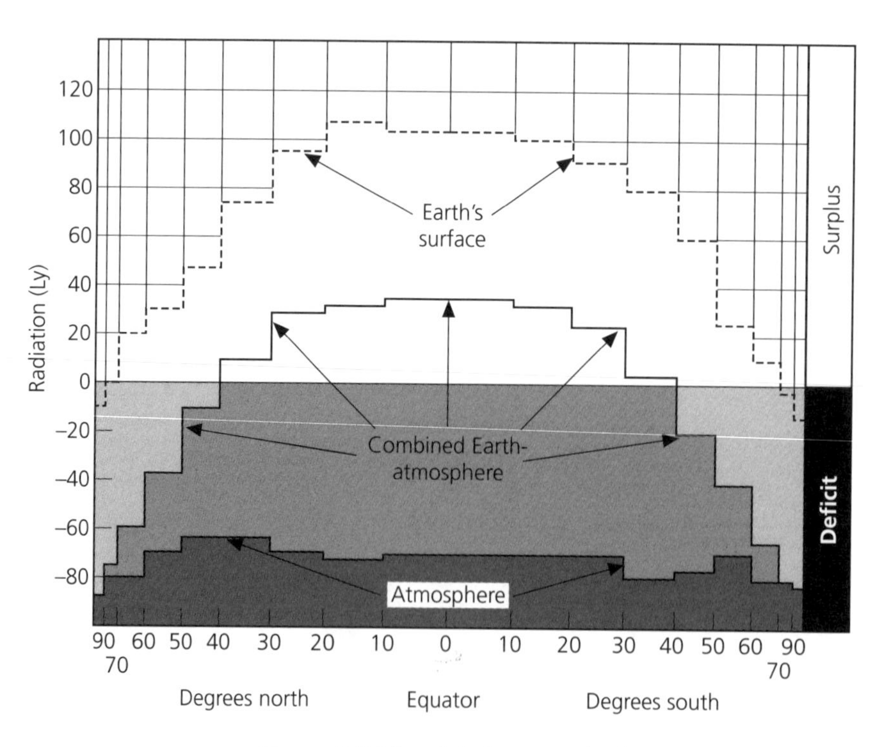

Figure 7.2 The global energy budget

This latitudinal energy imbalance causes a transfer of energy from the tropics to the middle and high latitudes. Planetary winds such as the westerlies, mid-latitude depressions, hurricanes and ocean currents such as the North Atlantic Drift, redistribute this energy. The energy transferred within the atmosphere is known as the **general circulation**.

6 The general circulation

The imbalance in energy receipt between the equator and the poles sets in motion the general circulation. The general circulation comprises three separate systems:

- the Hadley cells in the tropics and sub-tropics;
- the circumpolar vortex in mid-latitudes;
- the polar easterly winds.

6.1 The Hadley cells

Between the equator and latitude 30°, the atmospheric circulation in both hemispheres consists of two huge convective cells, shown in Figure 7.3.

- Intense insolation around the equator causes air to rise and creates low pressure at the surface. This is the powerhouse of the planet's general circulation.
- When the rising air reaches the **tropopause**, it spreads polewards.
- Poleward-moving air close to the tropopause eventually cools and sinks back towards the surface around latitudes 25–30°. This subsiding air has two effects: it causes high pressure at the surface; and because the air is so dry, it produces the hot deserts of the northern and southern hemispheres (e.g. Sahara, Australian).
- Surface winds known as the Trades blow towards the equator from the high-pressure belt of the sub-tropics. They complete the convective cell.
- Around the equator, where the Trade winds converge, air rises and there is massive instability. This is the **inter-tropical convergence zone** (ITCZ), associated with heavy convectional rainfall and intense thunderstorm activity.

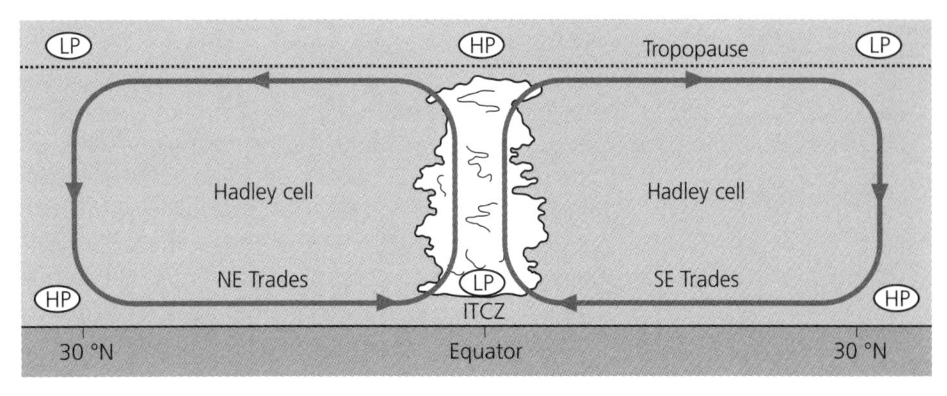

Figure 7.3 The convection circulation in low latitudes

The difference in pressure between the Icelandic 'low' and the Azores 'high' (the North Atlantic oscillation) has an important influence in the British Isles. With a large pressure difference a strong westerly flow develops. Smaller pressure differences give rise to blocking 'highs' and northerly/southerly winds.

6.2 Circumpolar vortex

Between latitudes 30° and 70° the general circulation takes on a completely different form. In the North Atlantic, high pressure around the Azores and low pressure near Iceland, together with the Earth's rotation from west to east, result in a narrow wave-like belt of fast-moving air called the **circumpolar vortex** (CPV), shown in Figure 7.4.

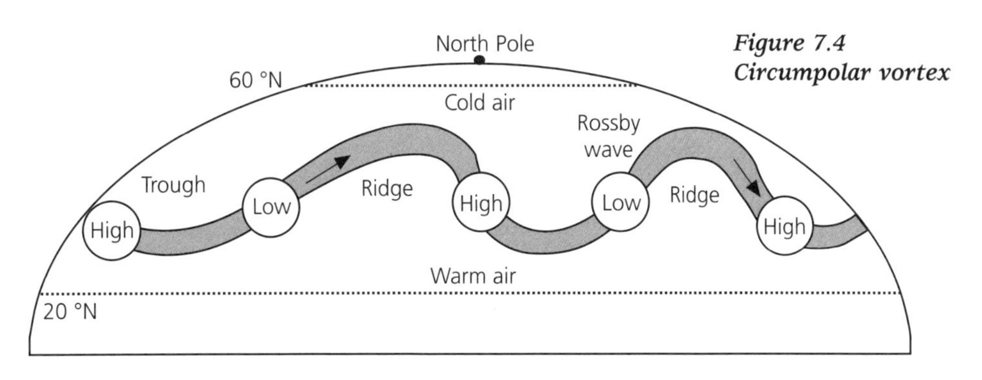

Figure 7.4 Circumpolar vortex

The CPV is located high above the surface near the tropopause and is responsible for the formation of travelling low-pressure storms or **depressions**, and small high-pressure cells or **anticyclones**.

INSET 1

Circumpolar vortex

The position of the CPV and the number of Rossby waves may remain unchanged for several weeks. The result is distinctive spells of weather. When the waves are shallow, surface winds are mainly from the west. Such a latitudinal or **zonal** circulation brings unsettled weather, with depressions and their associated belts of cloud and rain. Zonal flows bring cool, wet summers and mild, wet winters. When the Rossby waves are more sinuous, airflow is more longitudinal or **meridional**. This may cause extreme weather conditions. For example, high pressure often develops over western Europe, blocking the normal westerly flow. The result is exceptionally dry conditions, with unusually warm summers or abnormally cold winters.

6.3 Polar easterlies

This third element in the general circulation is less clearly defined. High pressure over the poles results in a weak pattern of surface easterly winds.

7 *The composition and structure of the atmosphere*

The Earth's atmosphere is a thin envelope of gases, barely 100 kilometres deep. About 99% of the atmosphere by volume is nitrogen (N_2) and oxygen (O_2). Other gases, present in only small amounts, but very important to the Earth's weather and climate, are water vapour (H_2O) and carbon dioxide (CO_2).

- As Figure 7.5 shows, the atmosphere comprises a series of layers defined on the basis of temperature. The **troposphere** is the lowest layer. It contains 75% of the atmosphere's gaseous mass and virtually all of the water vapour. The troposphere generates the world's weather and climate.
- Temperatures in the troposphere decrease with height at a rate of 6.5 °C per kilometre. Such a decrease is known as a temperature **lapse**.
- The tropopause separates the troposphere from the next layer – the stratosphere.
- Temperatures in the stratosphere increase with height – a phenomenon called **inversion**. The upper atmosphere (mesosphere and thermosphere) exert little influence on weather and climate.

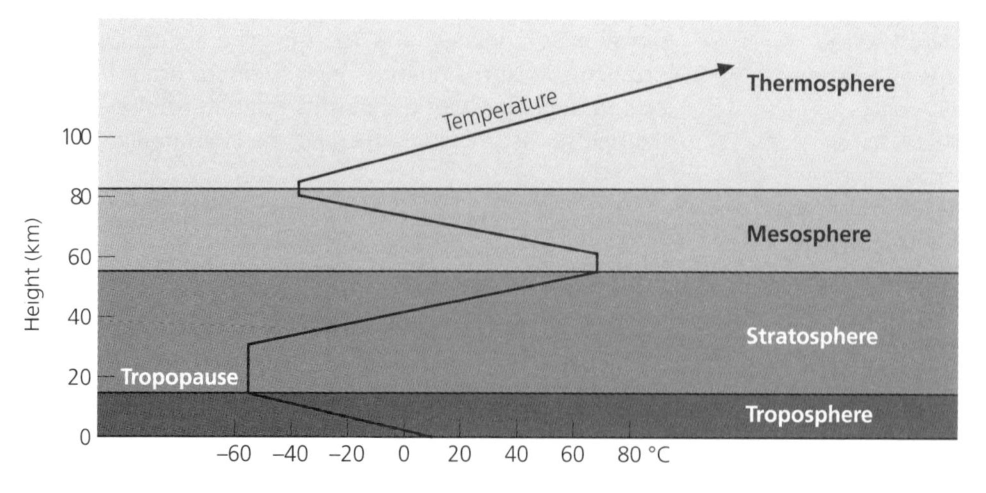

Figure 7.5 Structure of the atmosphere

8 Moisture in the atmosphere

Moisture is found in the atmosphere as a liquid (water droplets), as a solid (ice) and as a gas (water vapour). Figure 3.1 (p. 31) shows the phase changes of moisture.

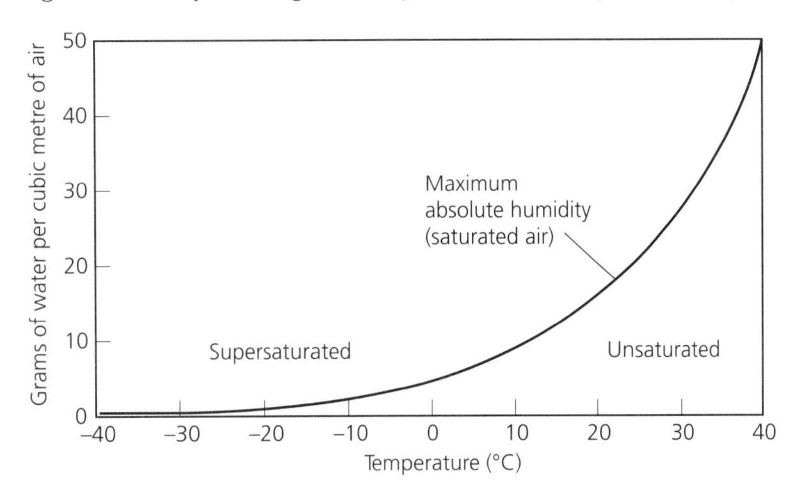

Figure 7.6 Temperature and absolute humidity

INSET 2

Humidity

There are two measures of humidity:

- **Absolute humidity** is the amount of water vapour, in grams, in 1 m^3 of air. Absolute humidity depends on temperature. Warm air can hold more vapour than cold air. For example, air at 27 °C can hold up to 25 grams/m^3, compared to just 4.4 grams/m^3 at –1 °C (Figure 7.6).
- **Relative humidity** is the ratio of the actual water vapour in 1 m^3 of air to the maximum amount the air can hold, expressed as a percentage. Thus, if 1 m^3 of air at 27 °C contains 15 grams of water vapour, its relative humidity is (15/25) × 100 or 60%. You should note that air at –1 °C would also have 60% relative humidity even though it contained only 2.64 grams of water vapour per cm^3.

If air cools sufficiently and reaches its dew-point temperature, condensation occurs. Cooling may result from:

- the expansion of rising air owing to a decrease in pressure (adiabatic expansion);
- air contacting a cold object – usually the Earth's surface;
- the mixing of cold and warm air.

Condensation causes dew, hoar frost and fog to form at ground level, and clouds to form in the atmosphere.

There is a limit to the amount of water vapour air can hold. When this limit is reached (i.e. at 100% relative humidity), the air is **saturated** and condensation takes place (Figure 7.6). Because the amount of vapour in the air depends on temperature, there is a critical temperature when saturation occurs. This is the **dew-point** temperature.

9 Condensation near the ground

Condensation is the phase change of moisture from vapour to liquid water (see Figure 3.1). It occurs both within the atmosphere and near the ground. Near the ground, condensation causes dew, hoar frost and fog.

9.1 Dew

Dew comprises deposits of water on vegetation surfaces and on the ground and is the result of condensation. A number of conditions favour dew formation (as well as frost and fog):

- clear night skies, allowing maximum heat loss through long-wave radiation and cooling of the ground;

- a gentle breeze, allowing the constant circulation of air and its chilling through contact with the ground to its dew point;
- high relative humidity, so that only a small temperature drop leads to saturation and condensation.

9.2 Hoar frost

Hoar frost is a white, crystalline deposit, usually formed overnight when temperatures drop below zero. It forms in similar circumstances to fog. In the early part of the night, dew forms. But as temperatures fall below zero, the dew freezes. The frozen dew provides the nucleus for the deposition of water vapour (i.e. phase change from vapour directly to ice), which forms a mass of white ice crystals.

9.3 Fog

Both fog and mist consist of water droplets suspended in the air. Mist is less dense than fog (i.e. visibility in excess of 1 km). Haze also restricts visibility. It consists of suspended particles of dust and smoke.

Fog is cloud at ground level, restricting visibility to less than one kilometre. Fog consists of tiny water droplets suspended in the atmosphere. There are two main types of fog: radiation fog and advection fog.

Radiation fog

Radiation fog results from the cooling of the atmosphere through long-wave radiation from the ground at night. Unlike dew, this cooling extends for some distance above the ground surface. To ensure sufficient cooling in depth, turbulence and wind speed must be greater than for dew formation. Clear skies and high humidity are also essential for radiation fog to form.

Radiation fog is most common in winter, when long hours of darkness give maximum cooling. Fog disperses either through an increase in wind speed or through a warming of the air (and subsequent evaporation) at sunrise. Sometimes in winter, radiation fog persists all day. At this time of year, the Sun has insufficient power to evaporate the fog.

INSET 3

Inversion fog

Inversion fog is a type of radiation fog that forms in valleys, as shown in Figure 7.7. In the evening, with clear skies and high humidity, the air on the upper slopes of a valley is chilled by radiative cooling. This cooling increases the density of the air, until it flows downslope. The cold air accumulates in the valley bottom, displacing warmer air. The result is a temperature inversion. If the cold air is chilled to its dew point, fog will form, filling the valley floor. Cold air stagnating in the valley floor in winter may produce exceptionally low temperatures. Valleys are often notorious frost hollows, frequently recording the lowest temperatures in a locality.

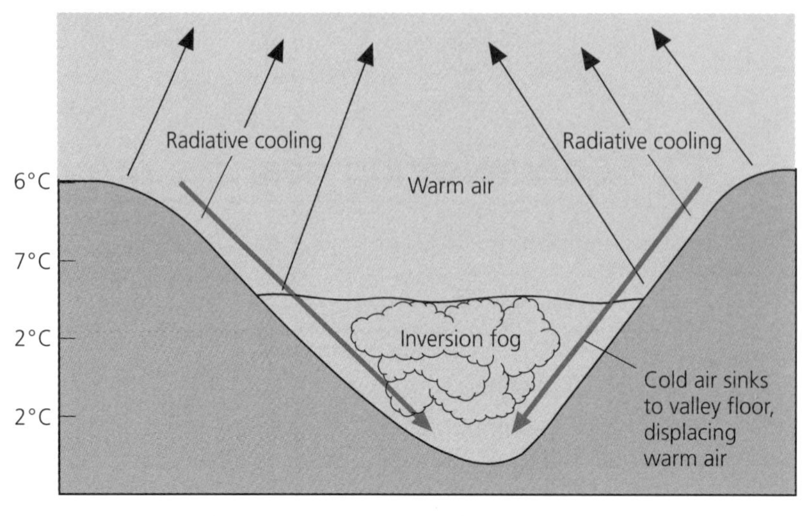

Figure 7.7 Formation of inversion fog

Advection fog commonly occurs around the coasts of Devon and Cornwall in summer. Tropical maritime air cools as it moves north-eastwards to form dense fog on the coast. The fog soon evaporates as it drifts inland.

Advection fog

Advection fog forms when a mass of relatively warm air moves horizontally across a cooler surface. As a result, the air is chilled to its dew point, and condensation occurs. Advection fog is most common around the coast and at sea (it is often known as sea fog). As the fog moves inland, it is soon warmed and evaporates.

If, at sub-zero temperatures, cloud or fog deposits moisture on trees, grass, fences, etc., the moisture freezes and leaves a coating of ice or **rime** on objects. Fog that comprises water droplets at sub-zero temperatures is called **freezing fog**.

10 *Condensation in the free air*

Condensation in the free air forms cloud. In 1803 Luke Howard proposed a simple classification of clouds. Based on their appearance, he recognised three main cloud types:

- cumuliform clouds (with flat bases and a bulbous, cauliflower-like shape);
- stratiform clouds (in layers or sheets);
- cirrus clouds (with a wispy, fibrous appearance).

Cumuliform clouds form in unstable conditions by **adiabatic cooling** (see Inset 4). Stratiform clouds form in stable conditions through contact with a relatively cool land or sea surface.

Cooling of the atmosphere, leading to condensation and cloud formation, can occur in three ways:

- when air comes into contact with the cold ground or ocean surface;
- when air rises through the atmosphere, expands and cools – adiabatic cooling;
- when a relatively warm mass of air mixes with a cooler one.

INSET 4

Adiabatic cooling

Atmospheric pressure decreases with height. Thus when a parcel of air rises, it encounters lower pressure. As a result, the air parcel expands and uses up energy, and its temperature falls. This pressure-related fall in temperature is adiabatic cooling. Most cumuliform clouds form by adiabatic cooling. Note that there is no exchange of heat between the air parcel and the surrounding atmosphere. The rate of adiabatic cooling is 10 °C per km for dry air and 7 °C for saturated air.

Confusion about lapse rates often leads to misunderstanding of stability/instability. The ELR simply describes the background temperature of the atmosphere at different heights. The DALR and SALR describe temperature changes which occur in parcels of rising air.

10.1 Lapse rates

A temperature **lapse** is a decrease in temperature with height. This is the normal situation in the troposphere. There are three different lapse rates:

- **Environmental lapse rate** (ELR): this is the vertical distribution of temperature in the atmosphere at any given time. In the troposphere, it averages 6.5 °C per kilometre.
- **Dry adiabatic lapse rate** (DALR): this is the rate of cooling of a rising parcel of dry air. The DALR is 10 °C per kilometre.
- **Saturated adiabatic lapse rate** (SALR): this is the rate of cooling of a rising parcel of saturated air. The SALR is approximately 7 °C per kilometre. Because condensation occurs in saturated air, there is a release of latent heat. As a result, saturated air cools more slowly than dry air.

10.2 Atmospheric stability and instability

Absolute instability

If a parcel of air is warmer than its surroundings, it will be less dense and therefore buoyant. If displaced (e.g. by the Sun heating the air, by turbulence or by uplift across a hill or mountain), such an air parcel will rise freely. This condition is **atmospheric instability**.

In Figure 7.8(a), the air parcel at A is warmer (and therefore less dense) than the surrounding atmosphere (ELR). Once displaced, the air parcel rises freely, cooling at the DALR. Above 1,000 m, cumuliform clouds develop and the air parcel cools at the SALR. If the clouds are thick enough, showers and thunderstorms may occur. The air parcel continues to rise until it becomes cooler (and therefore heavier) than the surrounding air (i.e. at 2,500 m).

The conditions of stability/instability compare the temperature of an air parcel with its surroundings. An air parcel is unstable if it is warmer than the surrounding atmosphere. If it is cooler than its surroundings it is stable.

Conditional instability

Often air masses approaching the British Isles are **conditionally unstable**. At ground level, the air is stable. However, if forced to rise (e.g. when crossing a mountain range), the air becomes unstable and rises freely, producing extensive cloud and relief (orographic) rain in upland areas.

In Figure 7.8(b), the air parcel at A is cooler (and therefore more dense) than the surrounding atmosphere (ELR). The air parcel is forced up as it approaches a mountain barrier, cooling at the DALR. Condensation occurs when the air parcel reaches its dew-point temperature – at 1,000 m. Above 1,000 m, cloud forms. At this level, the air parcel is unstable, being warmer (and therefore lighter) than the surrounding atmosphere. As a result, the air parcel rises freely. It continues to rise until it cools to the same temperature as the surrounding air (i.e. 2,500 m).

Absolute stability

When an air parcel is cooler than its surroundings, it is denser and heavier. If displaced, it will return to its original level. This condition is known as **atmospheric stability**.

In Figure 7.8(c), the air parcel at A is cooler (and therefore more dense) than the surrounding atmosphere (ELR). The parcel is stable at A and remains stable throughout the lower atmosphere. Unless forced aloft, the air parcel at A will, if displaced, always return to its original level. There will be no tendency for air to rise, and skies should remain cloudless.

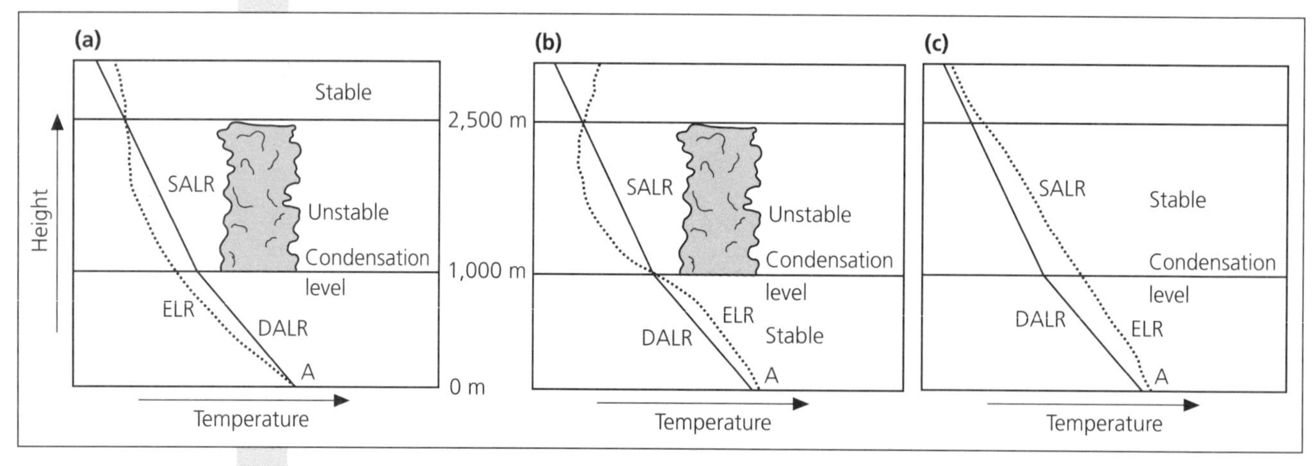

Figure 7.8 Atmospheric stability and instability: (a) absolute instability; (b) conditional stability; (c) absolute stability

11 Precipitation

Precipitation is moisture that falls from clouds. It includes rain, snow, sleet, hail and drizzle.

11.1 Intensity and duration

- **Showers** are high-intensity events that are localised and relatively short-lived. Rainfall intensities may exceed 50 mm an hour. However, most showers last only a few minutes and the total amounts of precipitation are usually small.

INSET 5

Formation of precipitation

Precipitation develops when the minute particles of water and ice that form clouds increase in size to form droplets and ice particles. Eventually, these droplets and ice particles fall out of clouds as precipitation.

According to the **Bergeron–Findeisen theory**, clouds above the freezing level contain both ice particles and supercooled water droplets (i.e. water droplets with a temperature below freezing). The ice particles grow at the expense of the supercooled water droplets (by deposition) until they become large enough to fall out of clouds. If temperatures near the ground are above freezing, the ice particles melt and fall as rain.

The Bergeron–Findeisen theory explains precipitation in middle and high latitudes, where clouds are below freezing. However, in the tropics, rain often falls from clouds with temperatures above freezing. In this situation, the **collision theory** explains precipitation. Rain droplets grow by collision with other droplets. The bigger droplets sweep up the smaller droplets, until they fall out of the cloud as rain.

- More organised bands of cloud and precipitation occur along fronts in depressions. This **general precipitation** may last for several hours. Although general precipitation is often low intensity (2–3 mm an hour) the total amounts of precipitation falling in any one event may be high.

11.2 Types of precipitation

We classify precipitation into three types depending on the processes that cause air to rise and cool.

- **Convectional** precipitation occurs when air in contact with the ground is heated by the Sun. The warm air rises from the surface as a **thermal** or convection current. This type of precipitation falls as showers (including thunderstorms) from cumuliform clouds.
- **Orographic** (or relief) precipitation occurs when mountains cause mechanical uplift of air masses. In the British Isles, such air masses are often conditionally unstable. This orographic effect explains the high precipitation totals in mountains in the west. However, areas on the leeward side of mountain ranges often lie in a **rain shadow** (e.g. north-east Scotland) and have unusually small amounts of precipitation.
- Depressions bring precipitation associated with air rising along fronts.

12 *Pressure and winds*

12.1 Pressure

The mass of atmosphere above any point at the Earth's surface exerts a pressure. We measure this atmospheric pressure in millibars (mb). Average pressure at sea level is 1,013 mb. Normally sea-level pressures vary from around 920 to 1,050 mb.

Isobars are lines on weather charts that join places of equal pressure. As Figure 7.9 shows, they form distinctive patterns similar to relief features on contour maps. Because altitude has such a strong influence on pressure, isobars on weather charts are normally standardised to sea level.

- **Anticyclones** are areas of high pressure, delimited by circular, closed isobars. Pressure increases towards the centre of anticyclones.
- **Depressions** are areas of low pressure, also comprising circular, closed isobars. Pressure decreases towards the centre of depressions.
- **Ridges** are narrow extensions of high pressure from anticyclones.
- **Troughs** are narrow extensions of low pressure from depressions.
- **Cols** are areas of constant pressure between two 'highs'.

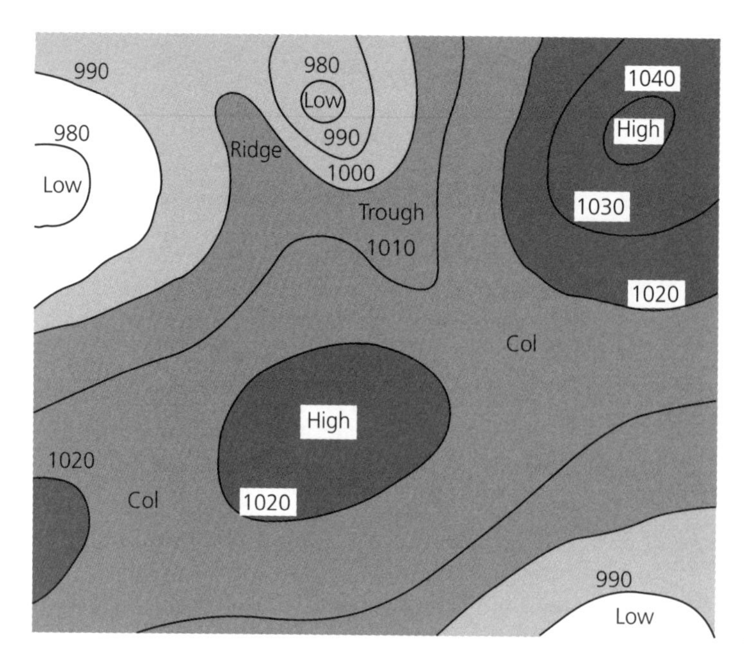

Figure 7.9
Pressure patterns

It is important to know how to determine wind direction on a weather chart.

- Wind direction is the direction **from which** the wind blows.
- Winds blow roughly parallel to isobars.
- In the northern hemisphere, winds circulate anticlockwise in a depression, and clockwise in an anticyclone.
- If you stand with your back to the wind in the northern hemisphere, low pressure is always to your left.

Backing and **veering** refer to changes in wind direction. Backing is an anticlockwise change of wind direction. Veering is a clockwise change of wind direction.

Pressure differences result mainly from differences in temperature. Cold air is relatively heavy and dense, and causes high pressure. Warm air is lighter and less dense, and is associated with lower pressure.

12.2 Winds

Three forces affect the horizontal movements of air or **winds**. These are shown acting on the air parcel at A in Figure 7.10.

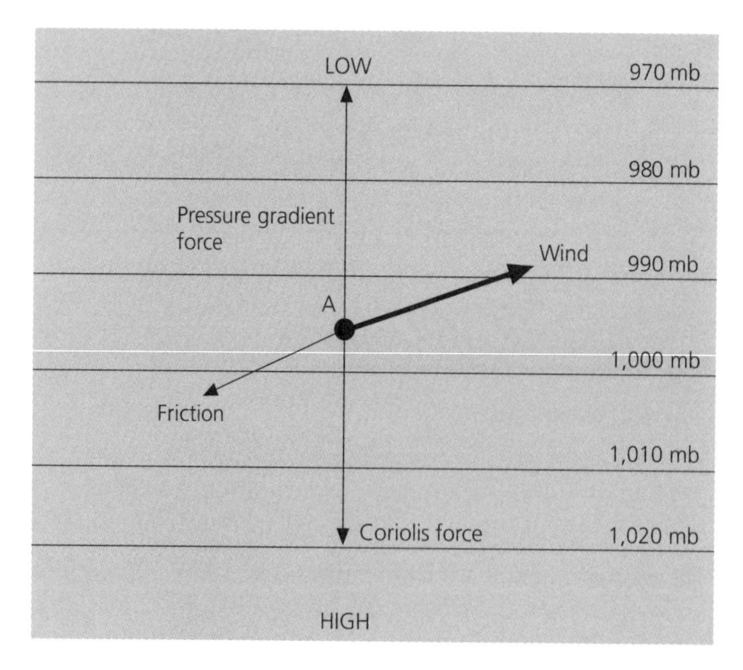

Figure 7.10
Forces acting on the wind

- The **pressure gradient** describes differences in atmospheric pressure between places. Pressure is the main force driving the wind. Winds blow from areas of high pressure to areas of low pressure, pushing A (Figure 7.10) towards the area of low pressure. In a sense, winds are equalising pressure differences on the globe. There is a simple rule: the steeper the pressure gradient, the stronger the wind.
- The force imparted by the rotation of the Earth – the **Coriolos force** – deflects the wind to the right of its path in the northern hemisphere, and to the left in the southern

hemisphere. When the pressure gradient and Coriolis forces balance, the resultant wind blows parallel to the isobars. This is the **geostrophic wind**. It blows at high level near the tropopause.

- **Friction** between the wind and the Earth's surface causes the wind to back, and cross the isobars at a slight angle. The greater the friction, the greater the angle formed by the wind at the isobars.

13 Air masses

Wind direction is the best guide to the type of air mass affecting an area. For instance, a north-westerly airstream usually indicates polar maritime; an easterly airstream suggests polar continental, etc.

An air mass is a large body of air with uniform temperature, lapse rate and humidity. Air masses form in areas of permanent anticyclone. Those that affect the weather and climate of the British Isles originate around the sub-tropical 'high', in Bermuda and the Azores; and in polar regions, such as northern Canada and Siberia. In these source regions, air can stagnate for several weeks. This allows the air mass to take on the temperature and humidity characteristics of these regions.

When air masses move away from their source regions, they undergo modification. The nature of this modification depends on the route or **track** taken by the air mass.

- Air masses moving towards the equator from source regions in high latitudes are warmed and become unstable (e.g. Am, Pm).
- Air masses moving towards the poles from source regions in low latitudes are cooled and become stable (e.g. Tm).
- Air masses following an oceanic track increase in humidity (e.g. Pm).
- Air masses following a continental track experience little change in humidity (e.g. Tc).

To understand the influence of an air mass on the weather, you need to answer a few basic questions:

- Is the air mass warmed or cooled from below?
- Is the sea warmer than the land or vice versa?
- Is the air mass stable or unstable?
- Does the stability of the air mass change as it crosses land or sea?
- Does the stability of the air mass change between day and night?

We classify air masses according to their source region and their track. Air masses that affect the British Isles have three types of source region: tropical, polar and arctic (see Figure 7.11). But by the time they reach the British Isles, they will have followed a long oceanic or a continental track, and will have been substantially modified.

Data concerning air masses in the British Isles are given in Tables 7.1 and 7.2.

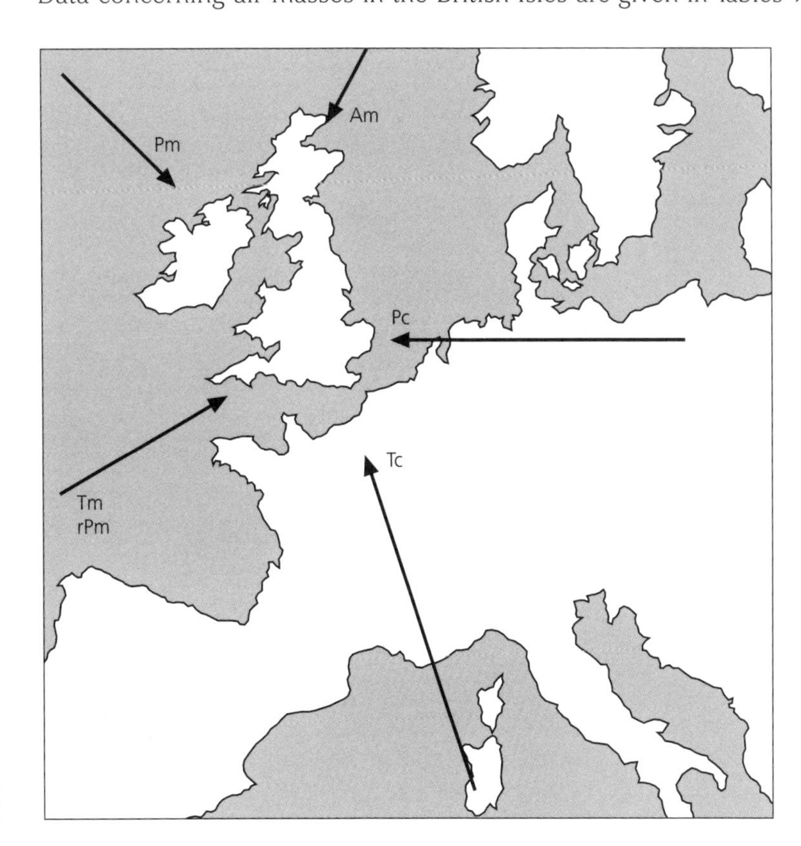

Figure 7.11 Air masses affecting the British Isles

Air mass	Kew	Stornoway
Am	6.5	11.3
Pm	24.7	31.5
rPm	10.0	16.0
Pc	1.4	0.7
Tm	9.5	8.7
Tc	4.7	1.3
Anticyclones	24.3	13.8
Depressions	11.3	11.8

Table 7.1 Percentage frequency of air masses at Kew (London) and Stornoway (north-west Scotland)

Air mass	Winter	Summer
Arctic maritime (Am)	A very cold air mass. Reaches the British Isles on a northerly airstream. Temperatures well below average (Jan. max. –1 to 2 °C). Unstable. Wintry showers especially in northern Britain and on exposed north-facing coasts. Brings our most severe winter weather.	Brings a cool northerly airstream with temperatures well below average (July max. 12–13 °C). Unstable. Rain showers more especially in the north.
Polar maritime (Pm)	Brings average temperatures in winter on a north-westerly airstream. Unstable after crossing the North Atlantic. Showers of rain and sleet, particularly in western areas. Instability dies down at night. There may be clear skies and frost.	Cool conditions with daytime maxima in July only 16–17 °C. Unstable. Showers in the west with possibility of thunderstorms.
Polar continental (Pc)	Arrives from the Continent on an easterly airstream. A cold air mass, warmed as it crosses the North Sea. Unstable on reaching eastern Britain. Wintry showers that die out towards the west. Daytime temperatures only just above freezing. Frost at night.	The air mass is warm in its source region, but cools and becomes stable as it crosses the North Sea. Advection fog common along the east coast north of the Humber in spring and early summer. Inland clear skies and temperatures of 20–25 °C.
Returning polar maritime (rPm)	Similar to Tm air in both winter and summer. A polar air mass forced further south than usual; it approaches the British Isles from the south-west.	
Tropical maritime (Tm)	Source region is the Azores. Comes to the British Isles on a south-westerly airstream. A humid, stable and mild air mass. Temperatures well above average (Jan. max. 10–13 °C). Low stratus cloud and fog on high ground.	Stable in summer after being cooled by the Atlantic. Some advection fog around south-west coasts. This quickly evaporates inland. Clear skies and temperatures around 25 °C.
Tropical continental (Tc)	Does not occur in winter.	Occasionally affects the British Isles. The air mass comes from north Africa and is hot. Very low humidity and largely cloudless. Heat wave conditions (28–30 °C). Poor visibility (haze) because of pollution from the Continent.

Table 7.2 Air masses and weather in the British Isles

14 Depressions and fronts

Depressions bring unsettled spells of weather, with rapid changes of cloud, precipitation, sunshine and temperature. Frontal zones are associated with a predictable sequence of weather changes (see Table 7.3). Weather changes along fronts are caused by air rising throughout the troposphere. Rising air cools and condenses to give extensive belts of cloud and precipitation.

14.1 Depressions

Depressions are travelling areas of low pressure. They dominate the weather in middle and high latitudes. As part of the general circulation, depressions help to even out imbalances in the global energy budget. They export surplus energy from the tropics towards the poles. Depressions have the following features:

- They comprise two contrasting air masses: tropical air and polar air.
- The boundaries between tropical and polar air are called **fronts**.
- Fronts contain a mass of cloud and precipitation.
- Winds in the northern hemisphere circulate anticlockwise in, and blow towards the centre of, depressions.
- Winds change direction at fronts (i.e. they veer).

Depressions form along the circumpolar vortex where polar and tropical air meet. Those that affect the climate of the British Isles form over northern Canada. They develop rapidly as they cross the Atlantic Ocean, but within a week start to fill, and disappear from weather charts. At any time the North Atlantic weather chart usually contains several depressions, in various stages of development, strung out between eastern Canada and the British Isles.

14.2 Fronts

Fronts are the boundaries between warm and cold air in depressions, as shown in Figure 7.12. There are three types of front: warm, cold and occluded.

- At the passage of the **warm front**, temperatures rise as tropical air replaces polar air.
- At the **cold front**, warm air is replaced by cold.
- There is little change in temperature at the passage of an **occluded front** because the warm tropical air has been lifted above the surface (see Figure 7.13).

Warm air rises at frontal zones to produce a mass of cloud. The cloud fills most of the troposphere and brings prolonged precipitation. However, once a front has passed, the cloud clears and sunny intervals occur. This cyclonic weather is, therefore, very changeable.

Occlusions are a feature of the later stages in the life cycle of depressions. In an occlusion, the cold front overtakes the warm front and lifts the warm sector above the surface. A mass of thick cloud fills the troposphere, with extensive and prolonged precipitation.

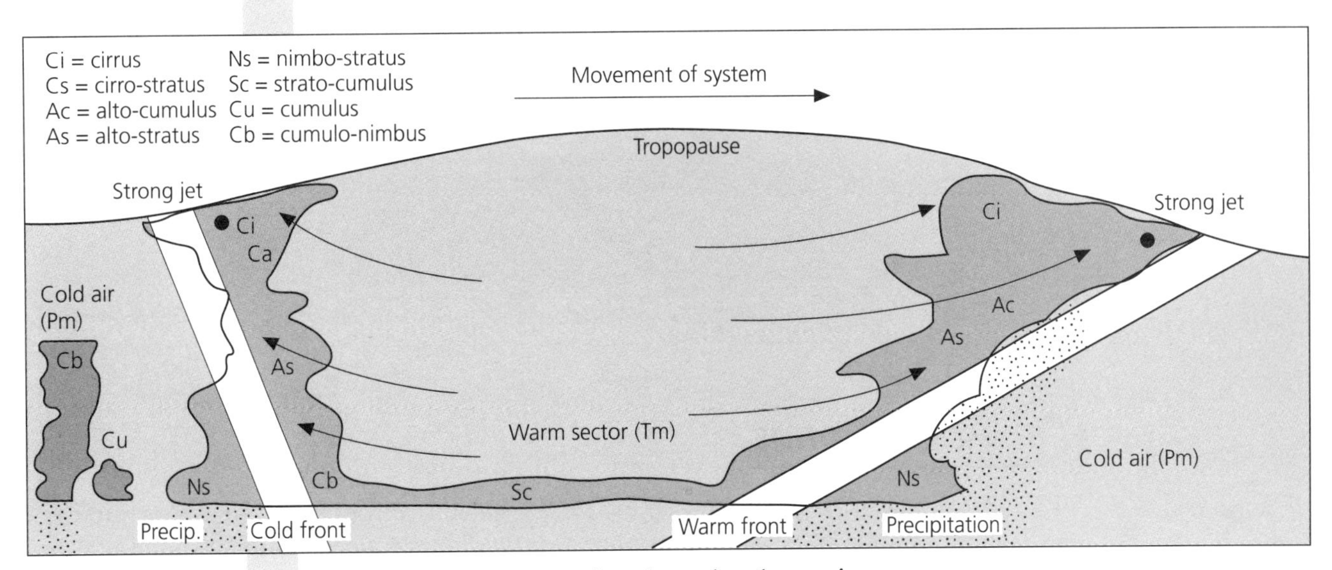

Figure 7.12 Cross-section through a depression

Element	In advance	At passage	In the rear
Warm front			
Pressure	Steady fall	Fall ceases	Little change or slow fall
Wind	Increases and sometimes backs	Veers and sometimes decreases	Steady direction
Temperature	Steady/slow rise	Rise	Little change
Relative humidity	Rises in the area of precipitation	May rise further	Little change
Cloud	Ci, Cs, As, Ns in succession; scud below As and Ns	Low Ns and scud	St or Sc
Weather	Continuous rain (or snow)	Precipitation almost stops	Cloudy, drizzle or light rain
Cold front			
Pressure	Fall	Sudden rise	Rise continues more slowly
Wind	Increasing, backing and becoming squally	Sudden veer, perhaps squally	Backing a little after squall, then steady or veering
Temperature	Steady but falls in rain	Sudden fall	Little change, variable in showers
Relative humidity	May rise in precipitation	Remains high in precipitation	Rapid fall as rain ceases
Cloud	Ac or As, then Cb	Cb with low scud	Lifting rapidly, followed by As or Ac; later further Cu or Cb
Weather	Rain	Rain, often heavy, with perhaps thunder and hail	Heavy rain for short period, sometimes more persistent, then fair with occasional showers

Table 7.3 The sequence of weather associated with the passage of warm and cold fronts

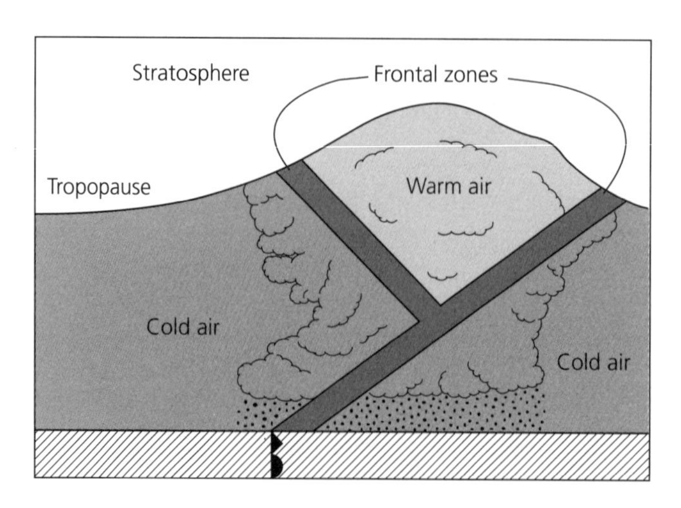

Figure 7.13 Cross-section through an occlusion

15 Anticyclones

Anticyclones are areas of high pressure. Within anticyclones the air sinks slowly towards the Earth's surface. This subsidence both warms the air (adiabatically) and prevents any upward motion, as shown in Figure 7.14. As a result, conditions are stable.

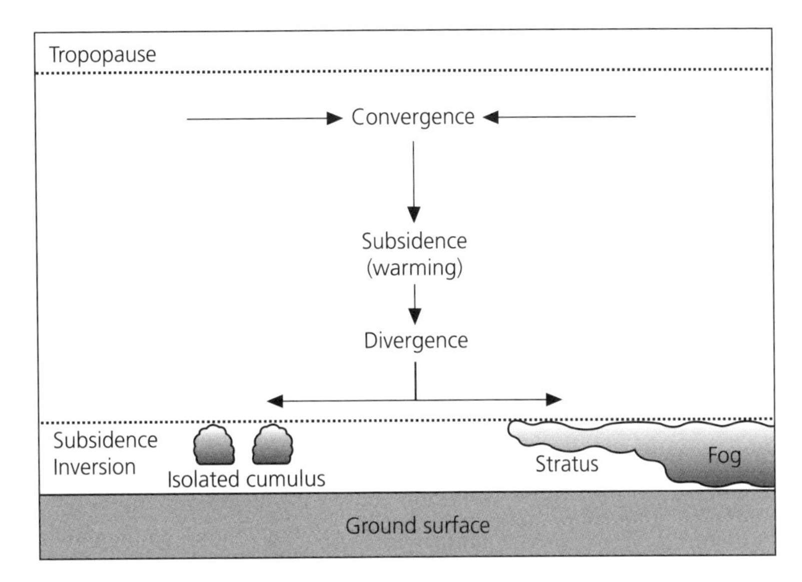

Figure 7.14 Possible weather in anticyclonic conditions

15.1 Anticyclonic weather

Anticyclones bring spells of calm, dry weather, with variable amounts of cloud. Cloud cover depends on the humidity of the air, and on whether subsidence reaches the surface. Sometimes cold air trapped near the surface causes an inversion and the formation of radiation fog or stratus cloud. The resulting weather in winter is known as anticyclonic gloom. Less humid anticyclones give rise to clear skies and long periods of sunshine.

15.2 Blocking

Sometimes an anticyclone establishes itself over north-western Europe and remains stationary for several days. Depressions, which normally reach the British Isles on a westerly airstream, are steered around the edge of the high. This situation is known as **blocking**. It produces extreme weather conditions: in winter, dry weather and freezing temperatures; in summer, drought and occasionally heat-wave conditions.

The contrasting features of anticyclones and depressions are given in Table 7.4.

Feature	Anticyclone	Depression
Surface pressure	High	Low
Wind direction	Clockwise in northern hemisphere	Anticlockwise in northern hemisphere
Airflow	Divergence at surface; convergence aloft	Convergence at surface; divergence aloft
Vertical air motion	Subsides	Rises
Wind speed	Weak	Moderate to strong
Precipitation	Generally dry	Wet
Cloudiness	Stratus or no cloud	Cloudy
Stability	Stable air with a subsidence inversion aloft	May be unstable
Temperature gradient	Little temperature contrast across the high	Strong temperature contrasts, especially at fronts
Speed of movement	Slow moving or stagnant	Generally mobile, moving west–east

Table 7.4 The contrasting features of anticyclones and depressions

16 Weather patterns

We can usually explain the weather at any particular place by referring either to weather systems, such as depressions and anticyclones, or to air masses. **Synoptic charts** present a summary of weather patterns. By referring to these charts, together with satellite images and radar, meteorologists can make accurate weather forecasts for two or three days ahead.

Table 7.5 explains how to interpret satellite images and Figure 7.15 shows how to identify cloud types from them.

	Black	Grey	White
Visible	Highly absorptive; low albedo; water (e.g. oceans, seas, lakes)	Moderate albedo; vegetation, crops	Highly reflective; snow, ice, thick clouds, desert surfaces
Infra-red	Strong signals; warm surfaces; land in the tropics	Moderate temperatures; low cloud	Weak signals; cold surfaces; high-latitude land and sea; high clouds

Table 7.5 Interpreting visible and infra-red satellite images

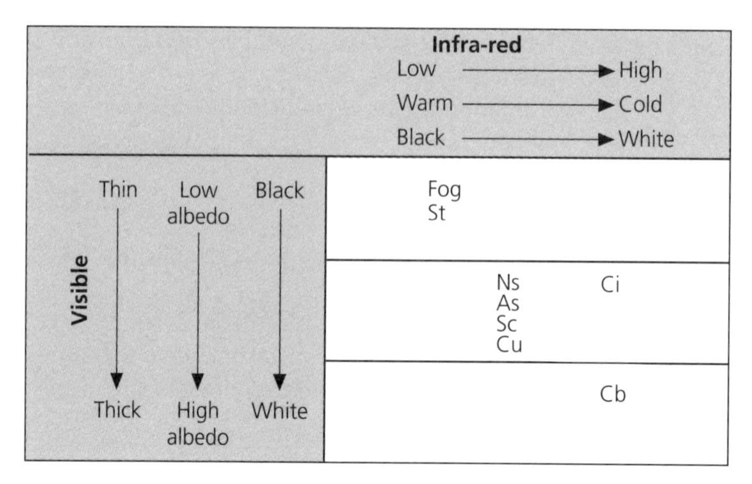

Figure 7.15 Identifying cloud types from satellite images

In order to analyse a synoptic chart and explain the weather in a particular place, you should answer the following questions:

General:

- Where are the main areas of high pressure and low pressure situated?
- Is the airflow zonal or meridional?
- Is there any evidence of blocking?

Area-specific:

- Which direction is the main airstream from?
- How steep/slack is the pressure gradient and how strong are the winds?
- Is the weather currently caused by a depression, an anticyclone or an air mass?
- Are there any fronts?
- Are the fronts active?
- How will the position of the fronts change in the next 24 hours?
- Are winds on-shore or off-shore?
- Is the air mass stable or unstable?

In answering each question, you will need to explain the implications for weather.

UNIT 8 Vegetation and soils

1 Ecosystems

Ecosystems are communities of plants, animals and other organisms (the **biotic** component) and the environment (the **abiotic** component) in which they live and interact (see Table 8.1). The physical environment provides the energy and nutrients that plants and animals need to survive and function.

Abiotic components	Biotic components
Rocks	Plants (primary producers)
Relief	Animals (herbivores, carnivores, omnivores)
Atmosphere (gases) and climate	Detritivores (fungi, microbes, etc.)
Soil	People
Water	
Solar radiation	
Fire	
Gravity	

Table 8.1 Components of ecosystems

Ecosystems exist at different scales: from a single oak tree to the Amazon rainforest and even the Earth itself. Those ecosystems that extend over large geographical areas (e.g. tropical rainforest) are known as **biomes**.

Most ecosystems are **open systems**, as shown in Figure 8.1. This means that both energy (e.g. solar radiation) and materials (e.g. minerals from weathered rocks, and water) cross ecosystem boundaries.

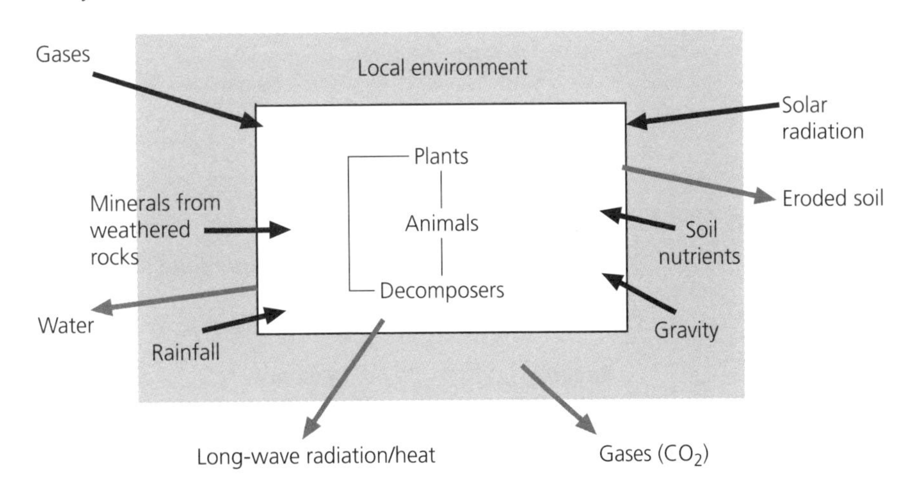

Figure 8.1 Inputs and outputs in an open ecosystem

Plants and animals interact with the physical environment and with each other. These interrelationships bind the various parts of ecosystems into a coherent whole. We refer to this quality of wholeness in ecosystems as **holisticity** (see Inset 1).

INSET 1

Interrelatedness in ecosystems

Because ecosystems are holistic, change in any one component often has far-reaching and unforeseen consequences. Thus a hill sheep farmer who increases the density of sheep on upland pastures may inadvertently cause damage to the ecosystem. Overgrazing may destroy the vegetation cover, resulting in accelerated soil erosion through increased run-off and increased sediment loads in streams. This in turn may destroy freshwater insect larvae and affect the fish and bird populations that depend on them.

2 Flows of energy

Sunlight, captured by the leaves of green plants, is the primary energy source for most ecosystems. This energy is then transferred along **food chains** and interlocking food chains known as **food webs**. The flow of energy within ecosystems occurs in a number of stages or **trophic levels** (T).

- T1: Green plants intercept sunlight and, in the process of **photosynthesis**, convert sunlight, water, CO_2 and mineral nutrients into carbohydrates. Green plants are the **primary producers** in ecosystems.
- T2: Plant-eating animals or herbivores convert some of the energy into animal tissue. Herbivores are the **primary consumers** in food chains.
- T3: Meat-eating animals or carnivores prey on herbivores. Carnivores occupying the third tropic level in a food chain are **secondary consumers**.
- T*n*: At the end of each food chain, there is a top or apex predator. Depending on the length of the chain, this animal may be a **tertiary** or **quaternary consumer**.
- At each trophic level, **detritivores** such as fungi and microbes decompose dead organic matter and animal faeces, consuming energy and releasing gases (CO_2, CH_4) and mineral nutrients.

At each trophic level in a food chain, there is a loss of energy. This is because organisms convert only a small proportion of the energy they consume into living tissue. Most is used to keep the organism alive and is lost as heat in respiration. As a result:

- There are limits to the number of trophic levels in food chains.
- There is a reduction of biomass at each trophic level, as shown in Figure 8.2.
- There is a reduction in the population of animals at each trophic level.

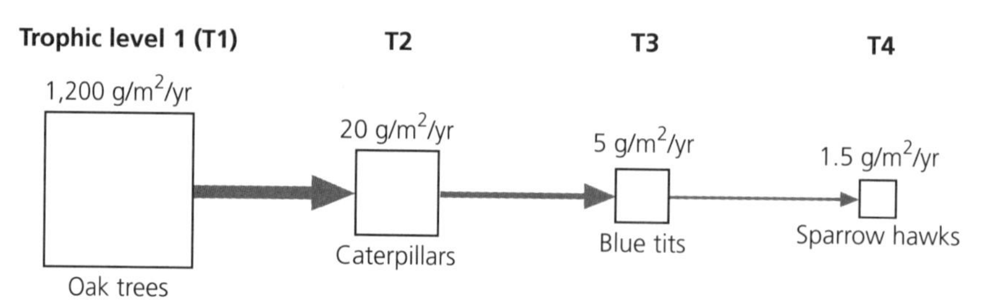

Figure 8.2 A simple food chain in an oak woodland

Ecosystems in harsh environments, such as deserts (see Figure 8.3) and tundra, are vulnerable to change by human activities. These ecosystems are fragile because they are relatively simple. They have few species, slow cycling of nutrients and short food chains. In contrast, complex ecosystems such as the tropical rainforest are far more resilient and able to withstand change.

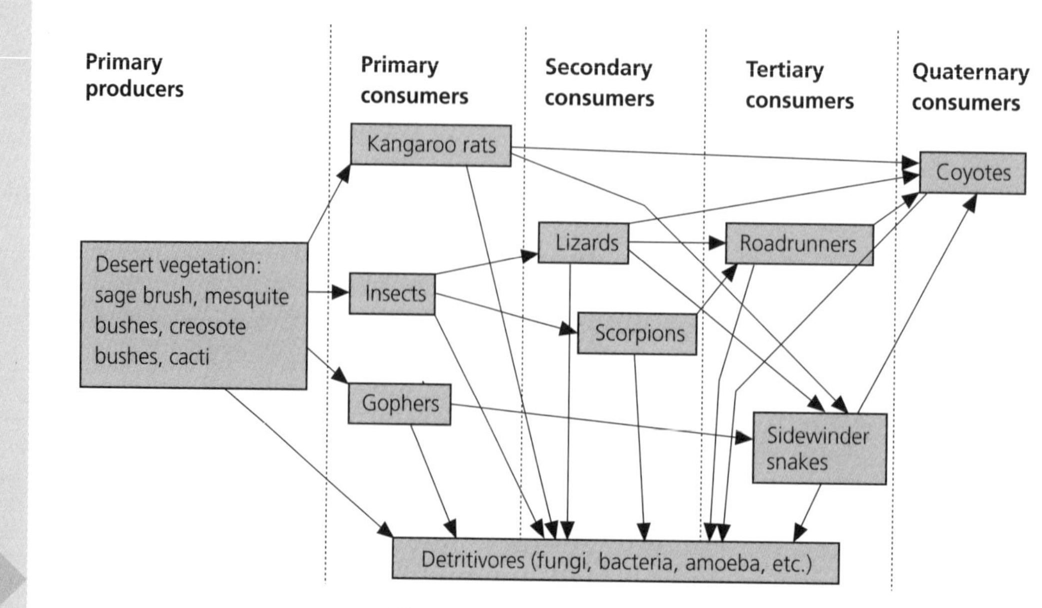

Figure 8.3 A desert food web

Most natural ecosystems can adjust to change and temporary disequilibrium through the operation of negative feedback loops (Inset 3). Such loops that restore stability in ecosystems may be destroyed through human activities.

INSET 2

Dynamic equilibrium

Most natural ecosystems, unaffected by people, are in a state of dynamic equilibrium. They are dynamic (rather than static) in the sense that they have continuous inputs, throughputs and outputs of energy and materials. From year to year there may be small fluctuations in animal populations and plant productivity. However, in the long term they remain stable, showing no fundamental changes over time.

INSET 3

Change and feedback in ecosystems

Change in ecosystems produces two responses: positive feedback and negative feedback.

- **Positive feedback** occurs when change leads to further change – a kind of snowball effect. In ecological succession, some plant species change the soil and microclimate. This allows new species to invade. They in turn modify the environment until other species take over and become dominant.
- **Negative feedback** leads to self-regulation, which restores ecosystems to balance. In the Arctic tundra, a glut of berries and edible seeds in a particular year may cause large increases in the population of small rodents. Animals such as arctic foxes and snowy owls respond to this abundance of prey by increasing their numbers. By predation, these carnivores restore balance between the rodent population and the environment.

3 *Nutrient cycles*

Nutrients are the chemical elements and compounds needed by plants and animals. They cycle between the living organisms and the physical environment within ecosystems. There are three sources of nutrients:

- Rocks are the source of most nutrients. On weathering, rocks release nutrients such as potassium, calcium and sodium into the soil, where they are absorbed by the roots of plants.
- Plants obtain some nutrients, such as nitrogen and carbon, directly from the atmosphere. Some mineral nutrients are also dissolved in rainwater. There are plants in the tropical rainforest with aerial roots that rely solely on the mineral nutrients in precipitation.
- Eventually, most mineral nutrients return to the soil as **plant litter**. Here the dead leaves, roots and stems are broken down and mineralised by fungi and microbes in the soil.

INSET 4

Primary productivity in ecosystems

There are two measures of primary productivity in ecosystems:

- **Gross primary productivity** (GPP) is the amount of energy fixed in photosynthesis. It is measured in grams/m^2/year.
- **Net primary productivity** (NPP) is the amount of energy fixed in photosynthesis minus the energy lost in respiration. It is also measured in grams/m^2/year.

The net primary productivity of selected biomes is given in Table 8.2.

Biome	NPP (grams/m^2/year)
Tropical rainforest	2,200
Temperate deciduous forest	1,200
Savanna grasslands	900
Boreal coniferous forest	800
Temperate grassland	600
Tundra and alpine	140
Desert and semi-desert	90

Table 8.2 Net primary productivity of selected biomes

Shortages of nutrients in an ecosystem may limit plant growth and influence species composition. For example, soils that contain free calcium usually support a richer flora than acidic soils.

Human activity may interrupt nutrient cycles and deplete nutrients in ecosystems. Deforestation often results in the leaching of mineral nutrients from the soil.

Nutrient cycles vary in their speed. In the tropical rainforest, high temperatures and humid conditions speed up the process of decomposition and cause rapid nutrient cycling (see Figure 8.4).

In the boreal coniferous forest, low temperatures slow down the activities of the decomposers. As a result, several years of leaf litter accumulate on the forest floor. Sometimes the nutrients tied up in the litter rely on wildfires to release them.

The richness of a nutrient cycle depends partly on the vegetation. Conifer trees require few nutrients. Unused nutrients weathered from rocks are removed from the soil. Oak trees are far more demanding. They take up many more nutrients from the soil and thus sustain a much richer nutrient cycle.

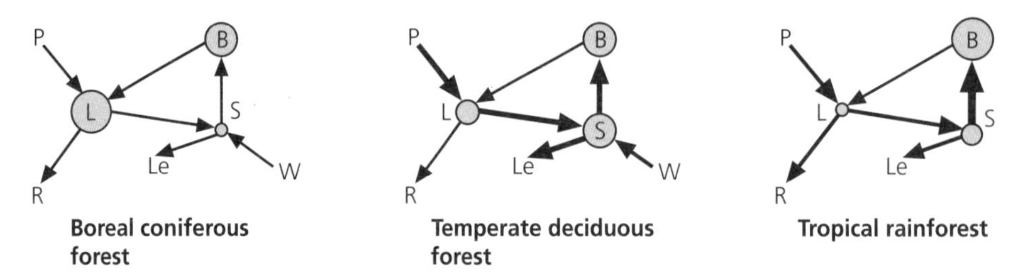

Figure 8.4 Nutrient cycles in three forest ecosystems

4 Ecological succession

Many ecological successions have their greatest biodiversity and productivity at an early stage. In forest successions, a diverse flora of herbs, grasses, ferns, etc. is often shaded out by forest trees. Productivity is often highest when young saplings are growing vigorously. At the climax stage, biomass acts as non-productive supporting structures such as trunks and branches.

The sequence of vegetation changes on a site through time is called **ecological succession**.

- **Primary succession** describes vegetation changes on previously unvegetated sites (e.g. sand dune, mudflat, bare rock). Primary succession in a deglaciated area is shown in Figure 8.5.
- **Secondary succession** describes vegetation changes on sites where the original vegetation cover has been destroyed (e.g. the fires in Yellowstone National Park, USA, in 1988 which destroyed extensive areas of lodgepole pine forests).

Ecological succession has the following characteristics: over time the physical environment becomes increasingly favourable to plant growth; there is a progressive increase in nutrient and energy flows; biodiversity increases; and net primary productivity increases.

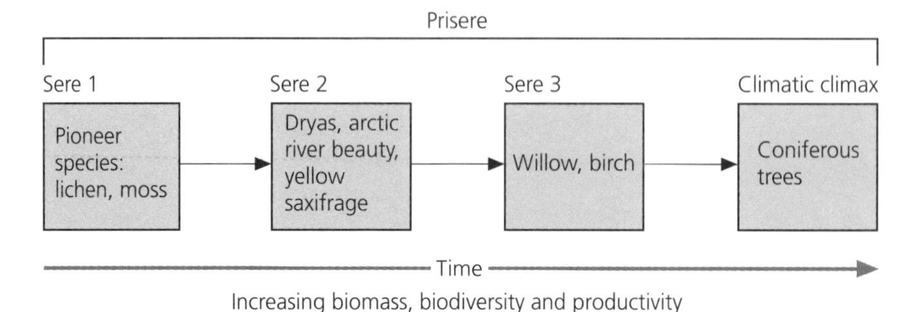

Figure 8.5 Primary succession in a recently deglaciated area

5 Climax vegetation

During succession each vegetation stage or **sere** modifies the environment (by increasing the depth of soil, nutrient levels, moisture storage, etc.). Such changes allow new species to invade, compete and dominate.

When the vegetation reaches a state of balance with the environment, it is known as **climax** vegetation. Providing there is no further environmental change, the climax vegetation will persist indefinitely.

The whole series of stages leading to climax vegetation is a **prisere**.

- When climate controls the main characteristics of the climax vegetation, we refer to it as the **climatic climax** (e.g. tropical rainforest).
- Where the vegetation has achieved stability, but is most strongly influenced by a non-climatic factor (e.g. steep slopes, poor soils), it is known as a **sub-climax**.
- Vegetation that is stable, but which owes its main characteristics to human activities (e.g. heather moorland) is known as a **plagioclimax**.

These types of climax community are shown in Figure 8.6.

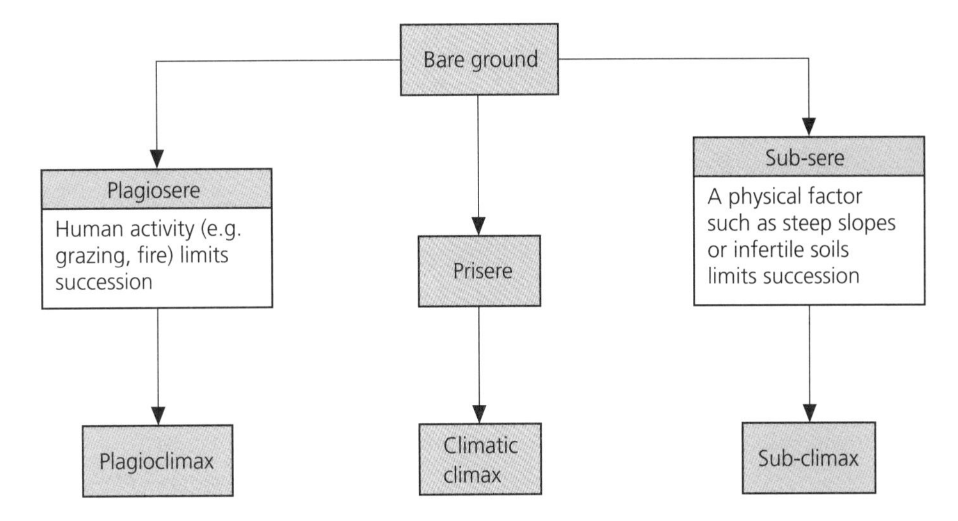

Figure 8.6 Types of climax community

6 Vertical structure of ecosystems

Climax vegetation often has a well-defined vertical structure. This is most obvious in forest ecosystems, where light intensity diminishes from the canopy to the forest floor. The temperate deciduous forest has four layers:

- A canopy of tall, broad-leaved trees (oak, beech, ash, lime, etc.). They are the ecological **dominants** that determine the living conditions for most other organisms in the ecosystem.
- An understorey of small trees, such as holly, hazel and elder, which depends on light which filters through the canopy.
- A herb layer on the forest floor.
- A moss/lichen layer on the forest floor.

The herb layer in a mixed oak woodland comprises many spring flowering plants, such as bluebells, wood anemones, violets and primroses. These species complete their flowering by the end of May. This is before the trees come into leaf and reduce light levels.

7 Xeroseres and hydroseres

A **xerosere** describes ecological succession on a surface where lack of water is a factor limiting plant growth. Succession on a bare rock surface (e.g. when a glacier recedes) is an example of a xerosere. The effect of each seral community on the environment is to increase soil depth, soil moisture, shade and shelter. Eventually, a stable climax vegetation succeeds.

Hydroseres occur where succession begins in a waterlogged environment such as a lakeshore. Here plant succession modifies the environment by infilling the lakeshore with dead plant remains and causing the build-up of sediment. As the environment gradually dries out, conditions allow the development of climax vegetation.

Xeroseres and hydroseres are shown in Figure 8.7.

The effect of ecological succession in extreme environments is often to promote a convergence of environmental conditions.

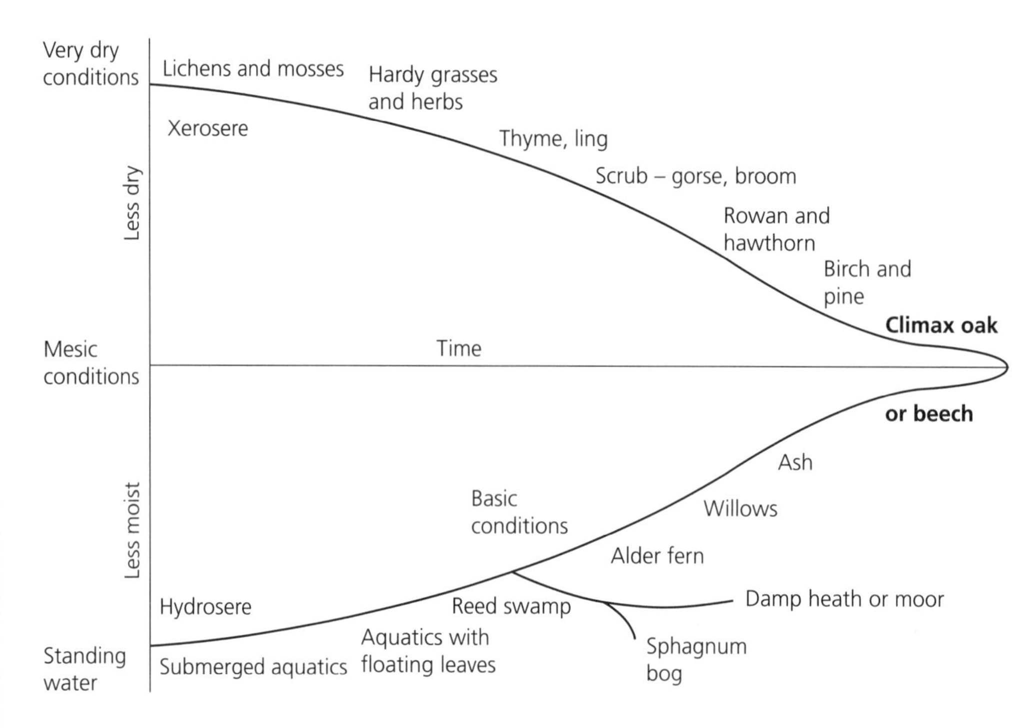

Figure 8.7 The relationship between primary successions and convergence to climax

8 The effect of human activity on natural ecosystems

The human impact on natural systems may be deliberate or accidental; direct or indirect.

Human activities modify natural ecosystems and cause:

- a reduction in biodiversity (number of species);
- the eradication of some species that compete with people for food (e.g. weeds and pests);
- the extinction (through habitat destruction) of animals with small populations (e.g. at the end of food chains);
- a reduction in flows of energy and the amount of sunlight photosynthesised;
- an impoverished nutrient cycle, with reductions in inputs of plant litter and increased losses of nutrients to leaching;
- accelerated soil erosion by wind and run-off;
- ecosystems to be maintained at an early successional stage (e.g. grasslands rather than forest in upland Britain, caused by grazing).

Soil, which is a mixture of mineral and organic material, is different from other superficial deposits which mantle rocks at the Earth's surface. Sand and clay are wholly mineral, while peat is wholly organic. Neither sand, clay nor peat can be classified as soil.

9 Soils

Soils are a mixture of mineral and organic material in which plants grow.

- The mineral fraction of the soil comes from the weathering of **parent material** (solid rock, boulder clay, glacial sands, etc.).
- The soil's organic material comes from the decay of plant litter.

Mature soils are differentiated into layers or **horizons**. Each horizon has a distinctive colour, depth, physical structure and chemical composition.

The **soil profile** is a cross-section of the soil from the surface down to the parent material, as shown in Figure 8.8. We recognise different soil types from the characteristics of their profiles.

Zone	Horizon	Description
Horizons of maximum biological activity, of eluviation and leaching	L, F, H	Loose leaves and organic debris partly decomposed
	A1	A dark-coloured horizon with a high content of organic matter
	A2 or Ea	A light-coloured horizon of maximum eluviation. Prominent in podsol soils but absent in brown earths and chernozems.
Horizons of illuviation and accumulation of suspended material from A or of maximum clay accumulation	B	Maximum accumulation of clay minerals or of iron and organic matter. Nature of accumulated materials indicated by following symbols: Bfe (irons); Bs (sesquioxides); Bt (clay).
	G	Horizon G for gleyed layers caused by waterlogging
	C	Parent material

Figure 8.8
The soil profile

10 Physical characteristics of soils

The main physical characteristics of soil are texture, structure and depth.

10.1 Soil texture

Soil texture refers to the size of mineral particles in the soil. Soil mineral particles range in size from clay (fine), to silt (medium) and sand (coarse). We can divide soils into a number of textural classes (e.g. sandy loam, silty clay).

- Parent material is the main influence on soil texture. Coarsely crystalline rocks, such as granite, weather to form sandy soils; fine-grained rocks, such as shale, produce clayey soils.
- Soil texture is important for cultivation and soil drainage. Sandy soils are easily workable and free-draining, but often suffer drought during summer. Clayey soils are naturally heavy and poorly drained. They are better suited to grass than to arable crops. Loamy soils have the ideal texture, being easy to work, well drained and yet able to retain moisture.

INSET 5

Triangular graphs

We identify a soil according to its texture by using a triangular graph. To do this we need to know the percentage of soil particles that are sand, silt and clay. Sand particles are more than 0.02 mm in diameter; silt particles are 0.002 to 0.02 mm; and clay particles are less than 0.002 mm. These percentages are then plotted on the graph's three axes. The example in Figure 8.9 shows a sandy clay soil, comprising 47% sand, 24% silt and 29% clay.

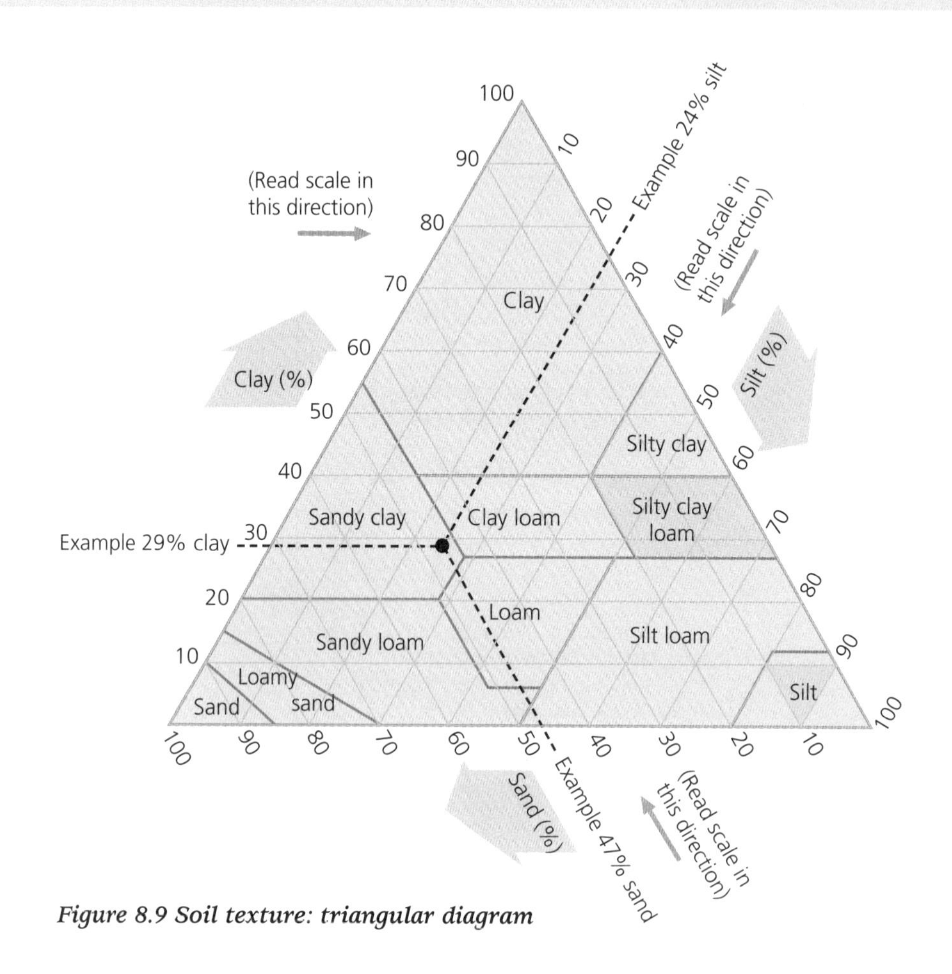

Figure 8.9 Soil texture: triangular diagram

10.2 Soil structure

Soil structure describes the aggregation of mineral particles and humus into larger units or **peds**. Soil peds have various shapes, as shown in Figure 8.10. Soil structure is important because it determines the extent to which water, air and plant roots can penetrate the soil. Crumb structures, associated with loamy soils, are ideal for cultivation.

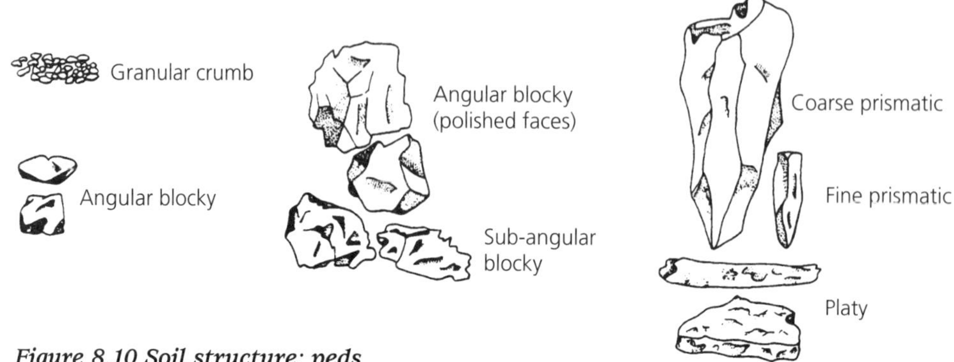

Figure 8.10 Soil structure: peds

Farmers need to manage soils if they are to retain the soil's structure.

- Using heavy farm machinery on saturated fields compresses the soil and causes permanent damage to its structure.
- Modern arable farming relies heavily on chemical fertilisers. As a result, its soils are often deficient in humus (derived from manure). This may lead to the breakdown of peds and increase the risk of soil erosion by run-off and the wind.
- Overcultivation depletes the soil's humus, destroying the soil's structure and making it vulnerable to erosion.

10.3 Soil depth

Soil depth is influenced by: the resistance of the parent material to weathering; the chemical composition of the parent material; climate; and time.

- Hard rocks, such as quartzite and dolerite, resist weathering and have only a thin soil cover.
- Shallow soils develop on soluble rocks such as limestone. Limestone mainly consists of $CaCO_3$. This mineral dissolves in rainwater and is removed in the soil solution, rather than adding to the mineral body of the soil.
- Shallow soils are typical of environments where rates of weathering are slow (e.g. in deserts owing to lack of moisture, and in the Arctic tundra and high mountains owing to low temperatures).
- Harsh climates limit plant growth and restrict the supply of organic material for soil formation and biological weathering.
- Soils develop slowly, taking thousands of years to reach maturity. Thus shallow soils occur in 'new' environments (areas of recent deglaciation, sand dune formation, volcanic eruption, etc.), where soils are young.

11 *Chemical characteristics of soils*

Soils provide plants with most of the mineral nutrients they need to grow.

Some nutrients, such as nitrates, phosphates and sulphates, are available in the soil solution. Other nutrients, such as calcium, magnesium, potassium and sodium, are found attached to the **clay–humus complex**. The clay–humus complex consists of tiny clay particles (i.e. secondary minerals such as illite, formed by the weathering of primary minerals) and humus.

- The surface of the clay–humus complex has a negative electrical charge, allowing positively charged mineral nutrients, or **cations**, to adhere to it (see Figure 8.11).
- Cation nutrients remain attached to the clay–humus complex until removed either by leaching or by the roots of plants.

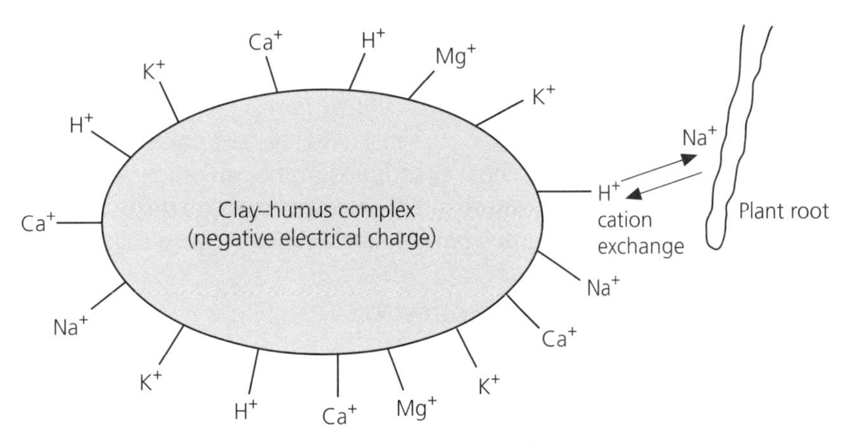

Figure 8.11 The clay–humus complex

- Plant roots remove cation nutrients from the surface of the clay–humus complex, in exchange for hydrogen ions – a process known as **cation exchange**.

INSET 6

The clay–humus complex

The surface of the clay–humus complex has sites for cation nutrients. The amount of space available on the clay–humus complex depends on the type of clay. A clay such as montmorillonite has a much larger surface area than kaolinite clay. As a result, montmorillonite has a far greater **cation exchange capacity**. Soils dominated by this clay have a high nutrient status.

Soil acidity is a measure of hydrogen ion concentration in the soil.
- Acidic soils, dominated by hydrogen ions and with few cation nutrients (bases), have a low pH value (3 to 5).
- Alkaline soils, found on calcareous rocks such as limestone and in hot deserts, have high pH values (8 to 11).
- Neutral soils, with pHs of around 7, are the most favoured for cultivation.

12 *Soil formation*

The influence of climate is more wide ranging than that of the other pedogenic factors. Not only does climate directly influence important soil-forming processes such as weathering, but it also has an indirect effect on other pedogenic factors such as vegetation and drainage.

Soil formation results from a combination of soil-forming or **pedogenic** factors:

$$s = f(c, v, p, r, t)$$

where:

s = soil | p = parent material
c = climate | r = relief
v = vegetation | t = time

12.1 Climate

Climate is the single most important pedogenic factor. Apart from its direct influence on soil formation, climate has an indirect influence through its effect on vegetation and soil drainage.
- Climate influences rates of weathering and the breakdown of parent material. Chemical weathering occurs three to four times faster in hot, humid climates than in temperate, humid climates. Weathering is slow in dry climates because most chemical weathering processes (solution, hydrolysis, oxidation) depend on moisture.
- Climate affects the vertical movement of moisture within the soil. Where annual rainfall exceeds annual evapotranspiration (e.g. in the British Isles), there is a surplus of moisture. Gravity pulls this surplus water through the soil. As a result, it washes soil particles from the upper part of the soil profile (**eluviation**) and deposits them lower down (**illuviation**). It also removes cation nutrients and clays in solution, a process known as **leaching**. The end product of eluviation, illuviation and leaching is an acidic soil with well-defined horizons. This general group of soils is called **pedalfers**.
- In some climates (e.g. the cool continental climate of the North American prairies), potential evapotranspiration exceeds precipitation during the year. In this situation, moisture is drawn towards the surface, and minerals such as $CaCO_3$ accumulate in the soil profile (**calcification**). These soils, which are alkaline, are known as **pedocals**.

At the global scale climate is the dominant pedogenic factor. At smaller scales differences in geology, slopes, vegetation and time are often most important in determining soil type.

12.2 Vegetation

- Vegetation is the main source of organic material. Where vegetation is sparse (e.g. hot deserts), soils are usually thin. Grassland soils, such as chernozems, are rich in humus. This is because grasses have a dense root network. When these roots die, they are already in place in the soil and decompose quickly.

- Some plant species, such as heather and ling, produce litter that forms an acidic humus called **mor**. When this mor humus mixes with rainwater, it forms organic acids. In moorland environments, these acids break down the clay–humus complex and remove mineral nutrients in solution. This is the process of **chelation**. When combined with a general downwashing of particles within the soil profile, it is called **cheluviation**. Cheluviation is important in the development of acidic, podsolised soils.
- In the boreal coniferous forest, pines, spruces, firs and larches produce needle litter that contains a high proportion of carbon (in lignins and waxes), which is slow to decompose. This needle litter accumulates on the forest floor, depriving the soils of humus. In these circumstances, forest fires play a vital part in the nutrient cycle, burning the litter and releasing the stored minerals into the soil.
- Vegetation provides physical protection to soils. It intercepts rainfall, reducing run-off and erosion (e.g. an oak woodland intercepts between 15 and 22% of rainfall). Plant roots bind the soil together, preventing erosion, especially on steep slopes. Vegetation also modifies the local climate. In forest ecosystems, interception and transpiration are high, and wind speeds are low. Thus there is less water to infiltrate the soil and cause leaching and eluviation.

12.3 Parent material

- The weathered parent material provides the mineral body of the soil. The parent material may comprise either solid rock, such as sandstone or chalk, or superficial material deposited on solid rock, such as glacial drift and loess.
- Where parent materials resist weathering or are highly soluble, soils are often thin.
- Parent material influences soil texture, nutrient availability and acidity.

12.4 Relief

Relief refers to altitude and slopes.

- Altitude modifies climate. In the British Isles, increasing altitude means higher precipitation, lower evapotranspiration and lower temperatures. In other words, the soil-forming environment is fundamentally changed.
- Slopes have a major effect on soil drainage. Thus, on valley sides we often find a sequence of soil types known as a **soil catena**, which reflects differences in drainage conditions (see Figure 8.12). For example, on flat interfluves, waterlogging is common. In such conditions, soils often have a gley horizon, caused by unoxidised ferrous iron. Meanwhile, partly decayed litter may accumulate as peat. The resulting soils are known as peaty gley podsols. On steep slopes, soils are often excessively drained, leached of nutrients and acidic.

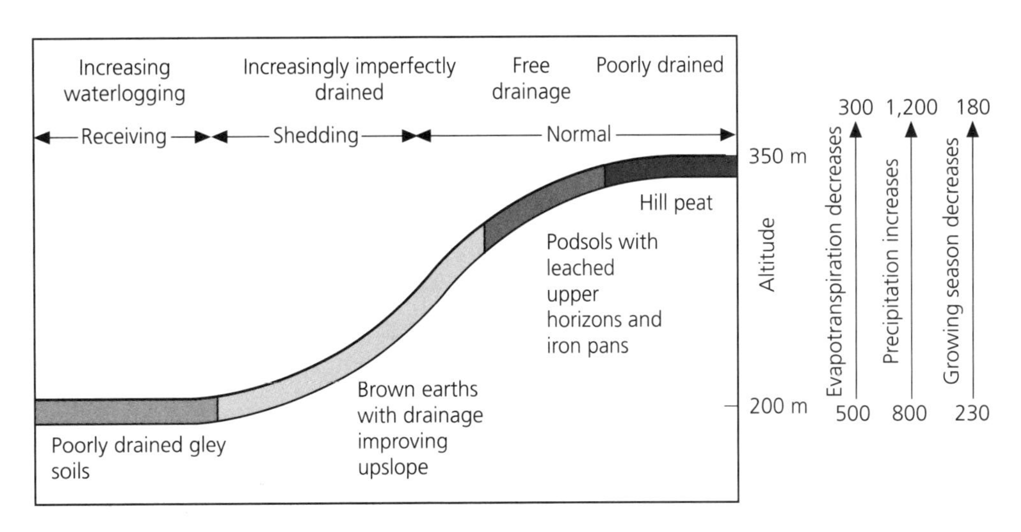

Figure 8.12 A soil catena in northern England

- Steep slopes often give rise to poorly developed soils. Slope processes such as soil creep and slumping cause a slow downslope movement of soil particles. The result is shallow, permanently immature soils.

12.5 Time

The characteristics of a soil depends partly on its age. If soil-forming processes have operated for only a few hundred years, soils will be thin and show limited development of horizons. Young and immature soils are a feature of 'new' environments such as sand dunes, emergent coastlines, lava flows and recently formed glacial moraines.

13 *Soil classification*

The zonal soil classification has a number of weaknesses:

- It is a classification of soil-forming environments, rather than soil profiles.
- It works well at the global scale.
- Many soils do not fit into the zonal scheme. These are classified as intra-zonal and azonal.
- In high latitudes climate may be too variable for soils ever to achieve an equilibrium state.

There are many different classifications of soil. The **zonal** classification, shown in Figure 8.13, is the simplest and best-known classification at the global scale.

A **zonal soil** is mature and in equilibrium with the environment, and owes its main characteristics to climate. The concept of zonal soils is similar to climatic climax vegetation, described earlier in this unit. Well-known zonal soils include podsols, brown earths, chernozems and tropical red soils. At the global scale, these soils correspond with broad climatic and vegetation zones.

Climate is not always the dominant factor influencing soil types; nor are all soils mature. An area of limestone in lowland Britain might support its own distinctive calcareous soils known as rendzinas, rather than acid brown earths. Soils like rendzinas, which are stable and mature, but owe their characteristics to non-climatic factors, are **intra-zonal** soils.

Azonal soils also depart from the zonal norm. They are permanently immature. They include soils found on steep slopes (constant downslope movement of soil particles) and those on flood plains (where rivers provide a continuous supply of new mineral particles).

		COOL CLIMATES	WARM CLIMATES	
	Permafrost soils	**Tundra soils**		
MOIST CLIMATES	Pedalfers: Podsolic	Podsols Brown earths Prairie soils	Yellow and red podsols	Increasing leaching →
MOIST CLIMATES	Pedalfers: Lateritic		Tropical red soils Lateritic soils	
DRY CLIMATES	Pedocals	Chernozems Chestnut brown soils Brown soils Sierozems	Various tropical pedocals	

Figure 8.13 Zonal classification of soils

14 *Podsol soils*

Podsols (see Figure 8.14) are zonal soils of the boreal coniferous forest, moorlands and heaths.

- In the coniferous forest, low temperatures cause low rates of evapotranspiration. Although precipitation is modest, it none the less exceeds evapotranspiration. Thus, for most of the year, soil moisture moves downwards through the soil profile. Leaching removes soluble minerals and organic materials from the upper soil horizons. Eluviation also washes soil particles down the profile.
- Humic acids, derived from acidic mor and nutrient-deficient needle litter, destroy the clay–humus complex and remove nutrient cations. This is cheluviation.
- The combination of leaching, eluviation and cheluviation depletes the upper soil horizons of organic material, clays and soil nutrients. The upper horizons (E) consist of little more than bleached sand and have a white to ash-grey colour. This, together with high soil acidity (pH 3–5) is the podsol's most distinctive characteristic.
- Lower down the profile, deposition (illuviation) of the mineral and organic matter, washed down and leached from above, takes place. This B horizon, rich in iron and aluminium oxides, often has an orangish colour. Sometimes, the illuviation of iron oxide may form an impermeable iron pan, which impedes drainage.
- A feature of podsols is their sharp differentiation into horizons. In part this is due to the physical and chemical processes described above. Also important is the absence of earthworms, caused by extreme acidity. Normally, the activities of earthworms and other soil fauna would cause some mixing of horizons and make the soil profile more uniform in appearance.

Podsols have little value for agriculture. In the UK, areas of podsol soil such as the Breckland (Norfolk) are largely afforested.

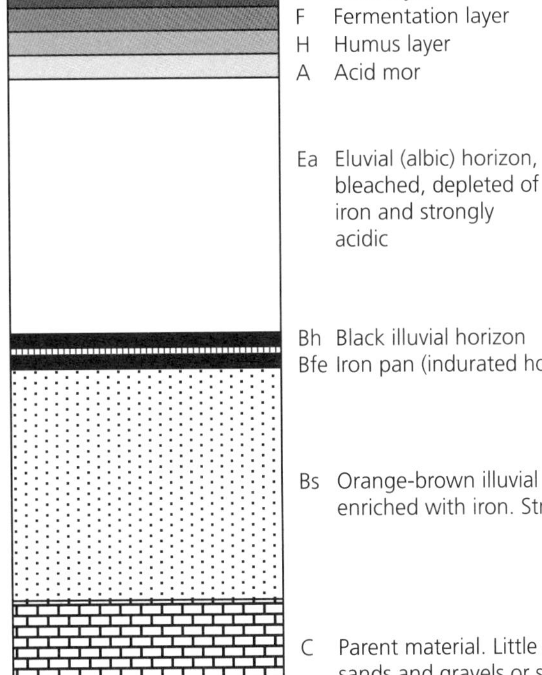

Figure 8.14
A humus iron podsol

INSET 7

Podsolisation

Figure 8.15 describes the chemical, physical and biological processes that lead to the formation of podsol soils. The parent materials of podsol soils (e.g. glacial sands and gravels) are often deficient in plant nutrients. The natural vegetation (conifers, heather, etc.) generates an impoverished nutrient cycle and produces litter that is often acidic and slow to decompose. The excess of precipitation over evapotranspiration causes leaching, eluviation and, where rainwater mixes with acidic plant litter, cheluviation. The result is a soil that is highly acidic, deficient in earthworms and differentiated into a sandy, bleached Ea horizon and a rusty brown illuviated horizon.

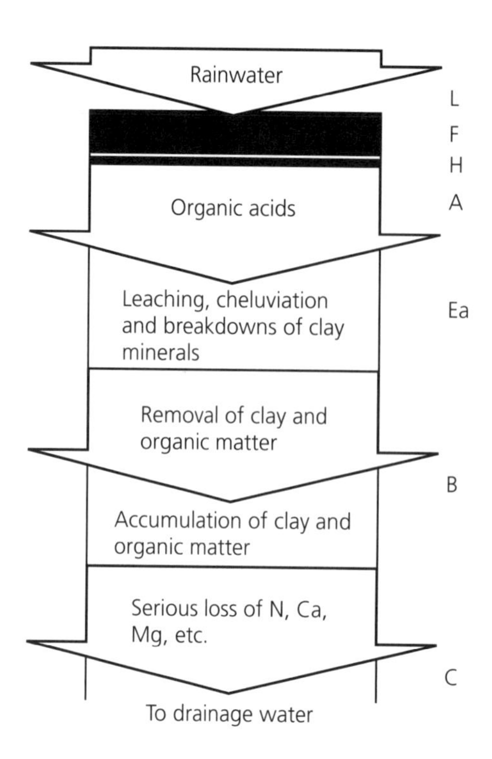

Figure 8.15 Podsolisation

15 Acid brown earth soils

Brown earth soils (see Figure 8.16) are the zonal soils that once covered most of lowland Britain. Today these soils are no longer natural: thousands of years of cultivation mean they bear little resemblance to the original soils. Brown earths originally developed beneath a deciduous forest of oak and birch, in a cool, temperate, humid climate.

- In lowland Britain, there is a small annual surplus of precipitation over evapotranspiration. Thus brown earth soils are slightly leached and mildly acidic (pH 6–6.5).

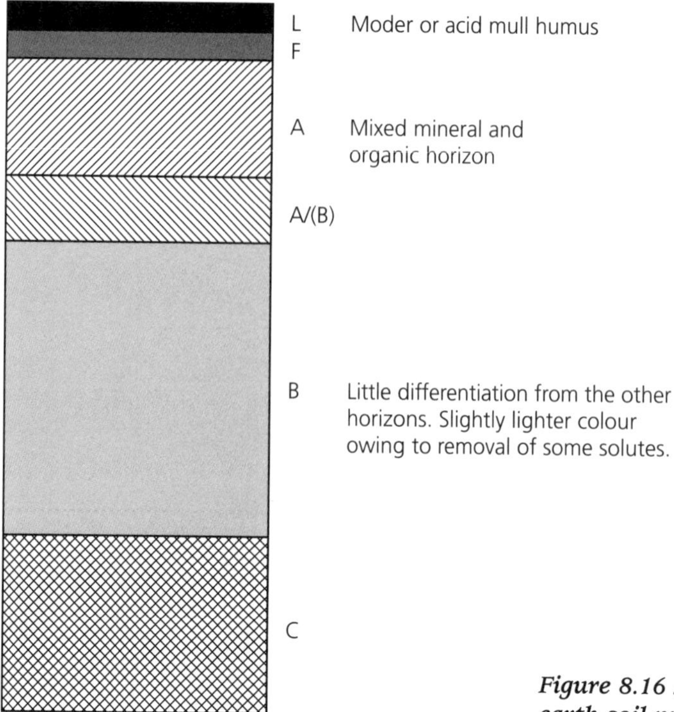

Figure 8.16 An acid brown earth soil profile

- Compared to podsols, brown earths are nutrient rich. Leaf litter from deciduous trees contains many nutrients and forms a mild, mull humus. This favours an abundance of earthworms, adding to the homogeneous appearance of brown earths (soil horizons are not sharply defined).
- In this midly acidic environment, the clay–humus complex does not break down, and soil nutrients are available for take-up by the roots of plants.

16 Human impact on soils

Farmers can modify some soil characteristics by:

- improving soil nutrient status through the addition of organic fertiliser (e.g. manure) or chemical fertiliser (e.g. phosphates, nitrates);
- reducing soil acidity by applying dressings of lime;
- improving soil drainage by underdraining with clay pipes;
- modifying soil texture by applying sand to clayey soils, and marl to sandy soils;
- improving soil structure by increasing humus levels in the soil.

Because soils are a non-renewable resource, farmers need to manage and conserve them by adopting good cultivation practice. Mismanagement may result in accelerated soil erosion, either by run-off or by strong winds. Soil erosion occurs when farmers:

- cultivate steep slopes;
- plough up and down, rather than across slopes;
- remove protective hedgerows that shelter soils from strong winds;
- prepare the soil as a fine tilth (for a seedbed) without any protective crop cover;
- overcultivate the land, leaving the soil deficient in humus and destroying the soil's structure;
- use heavy machinery on fields that are at field capacity, so that soils are compressed, impeding natural drainage and promoting run-off;
- exceed the carrying capacity of the land by overstocking, causing destruction of vegetation and exposing the soil.

UNIT 9 Population and migration

1 Fertility and mortality

Fertility is the occurrence of live births. Many factors influence fertility, including economic status, religion, government policies, female literacy, the economic value of children and the availability of contraceptive devices.

The **crude birth rate** (CBR) is widely used as a measure of fertility. The CBR is the ratio of the number of live births to the total population. It is usually expressed per 1,000 of the population. As a measure of fertility, the CBR has drawbacks because it is strongly influenced by age–sex structure. Regardless of how many children each woman produces, mature populations and populations with relatively few women will have low CBRs. However, the CBR is useful in calculating population change. Inset 1 describes alternative measures of fertility.

INSET 1

Other measures of fertility

General fertility rate: the number of live births in a year as a ratio of the number of women aged 15–44, expressed per 1,000 women. In the USA in 1994, the general fertility of Hispanic women was 99.2 per 1,000 compared to 60.6 per 1,000 for non-Hispanics.
Age-specific fertility rate: the number of live births to women in five-year age groups per 1,000 women. Age-specific fertility for 25–29-year-old Hispanic women in the USA in 1994 was 158.2 per 1,000 compared to 101 per 1,000 for non-Hispanic women.
Total fertility rate (TFR): the average number of live births to women who have completed their families. The reproductive TRF (i.e. the rate needed just to replace the population) is 2.1. The current global average TFR is 3.0.

Mortality fluctuates more than fertility.

- Famine, disease and war may cause brief periods of high mortality.
- Mortality decline (through improved medical technology, etc.) is nearly always more acceptable to a pre-industrial society than fertility control.

Mortality is the occurrence of death. Rates of mortality depend on many factors, such as age, diet, health care, economic status and disease. The **crude death rate** (CDR) is calculated in the same way as the CBR and has similar disadvantages. Age-specific mortality is similar to age-specific fertility. It has a peak in infancy and then declines until the mid-teens. Thereafter there is a slow increase until old age, when the rate rises very steeply. The **infant mortality rate** (IMR) is the number of children per 1,000 of the population who die in their first year. The IMR is a particularly sensitive indicator of the standard of living in a society.

2 Population change

The difference between the number of births and number of deaths accounts for population change at the global scale (migration has no effect at this scale). Thus:

- more births than deaths leads to population growth by **natural increase**;
- more deaths than births leads to population decline or **natural decrease**.

We calculate natural population change from crude birth rates and crude death rates.

INSET 2

Calculating rates of natural increase/decrease

% natural increase or decrease per year = (CBR per 1,000 – CDR per 1,000)/10
Example:

% global natural increase in 1997 = (26 – 9)/10 = 1.7%

The time taken to double a population can be estimated from the natural increase rates thus:

Doubling time = 693/(natural increase rate × 10)

Thus at 1997 rates of natural increase, it will take 693/17 = 40.06 years for the world's population to double.

2.1 Global population change

In 1999 the world's total population reached 6 billion. This figure reflects the unprecedented population growth in the last 200 years, and especially since 1950 (see Table 9.1). Population growth has resulted from an imbalance between births and deaths. While death rates in LEDCs have fallen rapidly, birth rates have remained high. Natural increase peaked (at around 2.2%) in the 1960s. Since then falling birth rates have reduced rates of natural increase to around 1.7%. Even so, the global population is expanding by 80 million a year. Latest estimates forecast a total population of more than 9 billion in 2050, with zero growth achieved only towards the end of the twenty-first century.

Continuing high levels of fertility in many LEDCs show:

- the difficulty of achieving universal acceptance of family planning;
- lack of resources to implement family planning programmes;
- the low status of women;
- the advantages of large families in rural societies.

Year	Population (bn)
1800	1.125
1850	1.402
1900	1.762
1950	2.556
2000	6.073

Table 9.1 World population growth, 1800–2000

2.2 Spatial patterns of global population change

There were great spatial differences in the global pattern of population change in the 1990s. The main features of this pattern and the implications for future population growth are as follows:

- Very low growth rates throughout most of the economically developed world. MEDCs' share of world population will fall from 20% to 12% between 1995 and 2050. Europe's population will shrink by 90 million during this period (see Figure 9.1). TFRs in much of Europe are already below replacement level.

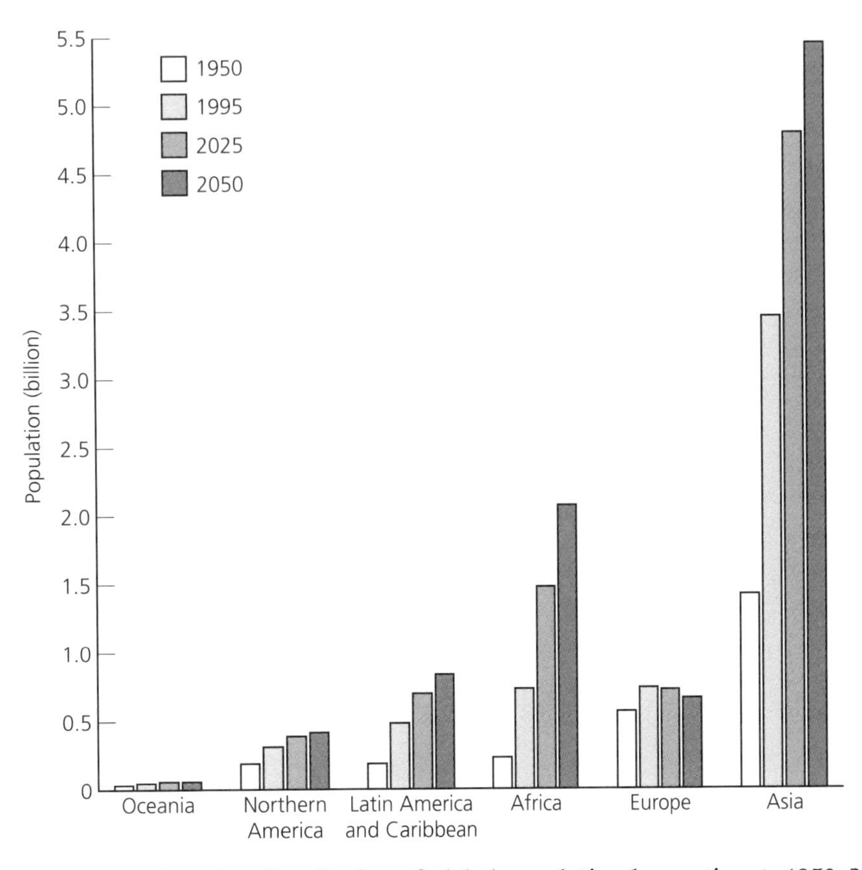

Figure 9.1 Changing distribution of global population by continent, 1950–2050

- Rapid, but declining rates of population growth in most LEDCs. But the youthful populations of most LEDCs mean than, even with declining fertility, there is great momentum for future growth.
- World population growth between 1995 and 2050 concentrated in Asia. India, China and Pakistan will contribute most to world population growth. India (with a TFR of 4 in 1995) will overtake China (with a TFR of 2.6 in 1995) as the world's most populous state by 2050.
- Very rapid population growth in most Islamic countries in south and south-west Asia (e.g. Pakistan, Iran) and in sub-Saharan Africa (e.g. Nigeria, Zaire).
- Moderate population growth in Latin America, where fertility levels are generally low and where initial population is relatively small.

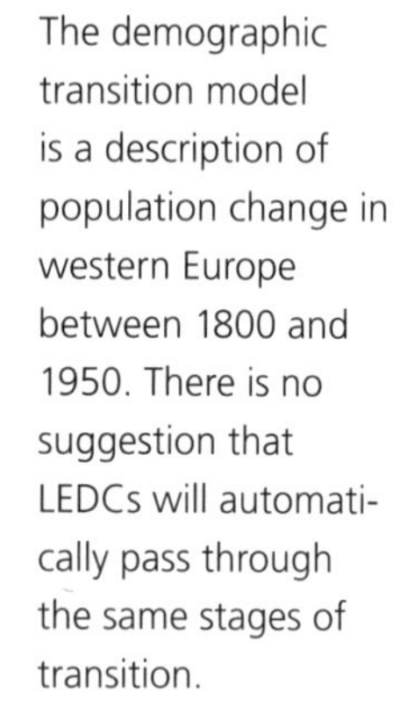
The demographic transition model is a description of population change in western Europe between 1800 and 1950. There is no suggestion that LEDCs will automatically pass through the same stages of transition.

2.3 The demographic transition

The **demographic transition** describes the shift from high fertility and mortality, to low fertility and mortality that occurred in Europe between 1750 and 1950. As Figure 9.2 shows, the transition involved four stages, and it was accompanied by economic growth and rising living standards. The model suggests that, if a country industrialises, it population growth will also decline.

- **Stage 1: Pre-industrial.** Fertility and mortality are high. There is little population growth. High fertility is needed to ensure the survival of the population. Children also provide a source of labour and security for parents in old age. Artificial contraception is unavailable. There is high mortality owing to poor nutrition, poor hygiene and lack of medical knowledge to combat disease.
- **Stages 2 and 3: Industrial.** Improvements in medicine, and in economic, social and environmental conditions, cause mortality rates to fall. In stage 2, fertility remains high and results in rapid population growth. The fertility decline in stage 3 lags behind mortality decline. Even so, the rate of population increase begins to slow. The fertility decline occurs because: children become expensive (long education period); the state provides for security in old age; artificial contraception is available; and infant mortality is low so that few children die in infancy.
- **Stage 4: Post-industrial.** Both fertility and mortality are at low levels. Population growth is either very slow or has ceased altogether. Further causes of low fertility include: women postponing marriage until their mid-twenties; more educated women with high-status jobs; more unmarried couples living together, who are less likely to have children than married couples; and more effective methods of birth control.

This demographic model provides an accurate description of population changes in Europe between 1750 and 1950. The changes were linked to economic growth, rising

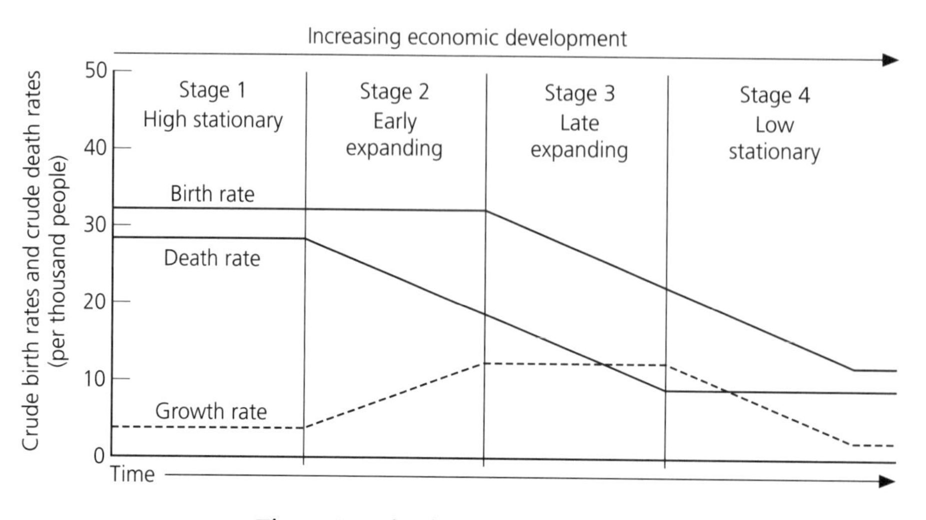

Figure 9.2 The demographic transition

living standards, improvements in medicine, and changes in societal values caused by urbanisation. However, the model does not describe accurately the experiences of most LEDCs in the last 50 or 60 years. There are several reasons for this.

- Absolute numbers of population increase and growth rates have been far higher in LEDCs than in nineteenth-century Europe. No countries in Europe had annual population growth rates of more than 1%.
- Mortality decline was a gradual process in nineteenth-century Europe. It followed improvements in living conditions brought about by economic growth and advances in tackling diseases such as smallpox and measles. In LEDCs, mortality decline has been more rapid. This decline is due largely to the application of modern medical techniques rather than to progress in living standards.
- Most LEDCs are less urbanised than countries in nineteenth-century Europe. The economic advantages of large families (most people still live in rural societies), low levels of literacy (particularly among women) and (in the absence of rapid urbanisation) the survival of traditional cultures and values have proved obstacles to lowering fertility levels.

3 Age–sex structure

The shape of population pyramids varies with scale. Pyramids are usually most unbalanced at a local scale where populations are small. This reflects the influence of migration, which often distorts age structures and sex ratios.

Age–sex structure is the composition of a population according to age groups and gender. We normally represent age–sex structure with a special kind of bar chart known as a **population pyramid**. Some examples are shown in Figure 9.3. Several factors influence the shape of population pyramids. Some are short term such as wars, epidemics and famines; others, such as fertility and mortality control, have a long-term effect. These long-term influences give rise to distinctive pyramid shapes.

- Broad-based pyramids, such as Figure 9.3(a), indicate youthful populations, with large proportions of children and high levels of fertility. If fertility increases over time, the pyramid is progressive. Some pyramids show the effects of high fertility in the past. An unusually large birth cohort may follow a 'baby boom', such as occurred in western Europe at the end of the Second World War (see Figure 9.3(b)). Today, these countries have unusually large numbers of older adults aged between 50 and 55 years.
- Rapidly tapering pyramids, again like Figure 9.3(a), suggest high levels of mortality, with significant reductions in numbers at each five-year age group. These populations usually have only small proportions of old people – hence their narrow apex.
- Straight-sided pyramids, such as Figure 9.3(b), with little reduction in the size of age groups between 0 and 60 years, suggest both low fertility and low mortality.
- Pyramids with a narrow base that broadens with age, such as Figure 9.3(c), indicate recent reductions in fertility. These pyramids are known as regressive.

Age structure can also be measured by a number of indices, as shown in Table 9.2.

Old age index	Aged/Adults
Dependency ratio	(Children + Aged)/Adults
Juvenility index	Children/(Adults + Aged)

Table 9.2 Indices of age structure

Migration has most effect on population structure at a local and regional scale. This is because migration is both age and sex selective. In most societies, young adults are most likely to migrate. Thus, places of recent net migrational gain often have more young adults than average; those suffering a net migrational loss have fewer. The migrational effects of gender are more variable. In southern Africa, males migrate more often than females, giving unbalanced sex ratios both in receiving (usually urban) and sending (usually rural) areas. In South America, the situation is reversed, with females more often migrating than males.

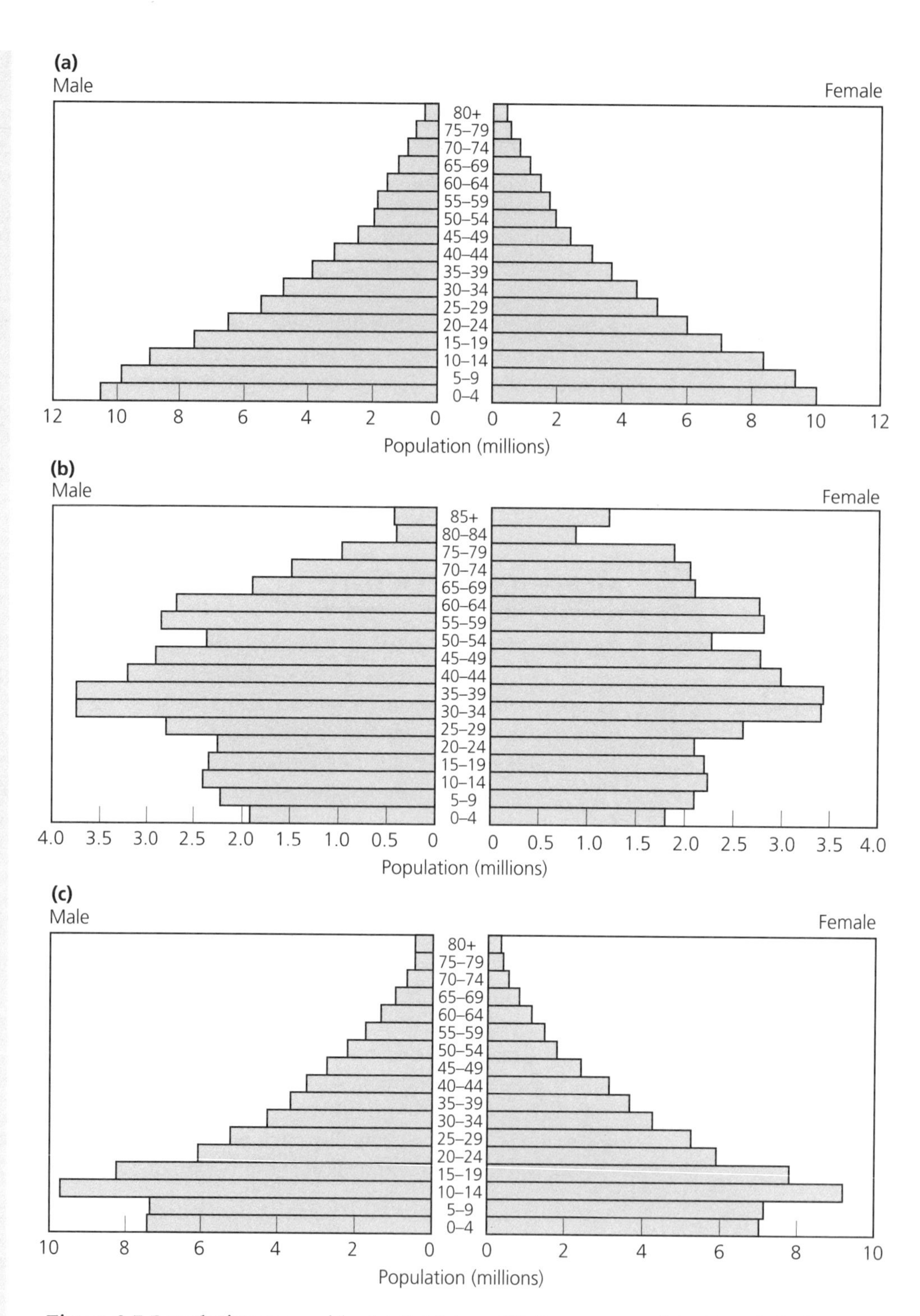

Figure 9.3 Population pyramids: (a) Pakistan, (b) Germany and (c) Bangladesh, 1999

3.1 The demographic impact of age–sex structure

The age–sex structure of a population has important implications for its future growth. Most LEDCs have youthful populations – the result of high fertility and low mortality in the last 50 years or so. With so many children entering young adulthood in future, rapid population growth is almost inevitable. In this situation, we say that the population has considerable **momentum**. In China, total fertility fell to 1.8 children per woman in 1998. This figure is well below the replacement level of 2.1 children per woman. Yet population momentum in China is such that, even if total fertility remains at 1.8, the population will continue to increase until 2030.

At a regional scale, migration often unbalances age–sex structure. Young adults are most likely to migrate from rural communities. This results in fewer babies and a general ageing of the population in rural areas. Ageing also occurs in communities that attract people on retirement. In the UK, the south coast is popular with retirees, leading to ageing populations in towns such as Eastbourne and Christchurch. The destinations that attract young adult migrants (e.g. large cities in LEDCs) experience the opposite effect: in-migration inflates the reproductive age groups and increases rates of population growth.

3.2 The economic impact of age–sex structure

Age–sex structure has important economic effects on the size of the workforce and dependency.

In Europe between 1960 and 1990, labour shortages were often met by policies that encouraged immigration.

- The economically active population in MEDCs are adults between 18–21 and 60–65 years. Sharp reductions in fertility could mean labour shortages in future. With a smaller workforce, businesses might have difficulty recruiting sufficient labour (perhaps forcing up wage rates) and tax revenues might fall. All of this has implications for the provision of services and pensions for the 'dependent' population (i.e. children and old people). Many countries in central and eastern Europe, which for the last 20 years or so have experienced low fertility and natural decrease, face this problem in the near future.
- An increase in the size of the 'dependent' population also puts economic pressure on governments. In LEDCs, high fertility has led to ever-increasing numbers of children and soaring demand for health care and educational services. In MEDCs, the problem is the increasing proportion of old people and how to provide state pensions and extra resources for health care. In Germany, for example, the proportion of over-65-year-olds will increase from 15.8 to 20.5% between 1998 and 2010. Most MEDCs have still to solve the problem of their 'greying' populations.

4 Population and resources

The concepts of optimum population, overpopulation and underpopulation refer to the balance between population, resources and development.

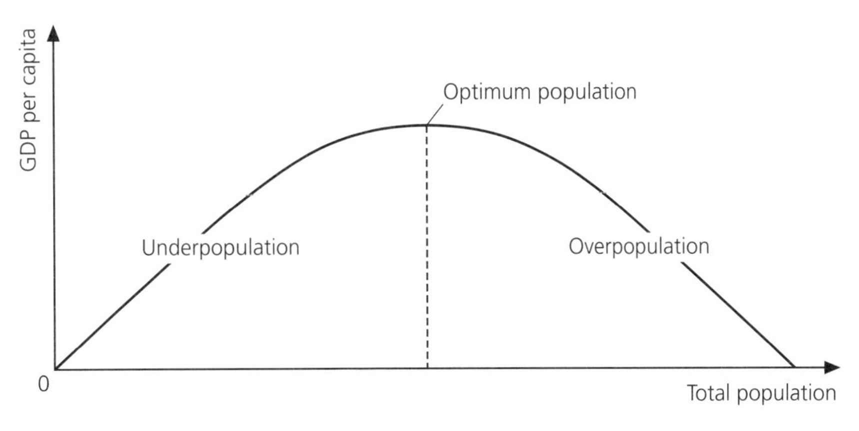

Figure 9.4 The concept of optimum population

- **Optimum population** (see Figure 9.4) is where the total population is just sufficient to allow resource development that gives the highest per capita standard of living.
- **Overpopulation** occurs when an excess of population in relation to resources and development reduces per capita standards of living below the optimum. In other words, a lower population would cause a rise in living standards.
- **Underpopulation** means there are too few people to develop fully the resources in an area and to raise standards of living to the optimum level.

In practice, the concept of optimum population is difficult to define. This is due to incomplete knowledge of any country's resource base; changes in technology; difficulties in measuring living standards; and the significance of human resources, especially education, skills, etc.

Governments are often acutely aware of imbalances between population and resources and develop policies to address the problems. These policies can approach the problem of population-resource imbalance by:

- promoting economic development and increasing the resource base;
- controlling migration and/or fertility and influencing the size of the population.

5 *Population policies*

Many countries that do not have population policies may try to influence fertility indirectly through fiscal measures such as child allowances and tax concessions for young married couples.

Most population policies in LEDCs aim to tackle the problem of rapid population growth (see Inset 3). Policies that aim to do this by reducing fertility are known as **anti-natalist**. For economic and political reasons, a few countries (e.g. Malaysia) have **pro-natalist** policies designed to increase population. These policies may be either voluntary or imposed on the people.

INSET 3

China's population policy

China's controversial anti-natalist population policy was a response to perceived overpopulation in the 1970s. Between 1950 and 1980 China's population increased from 560 to 985 million. Such growth threatened shortages of food, fresh water, fossil fuels and other natural resources. China's optimum population was estimated at 700 million. As a communist country, China gives priority to state interests over the rights and freedom of individuals. Thus, the government could impose its population policy in a way that would be impossible in democratic societies.

Initially, the policy limited couples to two children. But even this drastic step would not stop China's population being twice the optimum by the late twenty-first century. China responded by introducing a new one-child policy in 1979. Women who had more than one child incurred economic penalties or were coerced into abortions. Early marriage was discouraged. The policy had most success in towns and cities, where it was easier to enforce and where small families were more acceptable. But in rural areas the policy met considerable resistance: it was difficult to enforce and to explain to poorly educated farmers. Thus in rural areas a degree of relaxation was permitted. For instance, if a couple's first born was a girl, they might be allowed try for a boy (on marriage, boys bring their wives home to live with their parents, wives providing extra labour and support for boys' parents in old age).

Since 1980 China's population policy has caused a massive fertility decline. However, the impact of the policy on China's age structure will give rise to economic and social problems in future.

- The proportion of young people has fallen steeply, threatening labour shortages in cities.
- Thanks to improvements in health care and living standards, the proportion of old people has risen, increasing levels of dependency. While only 9% of China's population was over 60 years old in the early 1990s, by 2030 the proportion will reach 25%. With little state provision for pensions and retirement benefits, the burden of looking after old people will fall on today's single child.
- The preference for male children has led to female infanticide and selective abortion of girls. The resulting gender imbalance will eventually mean a shortage of marriageable women, threatening the tradition of universal marriage in China.

6 *Population distribution and density*

6.1 Measuring population density

Population density is the ratio of people to area. There are several population density measures:

- Crude population density is the number of people per unit area (usually per km^2 or per hectare). It gives little indication of the pressure of population on resources such as cultivated land, and is often too generalised for use at a small scale (e.g. in urban areas).
- Population density per km^2 of cultivated land gives a more accurate picture of population pressure, especially in many LEDCs, where most people live in rural areas. This measure could be refined further using the rural population density per km^2 of cultivated land.
- Residential population density per hectare gives a more precise picture of living conditions in urban areas. Inner city zones in MEDCs may include large areas of industrial, commercial and derelict land. Low crude population densities in such areas might give a misleading impression of living conditions.
- Average number of persons per room is the most detailed measurement of housing conditions and possible overcrowding.

6.2 Patterns of population distribution and density

Table 9.3 shows the relationship between population density and the presence or absence of natural resources.

(a) Population density related to local natural resources					
Economic activities	**Advantages/ disadvantages**	**Crude density**	**Scale**	**Settlement**	**Examples**
Resource-rich regions with resources fully developed					
Agriculture	Favourable climate, hydrological conditions, soils, relief	Moderate–high depending on farming intensity	Regional	Farms, villages, small urban (market) centres	Nile valley and delta (high density); arable farming areas of East Anglia (moderate density); Great Plains of USA (low density)
Mining, quarrying, forestry	Local energy, mineral and timber resources	Low	Local	Villages and small urban centres	19th-century coalfields in western Europe; Carajas in Brazil; Witwatersrand in South Africa
Resource-rich regions with resources poorly developed					
Sporadic primary activities	Remoteness, underpopulation, lack of capital for development, recent colonisation	Low	Regional–continental	Sparse: some pioneer villages on settlement fringe	Tropical rainforests in Amazonia, central Africa Africa and Indo-Malaysia
Resource-poor regions					
None	Extreme cold, extreme aridity, mountainous	Very low	Regional–continental	Few permanent settlements	Drylands (tropical/sub-tropical deserts, mid-latitude deserts); polar and sub-polar regions, major mountain ranges
(b) Population density unrelated to local natural resources					
Economic activities	**Advantages/ disadvantages**	**Crude density**	**Scale**	**Settlement**	**Examples**
Industry, trade, services, etc.	Accessibility (by land and/or sea), external economies, initial advantages, inertia	Very high	Local–regional	Many large urban settlements, conurbations and cities	Most of the world's major urban agglomerations, including NE USA, Pacific coast of Japan, SE Brazil and NW Europe

Table 9.3 Population distribution and density

At a global scale, the distribution and density of population is very uneven. We can interpret this pattern in three ways:

- In regions of maturity (i.e. fully explored and settled), population density reflects the availability of local natural resources – favourable climatic conditions, fertile soils, fossil fuels, etc.
- In regions still in the process of colonisation, density patterns may be unrelated to local resources, which have yet to be exploited.
- In some highly urbanised regions, population density is no longer related to local resources; in such regions, high population densities are based on the production of services and manufactured goods and sustained by trade.

7 Migration

Migration does not include transient population movements, such as tourism and commuting.

Migration is the permanent or semi-permanent change of residence of an individual or group of people. Net migration is the difference in numbers of in-migrants and out-migrants.

- When in-migrants exceed out-migrants, there is a **net migrational gain**.
- A **net migrational loss** occurs when there is an excess of out-migrants over in-migrants.

Migration, together with fertility and mortality, determines the population growth and population structure of an area.

7.1 Types of migration

Table 9.4 lists types of migration. Rural–urban and urban–rural migration have been responsible for significant shifts in population distribution in many countries. In LEDCs, the net migrational gain of urban areas at the expense of rural areas results in **urbanisation**. Meanwhile, movements in the opposite direction in MEDCs have led to the process of **counter-urbanisation**. Some migrations, such as **stepwise migration** and **chain migration**, do not fit the simple classification of Table 9.4. Stepwise migration describes movement through a settlement hierarchy (e.g. from villages to small towns and cities). Chain migration links migration flows to kinship ties between, for example, a city and a particular rural region.

Table 9.4 Types of migration

Criterion	Detail
Scale	International, inter-regional, intra-urban
Direction	Rural–urban, rural–rural, urban–rural, urban–urban
Distance	Long distance, short distance, regional/international
Decision making	Forced, voluntary
Causes	Economic, social, political, environmental

7.2 Causes of migration

Many factors influence the decision to migrate. At the simplest level, we divide these factors into two groups: push and pull.

- **Push factors** are the negative aspects of the current place of residence. They may be economic, social, political and environmental. They include factors such as lack of employment, low wages, poor housing, poor educational opportunities, political persecution, war and many others.
- **Pull factors** are the attractions of places of destination. Often they are the inverse of push factors: better employment and educational opportunities, better housing, higher wages and so on.

If the perceived push or pull factors are strong enough to overcome forces of inertia (cost of moving, disruption of social networks, etc.), migration will occur.

7.3 Perception and migration

At the level of the individual, **perception** has a strong influence on migration. Perception is the subjective view that a person has of the environment, derived from personal experience, the experience of others, the media, etc. Through perception an individual migrant builds up a **mental image** of a potential destination. This mental image is often distorted and partial. Even so, it is this image, rather than objective reality, that is the basis of decision making. Migrants' mental images often fail to accord with reality. This is one reason why for every migration there is a movement in the opposite direction – a counter-movement of disillusioned migrants back to their place of origin.

7.4 Lee's migration model

Lee's model, shown in Figure 9.5, develops the ideas of push and pull factors and perception. According to Lee, a potential migrant will assess the **place utility** of his or her current place of residence and potential place of destination. Place utility depends on the migrant's perceptions and mental images. Both origin and destination will have positive attributes and negative attributes. These positive factors in the place of destination are the same as pull factors. Negative attributes in the place of origin are push factors.

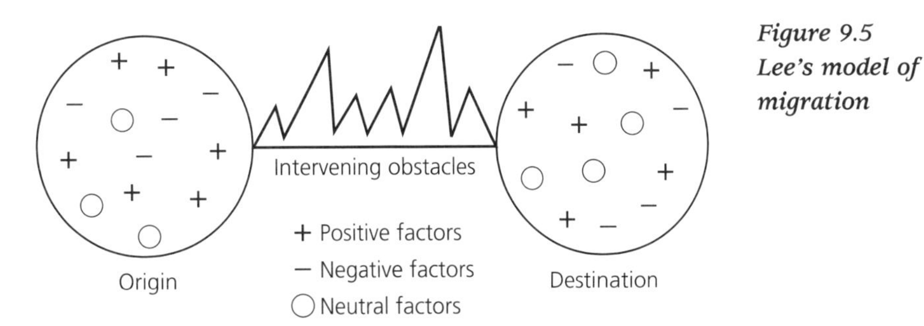

Figure 9.5 Lee's model of migration

For example, a redundant farmworker might regard the lack of employment opportunities in his village as a negative attribute, but the social network of the rural community as a positive one. Other factors might be neutral and not have any influence on his decision. If the farmworker assesses the advantages of a possible destination (i.e. its place utility) to be greater than those of his present location, he may decide to migrate.

However, Lee's model takes account of another factor: intervening obstacles. These may include physical distance or physical obstacles (poor communications, cost of movement, mountain barriers, etc.) between place of origin and place of destination; political obstacles, such as international borders; legal obstacles, such as problems of obtaining work permits, etc.

7.5 Consequences of migration

Migration affects populations unequally: some people and groups are more likely to migrate than others are. In other words, migration is a selective process influenced by factors such as age, gender, education, occupation and stage in the family cycle. The selectivity of migration may cause unbalanced age structures and sex ratios in both receiving and sending areas.

Because young adults are more likely to migrate than older adults and the aged, populations suffering a net migration loss often experience ageing. Populations undergoing net migration gain often experience the opposite effect, with disproportionate numbers of young adults and children. However, migration on retirement, which is increasingly common in MEDCs, will create a top-heavy pyramid with a large proportion of old people.

The effect of migration on sex ratios varies with culture. While in South America women are more likely to migrate than men, in sub-Saharan Africa men form the bulk of migrants. More educated people are often more mobile than less educated. Critical stages in the family cycle, such as starting a family and children leaving home, are often associated with household movement.

Regions experiencing heavy net migrational loss may suffer an absolute decrease in population. This phenomenon, known as **depopulation**, has affected many remote rural areas in western Europe in the last 150 years. In areas such as north-west Scotland and the Massif Central in France, it even continues today (see Figure 9.6).

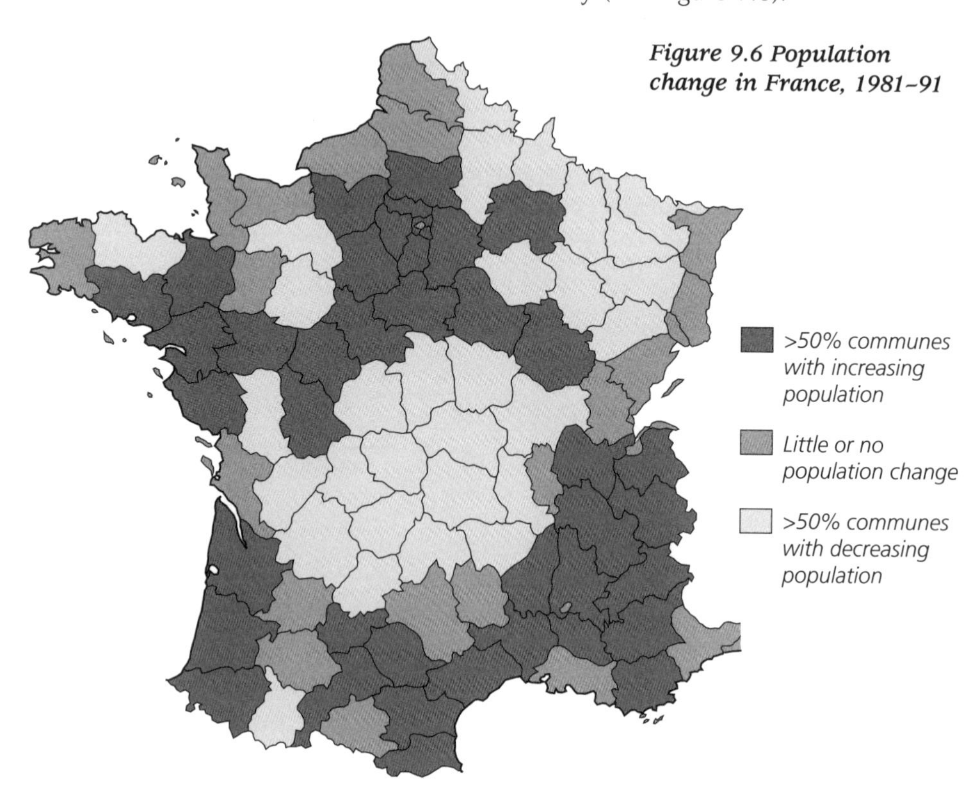

Figure 9.6 Population change in France, 1981–91

Gravity models belong to a group of general interaction models. These models (Huff, Reilly, etc.) assume that the movement of people, goods and ideas is:

- directly proportional to some measure of the size or attractiveness of sending and receiving places;
- inversely proportional to the distance separating the places.

INSET 4

Ravenstein's 'migration laws'

E.G. Ravenstein formulated seven 'laws of migration' in the 1880s.

- Most migrations take place over short distances.
- Migration proceeds step by step.
- The number of migrants falls with distance from a destination.
- Each current of migration produces a counter-current.
- Long-distance migrants usually move to larger urban centres.
- Women are more likely to migrate than men.
- Urban populations are less migratory than rural populations.

7.6 Characteristics of migration flows

Most migration studies have shown that the volume of migration is inversely related to distance. This reduction in movement with distance is called **distance decay**. We normally expect numbers of migrants to fall rapidly over a short distance, and much more slowly over longer distances. The resultant distance decay curve has an exponential form.

Gravity models predict migration flows between two centres. They assume that migration flows are directly proportional to the population size of the centres, and inversely proportional to the distance separating them (see Inset 5).

Stouffer developed these ideas further. In Figure 9.7, migration between places A and B will occur if A and B complement each other (e.g. a shortage of labour in one place and a surplus in another) and if the distance (or cost of overcoming distance) is not too great. However, if an alternative destination C also complements A and is nearer to A than B is, migrants will divert to C. Thus, place C is an **intervening opportunity** between places A and B.

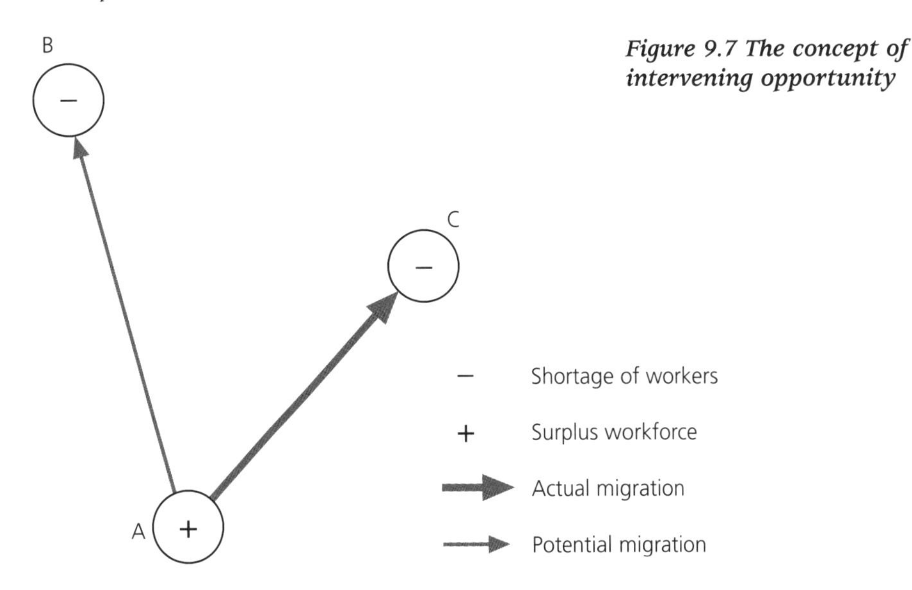

Figure 9.7 The concept of intervening opportunity

INSET 5

Gravity models

Gravity models are used to predict spatial interaction between places. This interaction may take the form of migration flows, commuter movements, traffic flows and so on. Newton's universal law of gravitation is the basic idea that underpins gravity models. It states that two bodies in the universe attract each other in proportion to the product of the square of their masses, and inversely as the square of the distance separating them.

The basic gravity model is:

$$I_{ij} = k(P_iP_j)/D_{ijb}$$

where I_{ij} is the predicted flow of migrants between place i and place j;
P_i is the mass (or population) of place i;
P_j is the mass (or population) of place j;
D_{ij} is the distance between places i and j;
b is a distance exponent (i.e. 2 in the classic model);
k is a constant or scaling factor.

Rural population and rural settlement

1 Defining rural areas

Most areas have a mix of rural and urban characteristics. There is an incline of rurality from extreme rural (e.g. Highlands and Islands of Scotland) to extreme urban (e.g. inner London).

There is no simple or universally accepted definition of the term **rural area**. Rural areas may be variously defined by criteria such as population size, population density, employment, sociology and land use.

National censuses often identify rural populations by administrative units. These units are determined by population size or population density. Thus, in England and Wales the rural population are those people who live in rural districts.

Rural societies have distinctive characteristics:

- Compared to urban societies they are more close-knit, have stronger family ties, attach greater importance to religion and have more traditional lifestyles.
- Extensive land uses, such as agriculture, forestry and recreation and leisure, dominate rural areas.

Paul Cloke used 16 variables to devise a **rurality index**. He identified four classes of rurality: extreme rural; intermediate rural; intermediate non-rural; and extreme non-rural. Most extreme rural areas in England and Wales are in the remoter parts of the Pennines, central Wales and south-west England.

2 Rural settlement

2.1 Settlement types and settlement patterns

The farm is the basic unit of rural settlement. Isolated farms are known as **dispersed** rural settlements. More often farms, dwellings and other buildings cluster to form **nucleated** rural settlements. There are two types of nucleated rural settlement: hamlets and villages.

When describing a settlement pattern from an OS map, you should comment on:

- the overall spatial distribution of settlement;
- the spatial distribution of different settlement types (i.e. farms, hamlets and villages);
- the density of settlement.

The term **settlement pattern** describes the spatial distribution of isolated farms, hamlets and villages in a region (see Figure 10.1). A dispersed settlement pattern is one dominated by isolated farms. Nucleated patterns mainly consist of hamlets and villages. In practice, most settlement patterns usually comprise all three elements.

2.2 Rural settlement patterns in Britain

The broad pattern of rural settlement in Britain has two contrasting elements: dispersion in upland Britain and nucleation in lowland Britain. The reasons for this contrast are both physical and cultural.

Physical factors

- In the uplands, the poor physical resources for farming (cold damp climate, thin acidic soils, poor drainage, short growing season, etc.) allow only low-intensity farming based on livestock. As a result, farms cover hundreds of hectares. Such farms are manageable only if the farm and its outbuildings locate centrally on the farm's own land. In other words, nucleation of settlement was often not an option in the uplands.
- In the lowlands, the physical resources for farming were more favourable. Farmers could earn a living from a much smaller area, allowing farms to cluster in villages.

Cultural factors

- Cultural factors also favoured dispersed settlement in the uplands. Historically, people have always had more freedom to act individually in the uplands. Often farmers were landowners and could therefore opt to site their farms on their own plots.
- During the Middle Ages, feudalism dominated lowland Britain. Land was owned by a small elite and peasants were allocated land in return for services on the lord of

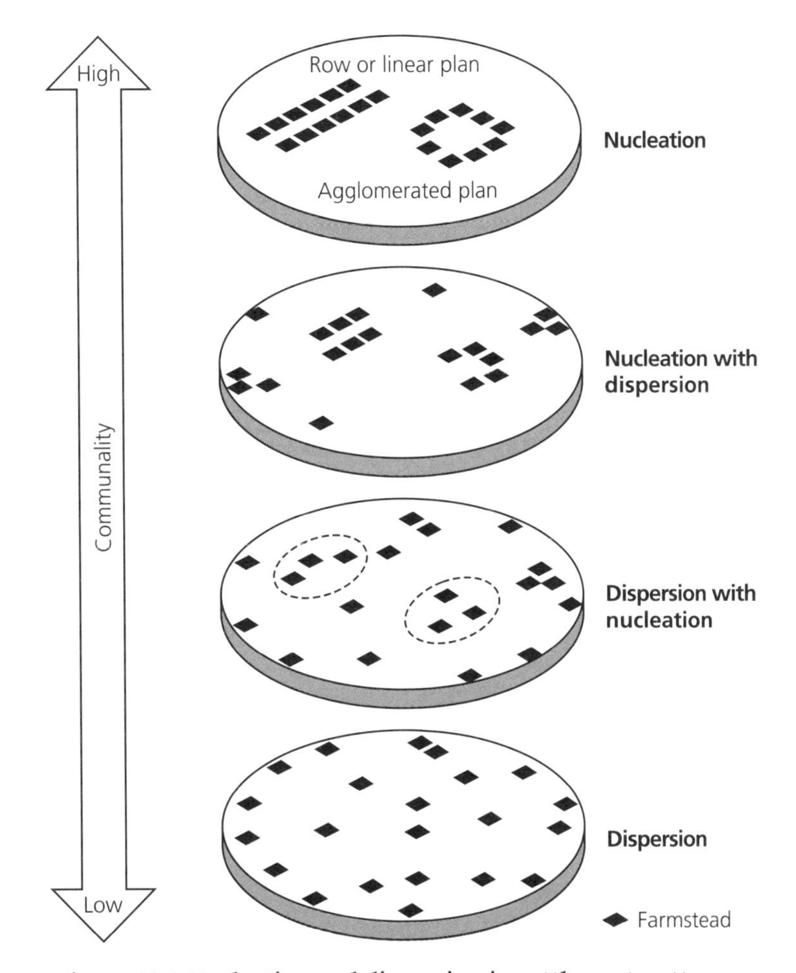

Figure 10.1 Nucleation and dispersion in settlement patterns

the manor's farm. Around each village, three or four large open fields were cultivated in strips. Farming required close co-operation between individuals. Such a system, based on communality, favoured nucleated settlement patterns.

INSET 1

Nearest neighbour analysis

Nearest neighbour analysis is a technique for measuring the degree of clustering or regularity in a settlement pattern. It involves a comparison of the actual spacing of settlements with the spacing expected if the pattern were random. The value of the nearest neighbour index varies from 0 to 2.1491. A zero index is where all settlement is concentrated in one location; a perfect regular spacing of settlements gives an index of 2.1491; and a random pattern has an index of 1.

Actual spacing is the average distance of each settlement to its nearest neighbour in kilometres.

Expected spacing in a random pattern is given by:

$$\frac{1}{2\sqrt{n/A}}$$

where n is the number of settlements in the pattern and A is the area (in km^2) of the territory being examined.

Nearest neighbour index = Actual spacing/Expected spacing

2.3 Village morphology

Villages are clusters of farms, dwellings and outbuildings in an arrangement that incorporates streets, lanes and open spaces. The spaces fall into three types: private space, communal space and public space. Private spaces include dwellings with their gardens and various outbuildings. Communal space belongs to the village community, rather than to individuals. It may include the village green, the church and churchyard, the village hall and so on. Public space includes roads, footpaths and areas in which there is free access for all, including strangers.

The arrangement of private, communal and public space gives rise to distinctive village forms or morphology. Some villages have a linear shape and consist of rows of buildings that face each other across a road or village green. Others are tightly clustered and compact, with more complex forms suggesting that they have evolved slowly. Both types of morphology may be regular or irregular and may or may not include a village green.

A range of physical and human factors influence village morphology. These include the site characteristics, the influence of roads and road junctions, the cultural values and lifestyles of the original founders, and the influence of planning (e.g. estate villages and villages with greens).

2.4 The colonisation and settlement of Britain

Most villages have a long history. In lowland England, most existing villages were recorded in the Domesday Book (1086). In fact, there is evidence to show that large-scale village settlement began in England in the Dark Ages (sixth to tenth centuries). Anglo-Saxon farmers, and later Scandinavian settlers from Denmark and Norway, colonised the lowlands. They cleared the primary forest for cultivation, and in the process established village settlement.

INSET 2

Origin of some place name elements in British settlements

Element	Meaning	Example
Anglo-Saxon		
Primary settlement		
-ing, -ingas	territory of the people of	Reading
-ham	homestead	Waltham
Later primary settlement		
-ton	enclosure	Orton
-borough, -bury, -burh	fortified place	Malmesbury
-bridge	bridge	Tonbridge
-ford	ford	Stratford
Early dispersal of daughter settlements		
-cot, -cote	outlying hut	Didcot
-field	clearing in wood	Sheffield
-ley	clearing	Shipley
-stead	place	Hampstead
-stoke	daughter settlement	Maxstoke
-stow	holy place	Wistow
-wick	outlying hut or dairy farm	Howick
Later clearing of woodland		
-den	pasture for swine in wood	Neasden
-hurst, -hirst	copse or wooded height	Longhirst
-holt	wood	Northolt
-weald, -wold	wood	Easingwold
-riding, -rod	cleared land	Glenridding
Scandinavian		
-toft	homestead or clearing	Burmantoft
-by	homestead	Whitby
-garth	enclosure	Dalegarth
-booth	summer pasture	Crawshawbooth
-thorpe	daughter settlement	Gunthorpe
-thwaite	clearing	Micklethwaite
-ergh	outlying hut	Sizergh

The evidence of Anglo-Saxon and Scandinavian colonisation is preserved in place names (see Inset 2). Anglo-Saxon place names dominate lowland England south of Watling Street. In the ninth century, the area to the north of Watling Street – the Danelaw – was a separate Danish kingdom. Here, and especially in East Anglia, the east Midlands and east Yorkshire, Danish and Norwegian place name elements such as -by and -thorpe are most common.

However, place names, as evidence of early settlement, are not wholly reliable.

- Archaeological evidence suggests that many village sites have been occupied since prehistoric times.
- Although some place names are wholly Scandinavian (i.e. both elements are Scandinavian in origin, e.g. Grimsby), many others comprise both a Norse and an Anglo-Saxon element (e.g. Skipton – first element Scandinavian, second element Anglo-Saxon).

You may be asked to reconstruct the evolution of primary settlement in an area from OS map evidence. In addition to place names you should use prehistoric sites (tumuli, stone circles, celtic fields, etc.), Roman and non-Roman evidence.

3 Site and situation

3.1 Village sites

Site refers to the land on which a settlement is built. A favourable village site is likely to offer a reliable water supply, good drainage, gentle slopes and shelter, and to be free from the risk of flooding and other natural hazards (see Figure 10.2). In the past, locations that had all or most of these qualities were at a premium. This is why many village sites have been occupied for millennia. Indeed, most villages in England were already in existence at the time of the Domesday survey.

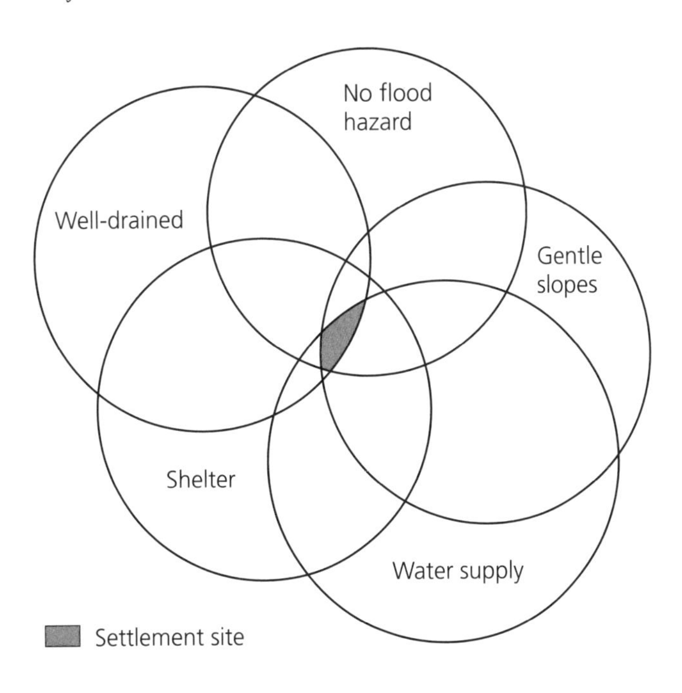

Figure 10.2 Factors influencing choice of settlement sites

INSET 3

Village sites in Upper Wharfedale and Littondale

The importance of site is shown by the location of villages in Upper Wharfedale (see Figure 10.3) and nearby Littondale in North Yorkshire. These steep-sided glacial valleys afford limited opportunities for settlement. Villages such as Buckden, Starbotton and Halton Gill developed at regular intervals along the sides of Wharfedale and Littondale, where tributary streams join the main valley. In the past, these streams provided a water supply. They were also responsible for the formation of alluvial fans of sand and gravels. These fans offered well-drained sites that, unlike the main valleys, had little risk of flooding.

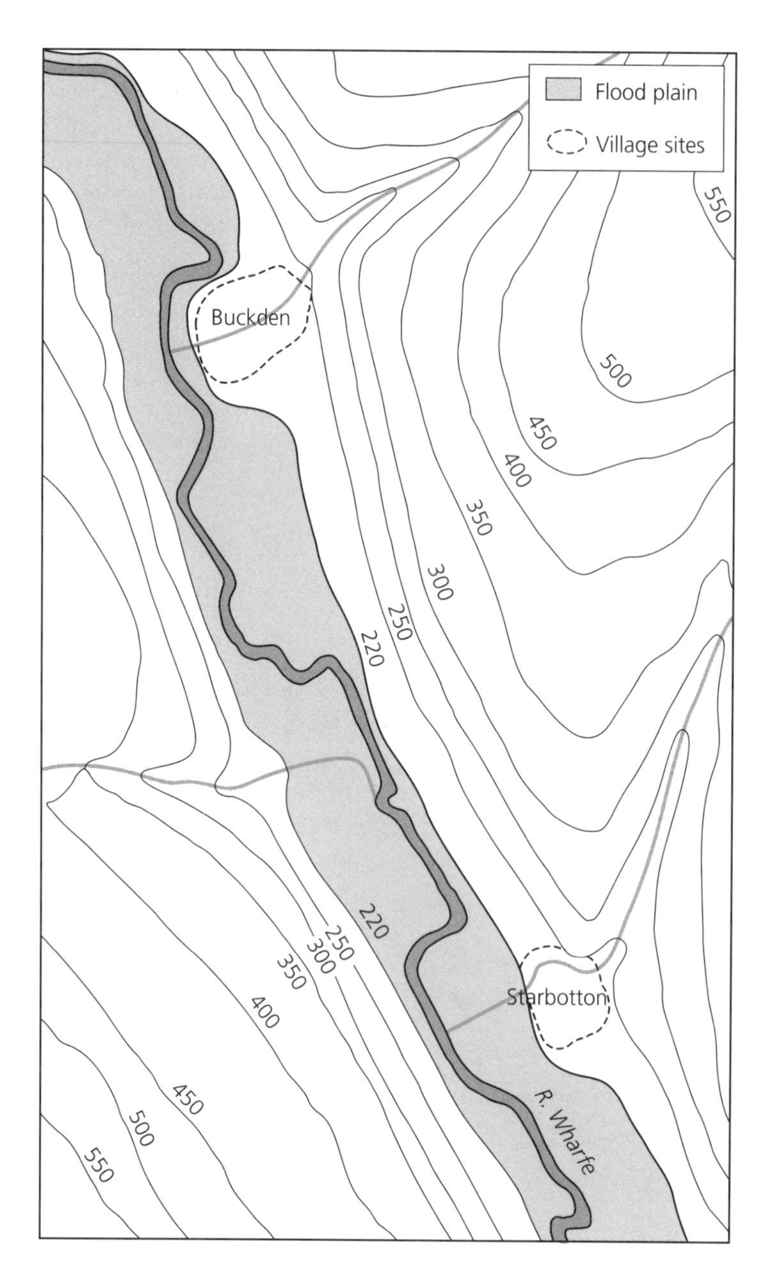

Figure 10.3* *Village sites in Upper Wharfedale

3.2 Village situation

The location of a village in relation to resources that lie beyond the site is referred to as its **situation**. As Figure 10.4 shows, situation can be considered at two scales. At a local scale, situation means location relative to resources, such as arable land, meadow, grazing and woodland. Situation also operates at a larger scale, within the context of the surrounding region.

The line of villages along the northern margins of the Vale of Pickering in North Yorkshire shows how situation in relation to local resources has influenced settlement. Villages such as Beadlam and Wombleton located close to soils that are a mixture of clays, hill wash and blown sand. These soils allow the cultivation of a range of arable crops. Meanwhile, meadows and marshlands for grazing were available in the low-lying lands of the Vale.

Thanks to the advantages of their regional situation, some villages grew and developed additional functions to agriculture. For instance, a location where routes converge owing to a bridging point, or ford, or a junction of valleys conferred a high degree of accessibility or **nodality** on some settlements (see Figure 10.4). As a result, these settlements often developed as market centres or central places.

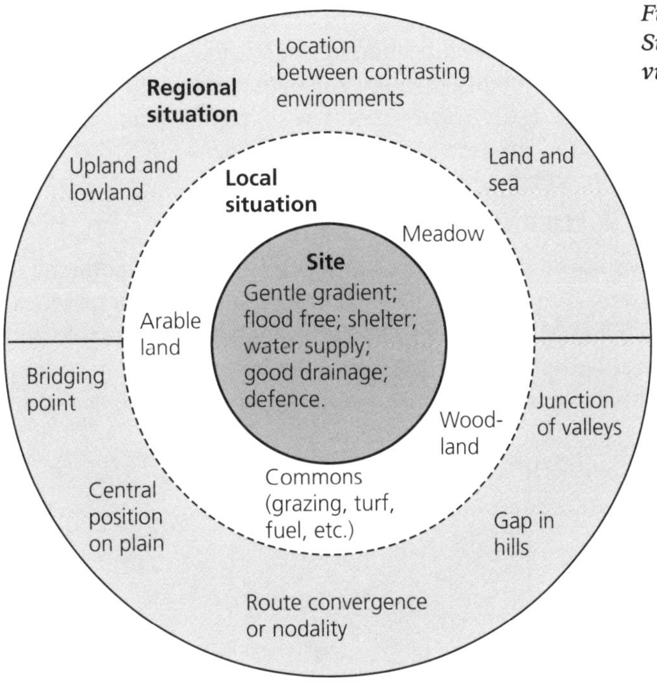

Figure 10.4
Site, situation and village development

4 Central places

Although some settlements function primarily as central places (e.g. market towns), most large settlements support additional economic activities. These activities include: manufacturing; mining and quarrying; tourism; transport, etc.

Central places are settlements that provide services for their own populations and for people who live in the surrounding area. This area with which a central place has functional ties is known variously as the **trade area** or **sphere of influence** or **hinterland** or **catchment area**.

INSET 4

Delimiting the trade area of a central place

Reilly's break-point model defines the trade area boundary between two central places. The model assumes that the trade area of a settlement is proportional in size to its population or number/range of services (i.e. **centrality**), and the location of competing settlements of similar status. The break-point formula for two settlements, A and B, is:

$$\text{distance of break-point from the smaller settlement B} = \frac{\text{distance between settlements A and B}}{1 + \sqrt{\dfrac{\text{population A}}{\text{population B}}}}$$

NB Various measurements of centrality and distance may be used. Distance may be expressed in kilometres, journey times or cost of travel.

4.1 Centrality

We can understand the number and range of functions or **centrality** of a settlement by the size of its catchment or the population it serves. Each function requires a minimum **threshold** population to support it. Some functions, such as a post office or pub, may have thresholds of just a few hundred people. These **low-order functions** will be viable even in relatively small settlements. Larger settlements will support several establishments offering the same low-order functions. **Higher-order functions**, such as clothes shops, car showrooms and primary schools, have larger thresholds. Thus, they are fewer in number and in rural regions will be confined to larger villages and market towns.

The availability of services in a rural region also depends on the cost of transport. The distance people travel to buy a particular good and service is its **range**. Generally, the

more expensive the good or service, the greater the range. However, the range of a good or service can change over time. Improvements in road networks, increased personal mobility through car ownership, and the development of new retail formats such as edge-of-town superstores have all increased the range of low-order items such as food in the last 30 years.

Central place theory does not attempt to describe **actual** settlement patterns. Rather, it explains how settlements **should** be organised, given certain simplifying assumptions about people's behaviour, geography and the economic system. The theory isolates the influence of threshold, range and distance on settlement patterns.

4.2 Hierarchy

The effect of threshold and range is to create a **hierarchy** of central places. An example is given in Figure 10.5. This central place hierarchy provides the population of Dorset with a full range of services. Functions with a low threshold and low range (e.g. essential food and household items) are available locally in many small centres. Higher-order functions that have larger thresholds and higher ranges are available only in a few larger centres.

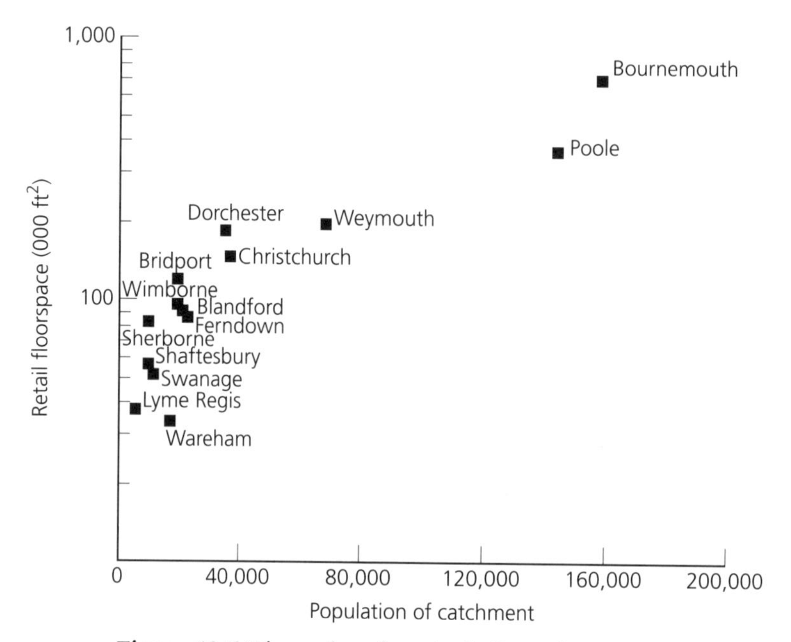

Figure 10.5 Hierarchy of central places in Dorset

A hierarchy of larger central places in the rural county of Norfolk in shown in Table 10.1. This hierarchy is based on two criteria: the shopping provision available in each centre; and the size of its population. Norwich, with a population of 190,000 and a retail floorspace of 187,500 square metres, is the highest-order centre. In contrast, the small towns in Table 10.1 have:

Regional centres	Sub-regional centres	Large towns	Small towns
Norwich	Great Yarmouth	Cromer	Attleborough
	King's Lynn	Dereham	Aylsham
		Diss	Gorleston
		Downham Market	Harleston
		Fakenham	Holt
		North Walsham	Hunstanton
		Thetford	Loddon
			Stalham
			Sheringham
			Swaffham
			Watton
			Wells
			Wymondham

Table 10.1 Hierarchy of larger central places in Norfolk

- approximately 9,300 square metres of retail floorspace;
- at least one large foodstore on the edge of town;
- a reasonable selection of national multiple (chain) stores;
- an average population of around 8,000.

Central place theory isolates the general principles that influence the spatial patterns and hierarchies of market centres. To do this, it makes a number of simplifying assumptions. Once we relax these assumptions, the regular triangular lattices of settlement and the step-like hierarchies distort and look more like real world patterns.

INSET 5

Central place theory

Central place theory, based on the concepts of threshold, range and hierarchy, describes an idealised distribution of market centres in a rural region. The idealised distribution provides a population with a full range of services at minimal travel cost. Central place theory makes the following assumptions:

- Shoppers travel to the nearest centre providing the goods and services they need.
- Transport costs are proportional to distance.
- Traders aim to maximise profits.
- Shoppers are perfectly informed, economically rational decision-makers.
- Perfect competition exists between services.
- The rural region is a plain where all parts are equally accessible, and population and resources are evenly distributed (i.e. it is an **isotropic surface**).
- There is no overlap between the trade areas of central places.

These assumptions produce a spatial distribution of central places that form a geometry of triangular lattices, as shown in Figure 10.6. The trade areas of individual central places are hexagonal in shape (i.e. they do not overlap); and the size of trade areas is proportional to the status of the central place. There is a hierarchy of central places. In this example, every central place serves two other central places and itself. This is known as a $K = 3$ hierarchy. It means that the number of central places at each lower level in the hierarchy increases by a factor of three, i.e. 1, 3, 9, 27, 81, etc.

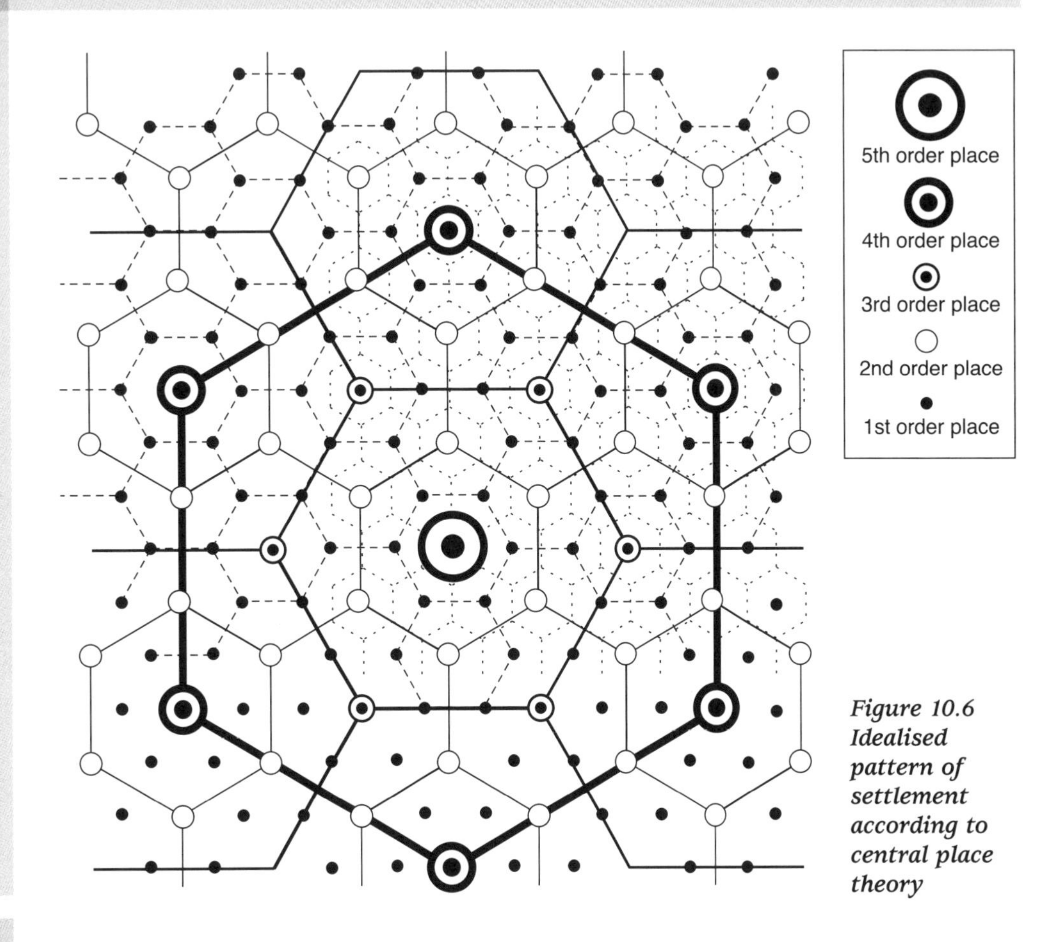

Figure 10.6 Idealised pattern of settlement according to central place theory

5 *Rural population and rural settlement change: UK*

In the last 30 years or so, changes to the rural settlement hierarchy in the UK have resulted from: population movements and their impact on services; the revolution in retailing; and planning policies.

5.1 Population movements

Since the early 1970s, two population movements have affected settlement hierarchies.

- At the national scale, a north–south movement of population has occurred from old industrial regions, such as central Scotland and north-east England, to the south-east and East Anglia. Although this migration has mainly affected urban settlements, industrial villages in former coalfields such as Durham and South Wales have also suffered depopulation and service decline.
- At the sub-regional scale, there has been an urban–rural shift of population (see Figure 10.7). This movement, which began in the early 1970s, is also known as **counter-urbanisation**. Counter-urbanisation continued throughout the 1980s, though at a slower rate. Metropolitan regions such as Merseyside and Strathclyde experienced heavy population losses. Meanwhile, between 1981 and 1991 the population of shire counties in southern England, stretching from Cornwall through to Norfolk and Lincolnshire, increased by more than 7%. Within this zone, many market towns (e.g. Kendal, Warwick) and rural areas within commuting distance of major employment centres grew strongly. Even so, the growth of population in these rural areas did little to maintain the central place status of villages. Often services continued to decline as they had done throughout the postwar period.

Because fertility and mortaility rates show little variation within the UK, population change at regional and sub-regional scales is due to migration.

Figure 10.7 Population change in the UK by type of district, 1981–91

The urban–rural shift of manufacturing and services has been accompanied by a similar decentralisation of population (see Inset 6). In the UK, the attraction of the countryside (the rural 'idyll') is particularly strong and reflects cultural values that are often quite different from those of other, more urbanised European cultures.

5.2 Rural depopulation

Depopulation is the absolute decrease of the population of an area or place. In the UK, depopulation usually results from net migrational losses in rural communities. Some regions, such as the north-west Highlands and Islands of Scotland and the northern Pennines, have suffered depopulation for decades. Lack of services and limited

INSET 6

Explaining the urban–rural shift

The advantages of decentralisation for businesses include lower taxes, less congestion, more space for expansion and a better quality of life for their workforces. The urban–rural shift of population has been facilitated by improvements in communications and rising real incomes:

- Thanks to e-mail, fax, Internet, personal computers, etc., many workers in service industries can operate from home, and need commute to an urban-based office only once or twice a week.
- Rising real incomes and increased levels of car ownership have made commuting from previously inaccessible rural areas possible.
- Personal mobility has also increased, owing to improvements in the road network (motorways, dual carriage trunk roads, bypasses, etc.).
- generous occupational pensions and earlier retirement have allowed many older adults on retirement to move away from their places of work in towns and cities. The most popular destinations for retirees are areas of high environmental quality, especially the coast of southern Britain, from Cornwall to East Anglia. Other attractive retirement areas include the National Parks and Areas of Outstanding Natural Beauty.

employment opportunities have been the main impetus to out-migration in remote rural areas. In lowland regions, declining employment in agriculture has been a major factor in population decline at the parish scale. For example, employment in agriculture fell by 70% in Norfolk between 1950 and 1980. With changes to the common agricultural policy and the lifting of tariff barriers by the World Trade Organisation in the next few years, further decline is likely.

Rural depopulation has triggered the decline of transport, retailing, educational and medical services in remoter rural areas of the UK, as Figure 10.8 shows. The result is that many small rural service centres have slipped further down the settlement hierarchy.

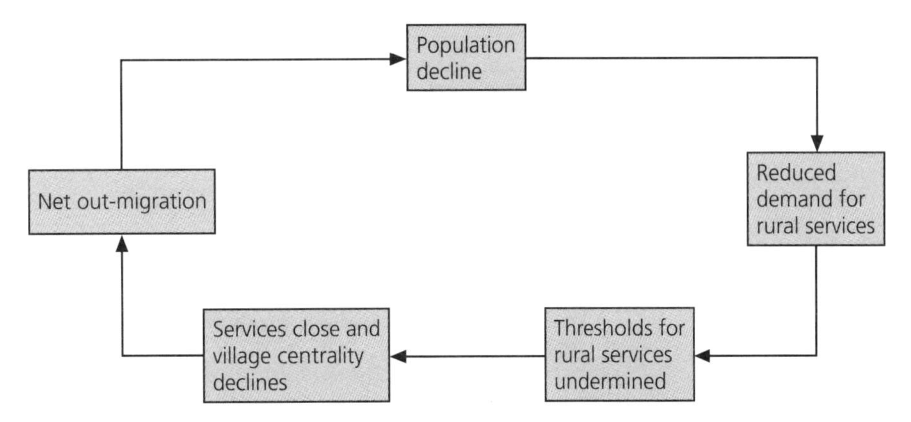

Figure 10.8 Rural depopulation and rural service provision: the vicious circle of decline

INSET 7

Types of rural area

We recognise two types of rural area: pressured rural areas and remote rural areas.

- **Pressured rural areas** are within commuting distance of large urban centres (e.g. north Warwickshire, north Cheshire). Villages have few traditional links with agriculture and the countryside. Many villages have expanded to accommodate population growth caused by in-coming commuters and their families. New housing estates have appeared, encroaching on the countryside, and barns have been converted to private dwellings. House prices have soared.
- **Remote rural areas** often continue to depend on agriculture. In the uplands, many remote rural communities are among the poorest in the UK. Incomes in hill farming are low and there are few job opportunities for young people. Net out-migration and depopulation has been a feature of these communities for the past 150 years. In some remote rural areas (e.g. western Highlands), a population revival has occurred in the last 20 years. Attracted by the quality of life and low cost of living, in-comers include retirees, people opting out of urban society and others who rely on modern telecommunications to work from home.

6 Declining rural services

6.1 Retailing

The importance of scale economies in retailing has led to the dominance of supermarkets and superstores in retailing during the last 30 years. This has put pressure on small, independent retailers. Unable to compete with the superstores operated by national multiples such as Tesco and Sainsbury, thousands of small shops have closed. The growth of car ownership (which is higher in rural areas than in urban areas) has given rural dwellers access to superstores often located in small towns at edge-of-centre sites. Meanwhile, fridges and freezers have become standard items in most households, encouraging weekly bulk shopping for food in large superstores. Because of these trends, support for general stores and food shops in rural areas has dwindled. Thus in Norfolk in 1997, 41% of villages were without a shop of any kind. And only in larger villages with populations of more than 1,000 was the village shop (and post office) reasonably secure.

6.2 Transport

The growth of car ownership has drastically reduced the demand for rural bus services in the postwar period, as Figure 10.9 shows. In Norfolk, 84% of villages have no daily bus service and 25% no bus services at all. Given the decline in village retail and health care services, the withdrawal of rural bus services has a severe impact on those groups – the old and the poor – without access to cars.

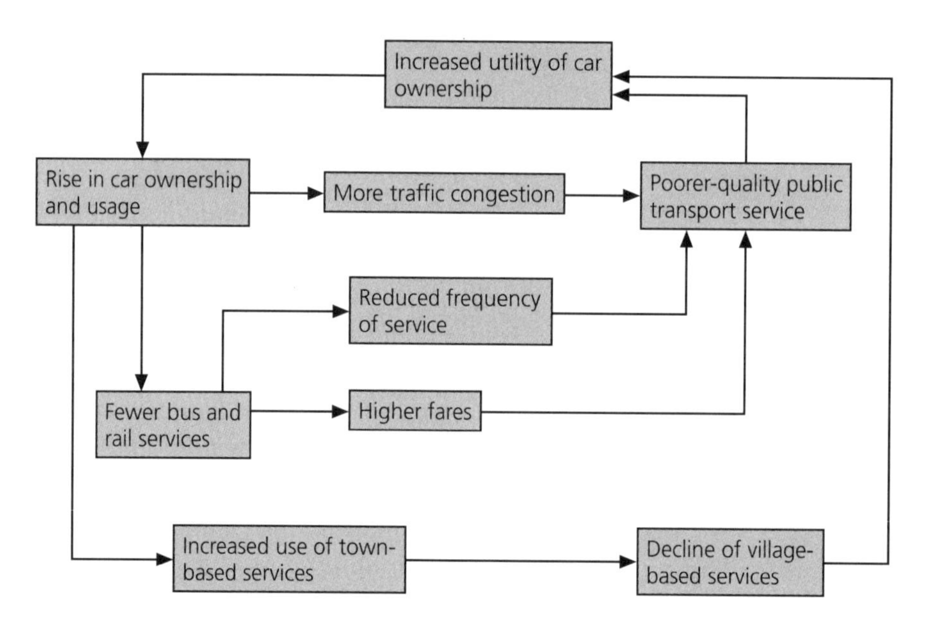

Figure 10.9 The effect of increasing levels of car ownership on public transport services

6.3 Education

Forty years ago, most villages had their own primary school. However, there are strong economic and educational arguments against small schools. Small schools are expensive to run (especially when there are fewer than 50 pupils on the school roll); offer only a restricted curriculum; and may be to the social disadvantage of pupils. Against this, village schools are a focus for rural communities, and with their closure children may face long journeys to school each day. Educational authorities in the UK have opted to close small village schools and bus children to larger schools in market towns and key villages.

Closure is most likely where there are falling school rolls. Falling rolls may have several causes: rural depopulation; the selective out-migration of young adults of child-bearing age from rural communities; and the in-migration of older adults without children.

7 Second homes and holiday homes

The growth of second homes and holiday homes in the countryside has three main causes:

- surplus housing stock as a result of depopulation;
- rising disposable incomes;
- increased mobility through car ownership and improved road networks.

Second homeowners favour properties around the coast, in National Parks and in other areas of high environmental quality. Occupied only at weekends or holidays, second homes and holiday homes contribute little to the support of local services. In rural areas where housing is in short supply, second homes inflate the rural housing market. This makes it difficult for young local people who wish to remain in the countryside to find affordable housing.

8 Planning policies in rural areas

National economic changes raise several important issues in rural Britain. Should rural services be given government support? Should some housing in rural areas be reserved for local people? Have influxes of communities and second home owners had an adverse effect on rural communities?

Planning authorities in rural counties such as Devon and Norfolk have introduced **key settlement policies** in an attempt to sustain rural services and halt depopulation. Allowing dispersed development of housing does not sustain village services. For instance, despite a 22% increase in Norfolk's rural population between 1971 and 1991, village services continued to decline.

Key settlements are usually large villages or small towns where planners concentrate new housing and services. In Norfolk, key settlements with the potential to support essential services for rural communities must have:

- significant existing employment;
- a selection of shops, including a post office;
- adequate public transport;
- a primary school;
- community facilities, such as a village hall, pub and sports club.

By concentrating population growth in larger centres, planners hope to ensure the viability of services. Thus, rural dwellers in smaller settlements should at least have essential services such as food shops, a pharmacy, a doctor's surgery and a primary school within easy reach. Without such policies, many rural dwellers would be forced to leave the countryside for the towns.

Key settlement policies clearly have an effect on the rural settlement hierarchy. They raise the status of those settlements designated for growth and accelerate the decline in others. Inevitably, such policies are often unpopular with the residents of villages not designated as growth centres.

Urban population and urban settlement

1 Defining urban populations and urban areas

Global figures on urban populations are only estimates. This is because:

- definitions of urban population used in censuses vary between countries;
- there is no agreement on the boundaries of urban areas.

Current estimates put the world's urban population between 40 and 55%.

Classifications of urban populations and urban settlements depend on census definitions. These vary from country to country. However, most definitions of urban population usually include one or more of the following criteria: population size; population density; distance between buildings within a settlement; economic activity; and legal or administrative urban boundaries.

Determining the size of towns and cities presents similar problems. The size of any town or city depends on the boundaries chosen. There are several possibilities. Each is likely to give a very different estimate of population (Inset 1):

- legal or adminstrative boundaries;
- the contiguous built-up area (including both the inner and outer suburbs);
- the contiguous built-up area and the physically separate exurbs;
- the contiguous built-up area and the surrounding commuter hinterland.

INSET 1

Estimates of London's population in 1991

Population	Area (km²)	Definition
4,230	3	Original 'city' of London
2,343,133	321	Inner London
6,393,568	1,579	Greater London (32 boroughs)
12,530,000	?	London metropolitan region

2 Urbanisation and urban growth

Urban growth *per se* does not necessarily mean that urbanisation also occurs. If the rural population grows faster or at the same rate as the urban population, without migration there will be no increase in the proportion of urban dwellers.

Urbanisation is the *proportion* of urban dwellers in a country or region. **Urban growth** is simply an increase in the number of urban dwellers. It is clear that when levels of urbanisation increase, there must be a relative shift of population from rural to urban areas. Such a shift occurs when:

- rural–urban migration produces a net migrational gain in urban areas, and a net migrational loss in rural areas;
- rates of natural increase are greater in towns and cities than in the countryside.

3 Global urbanisation

3.1 Urbanisation by continent

At the global scale, rapid urbanisation has occurred in the last 50 years. Thus, by 2005 half the world's population will live in towns and cities. At a global scale, Europe, North America, South America and Oceania are the most urbanised continents; Africa and Asia are least urbanised (see Figure 11.1). Although less than 40% of Asia's population lives in towns and cities, the absolute number of urban dwellers in Asia (around 1.4 billion) is by far the largest of any continent (see Figure 11.2).

Today, urbanisation is concentrated in the economically developing world, especially in Africa and Asia. This trend will continue so that by 2025 more than half the population in Africa and Asia will live in urban areas, and four out of every five urban dwellers will be in LEDCs. In Europe, North America and Oceania, urbanisation levels peaked in the mid-twentieth century and have fallen steadily in the last 30 years.

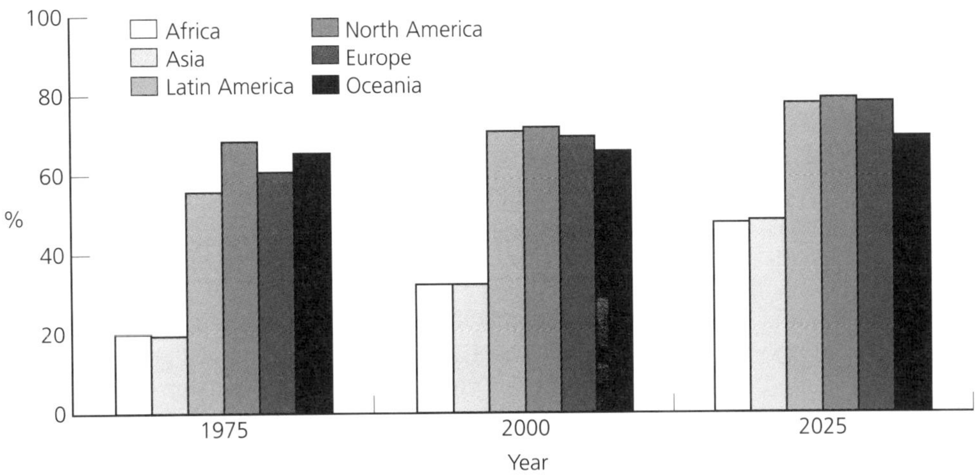

Figure 11.1 Population in urban areas by continent (%)

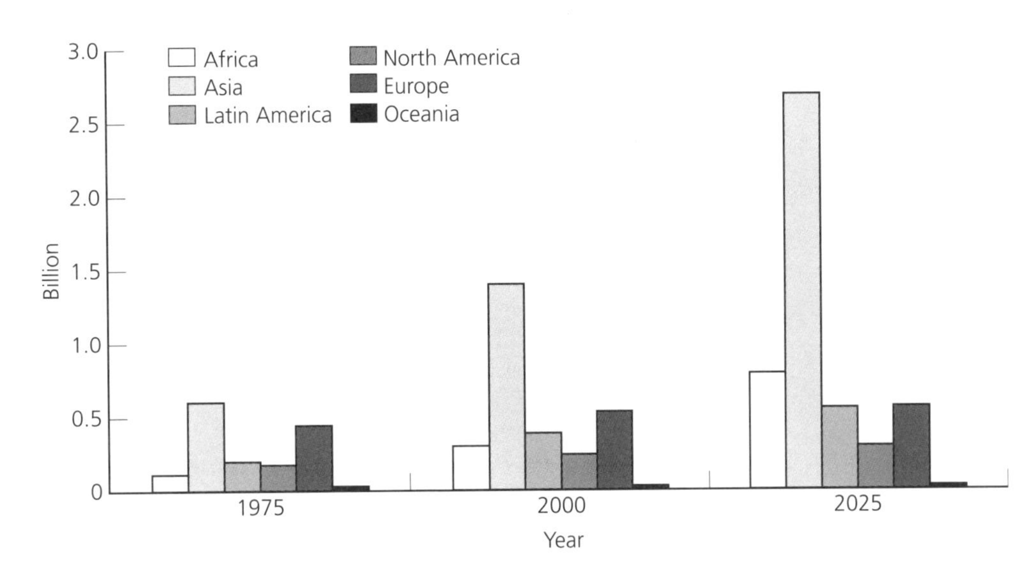

Figure 11.2 The urban population of the world by continent (billion)

3.2 Demographic causes of urbanisation

Urbanisation in LEDCs results from both natural increase in urban areas and large-scale rural–urban migration. On average, natural increase accounts for around 60% of annual urban growth in LEDCs: the remaining 40% is due to rural–urban migration. Where migration makes a major contribution to urban population growth, annual rates of increase are often very high (e.g. annual rate of growth 1990–5 was 5.74% in Dhaka and 4.35% in Djakarta).

INSET 2

Urbanisation in Peru

Peru's recent experience is typical of many countries in the economically developing world. Between 1990 and 2000 Peru's population increased by nearly one-quarter. This increase was, however, split unevenly between urban and rural areas. Thus while the urban population increased by 30%, the increase in rural areas was just 8%. Although natural increase remained high in rural areas (mainly owing to high fertility, as shown in Table 11.1), net out-migration to towns and cities, and especially to the capital and primate city of Lima, kept the rural increase to just 0.38% per year. This compared with an annual increase in urban areas of 2.26%.

	Infant mortality rate/1,000	Total fertility
Urban	35	2.8
Rural	71	5.8

Table 11.1 Urban and rural fertility and mortality in Peru

4 Urban growth and city size

Rapid urban growth in the last 50 years has had two important consequences for city size:

- There has been a huge increase in large cities with populations in excess of 1 million. In the early 1960s there were 113 million cities; by 1990 there were 281.
- The growth of these so-called **million cities** has been mainly concentrated in the economically developing world. As a result, the mean location of million cities shifted south between the 1920s and 1980s by approximately 10 degrees of latitude.

The largest cities, with a population of more than 10 million, are known as **mega cities** (see Table 11.2). Like million cities, the number of mega cities will increase rapidly in the next 25 years, with the increase mainly concentrated in LEDCs.

Rank	City	Population (m)
1	Tokyo	28.447
2	Mexico City	25.913
3	São Paulo	21.539
4	Seoul	19.065
5	New York	16.332
6	Bombay	15.138
7	Osaka	14.060
8	Shanghai	13.584
9	Calcutta	12.885
10	Rio de Janeiro	12.788
11	Los Angeles	12.410
12	Buenos Aires	12.232
13	Tehran	11.681
14	Manila	11.342
15	Beijing	11.299

Table 11.2 The world's largest cities, 1998

There are no simple explanations for rank-size and primate distributions. There is no clear link between city-size distribution and levels of economic development and urbanisation. Rank-size patterns and urban primacy occur in both MEDCs and LEDCs. Some factors associated with primate and rank-size distributions are described in Inset 3.

5 City-size distribution

We can describe the hierarchy of cities in a country by plotting the population of each city against its rank in order of size (both variables are plotted on a logarithmic scale). Analysis of a large number of national hierarchies has revealed two types of city-size distribution:

- a **rank-size distribution** which approximates a straight line, and where the second city is approximately half the size of the largest, the third city is one-third the size of the largest and so on (the so-called rank-size rule). Examples of countries with rank-size distributions are Sweden (see Figure 11.3), the USA, Australia and South Africa.
- a **primate city-size distribution**, where the largest city is much larger than all the other cities (i.e. at least more than twice the size of the second city). The largest city is known as the **primate city**. Examples of primate cities include London, Paris, Buenos Aires and Lima. The last of these is the primate city of Peru (see Figure 11.4).

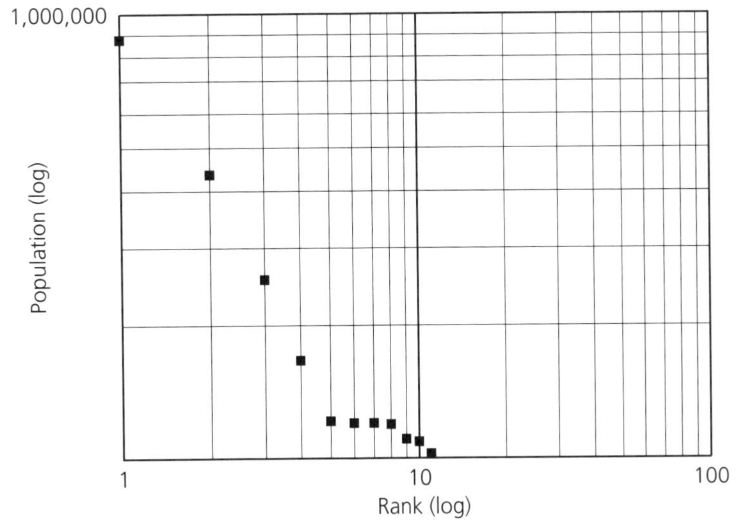

1,000,000
Population (log)
1
10
100
Rank (log)

Figure 11.3 City-size distribution: Sweden

10,000,000
1,000,000
100,000
Population (log)
1
10
100
Rank (log)

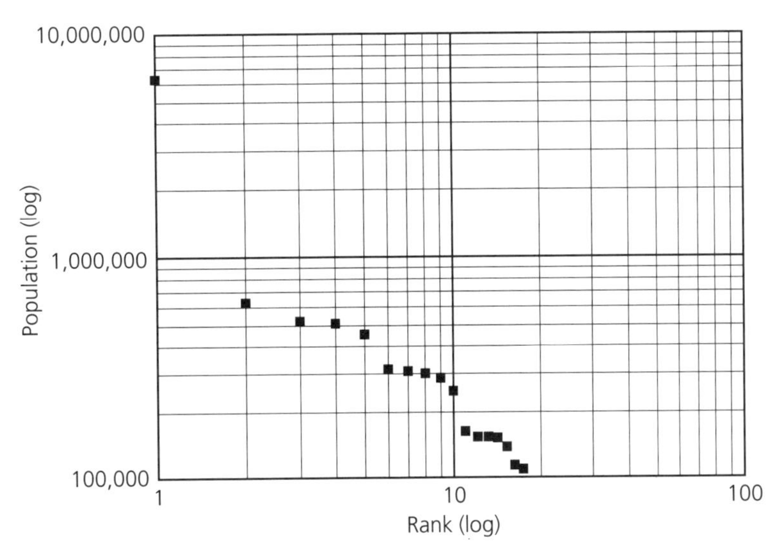

Figure 11.4 City-size distribution: Peru

INSET 3

Factors influencing city-size distribution

- 'Gateway' cities – often port cities that developed under colonialism. They articulate the biggest share of a country's trade to become primate cities (e.g. Buenos Aires).
- Cities that were once the centre of large empires are often primate cities (e.g. London, Vienna).
- Capital cities in countries with highly centralised government are often primate cities (e.g. Paris).
- Countries that, prior to unification, comprised many small independent states or colonies often have rank-size distributions (e.g. Germany, Australia).
- Small countries often have primate distributions. In a small country there may be little need for a second tier of cities. Thus the settlement hierarchy may be dominated by a single primate city (e.g. Copenhagen in Denmark).

Settlement hierarchies in many countries evolved before the emergence of a unified nation state. Thus, settlement hierarchies may have little relevance to modern nation-state boundaries.

6 World cities

Globalisation of the world economy grew rapidly from the early 1970s. Large industrial and service corporations (TNCs) and non-governmental organisations (NGOs), with factories and offices in many countries, were increasingly organised on a global scale.

These trends led to the emergence of a global hierarchy of world cities. Today, these world cities are the command and control centres of the global economy.

Three cities sit at the top of the global hierarchy: New York, London and Tokyo. They are the headquarters locations for many TNCs; centres of world finance; and provide international producer services in areas such as accounting, law, advertising and consultancy. Their importance has made them global hubs in international communications.

Below the truly global cities, we recognise three lower orders of world cities:

- cities linked to large international (but not global) areas, such as Los Angeles (Pacific Rim) and Singapore (south-east Asia).
- cities that link large national economies with the global system, such as Paris and São Paulo;
- cities that integrate important sub-regional economies with the global systems, such as Seattle–Vancouver (Pacific North-West) and Osaka–Kobe (Kansai).

7 Land use in cities

There is no general model of urban structure applicable to all cities. Urban structure models apply to specific regions. They reflect prevailing social, economic and cultural systems both today and in the past.

There is order and pattern in the spatial distribution of land use in cities. Urban structure models describe these patterns and the processes that generate them.

7.1 Urban structure models for MEDCs

Land use in cities in North America, Europe and Japan is the outcome of an economic system dominated by free market forces, mediated in the last 60–70 years by planning control. Within this framework, four basic structure models have been devised: the zonal model; the bid rent model; the sector model; and the multiple nuclei model.

Zonal model

The zonal model, shown in Figure 11.5, represents urban land use as a series of concentric rings or zones focused on the city centre. It assumes that a city grows outwards from a central core. Each period of growth adds a new zone of urban development. The width of each zone will depend on the density of the built area and on the efficiency of urban transport systems. The location of each zone will depend on its age and need for proximity to the city centre.

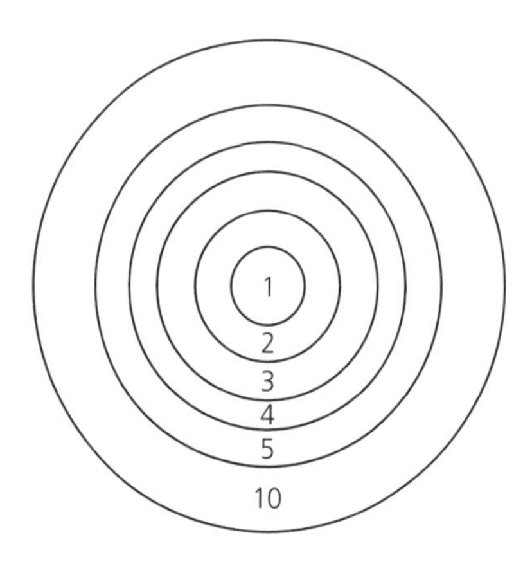

1 Central business district
2 Wholesale light manufacturing
3 Low-class residential
4 Medium-class residential
5 High-class residential
6 Heavy manufacturing
7 Outlying business district
8 Residential suburb
9 Industrial suburb
10 Commuters' zone

Figure 11.5 Zonal model

Bid rent model

The bid rent model, shown in Figure 11.6, provides an economic explanation for the zonal land use patterns described by Burgess. In a free market system, urban land is allocated on the basis of competitive bidding between different users. In the absence of planning controls, those users making the highest bid will gain control of the land. The city centre has the highest bid rent. Urban transport systems converge on the centre, giving it a high level of accessibility. From this initial advantage the city centre acquires other advantages – an appropriate stock of buildings, concentrations of service activities, prestige and so on. For commercial functions such as retailing, banking, accounting and leisure activities, the city centre is the most attractive location. A location in the **central business district** (CBD) gives the best access to consumers and allows firms to transact business easily. Thus, commercial activities outbid all other potential users for central sites. High-rise buildings dominate the CBD and reflect the high demand for land and shortage of space in the city centre.

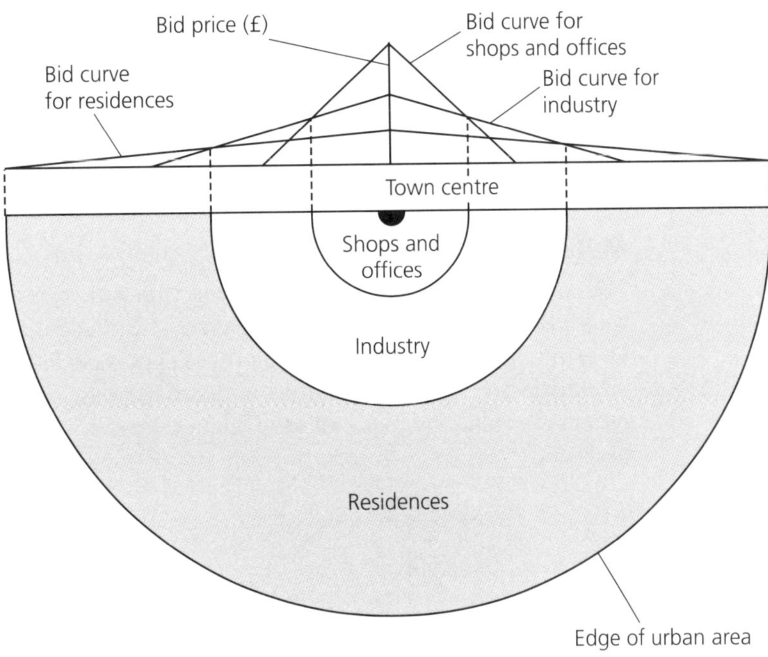

Figure 11.6 Bid rent model

Sector model

The sector model, shown in Figure 11.7, describes urban land use as a series of wedges or sectors that radiate from the city centre. These sectors often develop around transport corridors, such as roads, railways, canals and navigable rivers, where accessibility is high. Sectoral growth is directional and gives rise to the distancing between different income and ethnic groups. The process of sectoral growth is cumulative. For example,

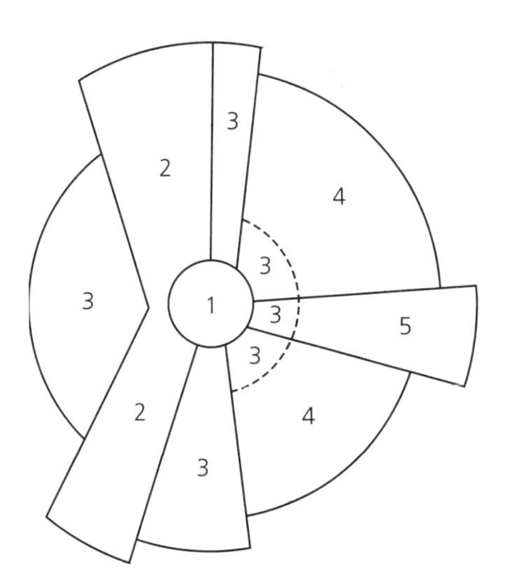

Figure 11.7 Sector model

high-class residential housing on one side of the inner city attracts similar development, producing an outward growth wedge. Expensive housing in this area effectively excludes lower-income groups.

INSET 4

Sociological processes of urban growth

The zonal model describes an expanding city and was based on Chicago in the 1920s. Waves of in-migrants to the city at that time produced dynamic growth. Burgess identified the process of growth as **invasion and succession**. Immigrant groups settled in cheap accommodation near the city centre. They displaced existing residents, who moved out into the next zone. The process had a ripple effect throughout the city, which culminated in the construction of new residential areas on the rural–urban fringe.

Hoyt's model describes a different process of growth called **filtering**. The process begins when new housing is built for high-income groups. Thus, high-income groups move to new housing and the next income group down occupies their old housing. In this way, the housing stock filters down the social hierarchy over time. You should note that **gentrification** is filtering in reverse.

There are situations when filtering cannot account for change:

- Sentiment and symbolism may cause high-income residents to remain in an inner-city suburb and for the suburb to retain its status (e.g. Clifton in Bristol, the New Town in Edinburgh).
- New housing is not built solely for high-income groups (e.g. local authority housing).

Multiple nuclei model

The zonal and sector models assume that cities develop around a single core. The multiple nuclei model, shown in Figure 11.8, describes cities that have several nuclei. Over time, each nucleus becomes more specialised. Thus, a city may develop functionally distinctive areas (port areas, industrial areas, outlying business districts, etc.) that reflect the location of specialised facilities, environmental attractiveness and rent-paying ability.

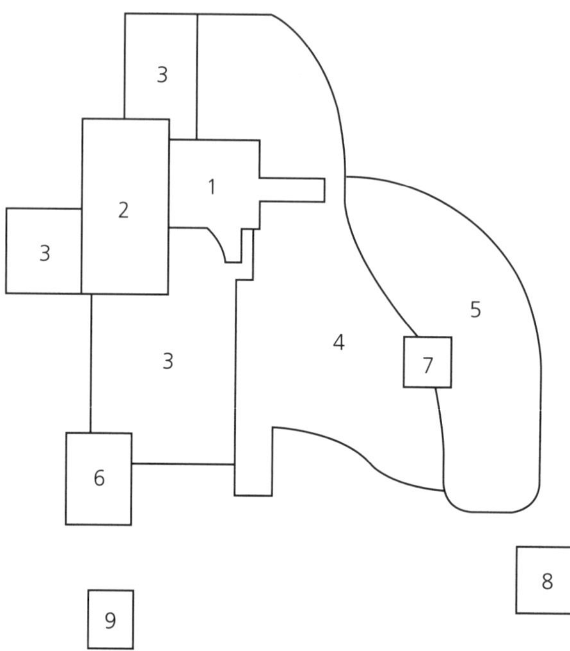

Figure 11.8 Multiple nuclei model

7.2 Urban structure models for LEDCs

Two factors distinguish cities in LEDCs from those in MEDCs: first, their rapid expansion in the last 50 years; and second, the extremes of wealth and poverty found within them. Urban structure within the economically developing world varies widely. Such differences stem from contrasts in culture and historical development. Despite recent modernisation, large cities in LEDCs usually show some trace of their pre-industrial origins.

The pre-industrial model does not take account of the impact of colonialism on city structure in LEDCs. Indeed, the diversity of urban structure is such that we recognise separate models for African, south Asian, south-east Asian and Latin American cities.

Pre-industrial city model

The pre-industrial city (see Figure 11.9) had a feudal social hierarchy. A wealthy (governing) elite group occupied the city centre (the area of highest status). The lower the status of the group, the more peripheral their location. Thus, an economic and social gradient extended from the city centre, with the poorest groups living on the edge of the city, and even outside its walls. Foreign and minority groups were often segregated in distinctive quarters of the city.

Figure 11.9 Pre-industrial city model

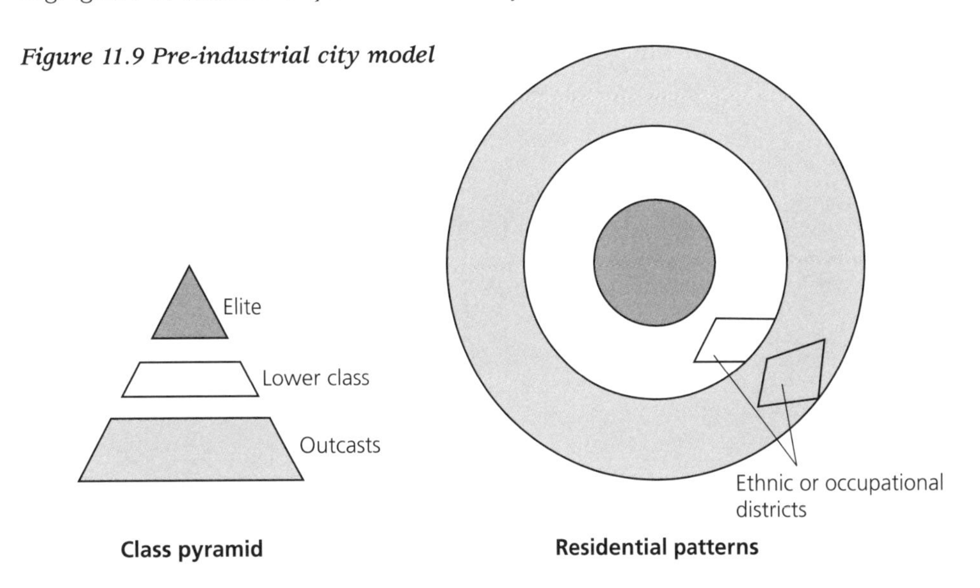

African cities

Many African cities have a high-density core occupied by indigenous groups, as shown in Figure 11.10. Around this core there is often a zone of low density. Previously occupied by a colonial elite, this zone has often been taken over by the indigenous administrative and governmental elite. The outer zones house high-density indigenous populations. Industry and squatter settlements occupy the periphery.

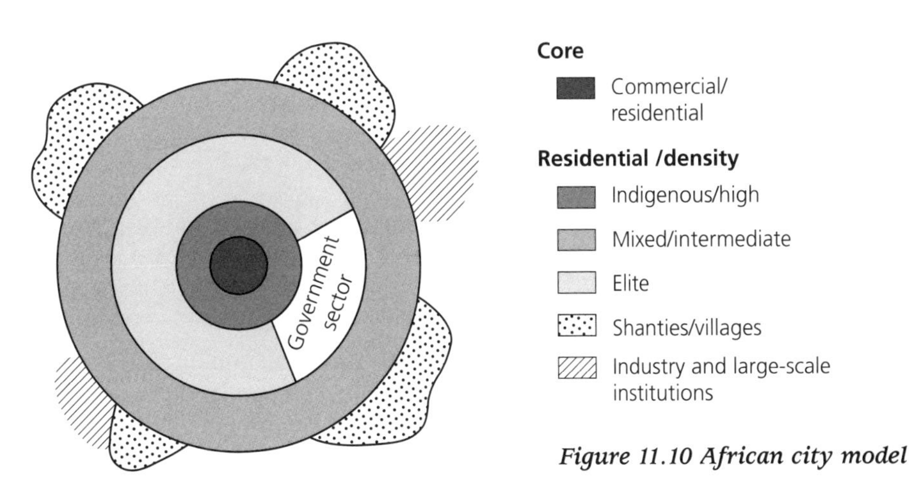

Figure 11.10 African city model

South Asian cities

Many of the largest cities in India – Delhi, Calcutta, Bombay and Madras – were founded as colonial cities and ports. A walled fort surrounded by a large open space is often located at the centre, as shown in Figure 11.11. The CBD is quite separate, and it is around this that low-density neighbourhoods, occupied by Europeans, once clustered. The indigenous population lived in unplanned, high-density districts away from the Europeans.

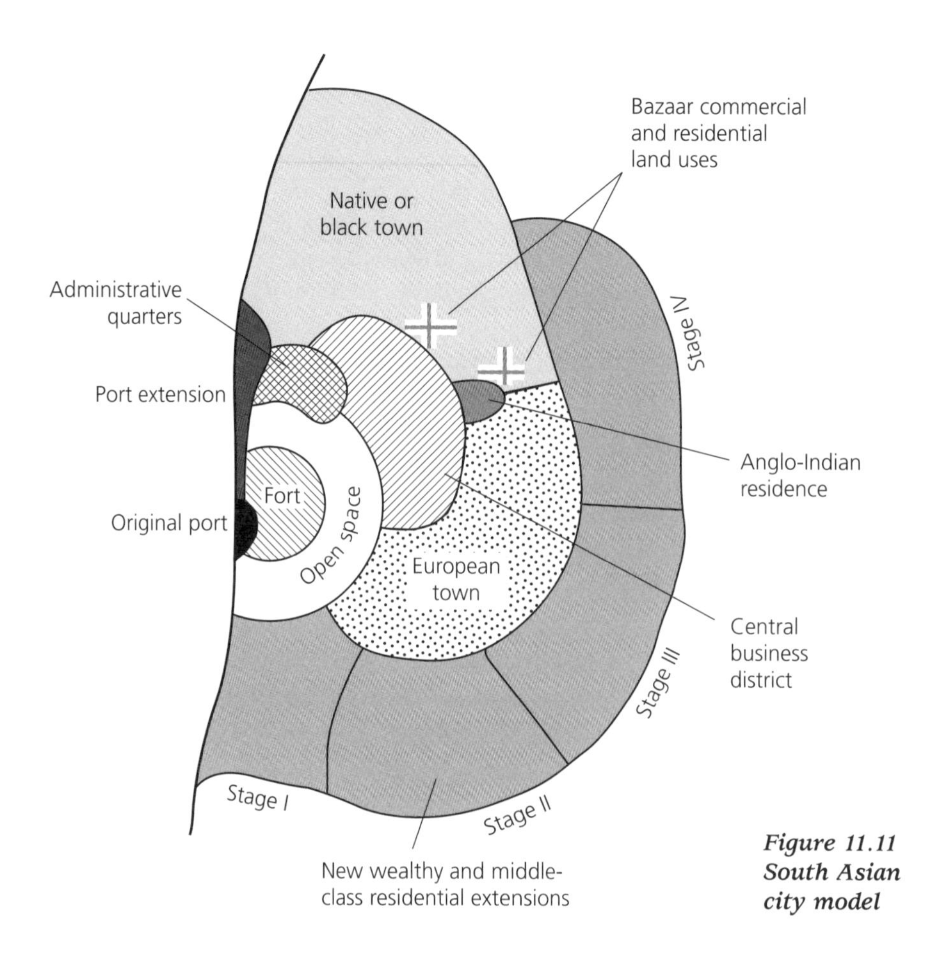

Figure 11.11 **South Asian city model**

South-east Asian cities

The most prominent south-east Asian cities in colonial times were trading centres. The traditional centre includes bazaars and other commercial uses, as shown in Figure 11.12. There is a western-style CBD with distinct commercial enclaves developed by Chinese, Indians and Europeans. Squatter settlements, new industrial zones and agriculture

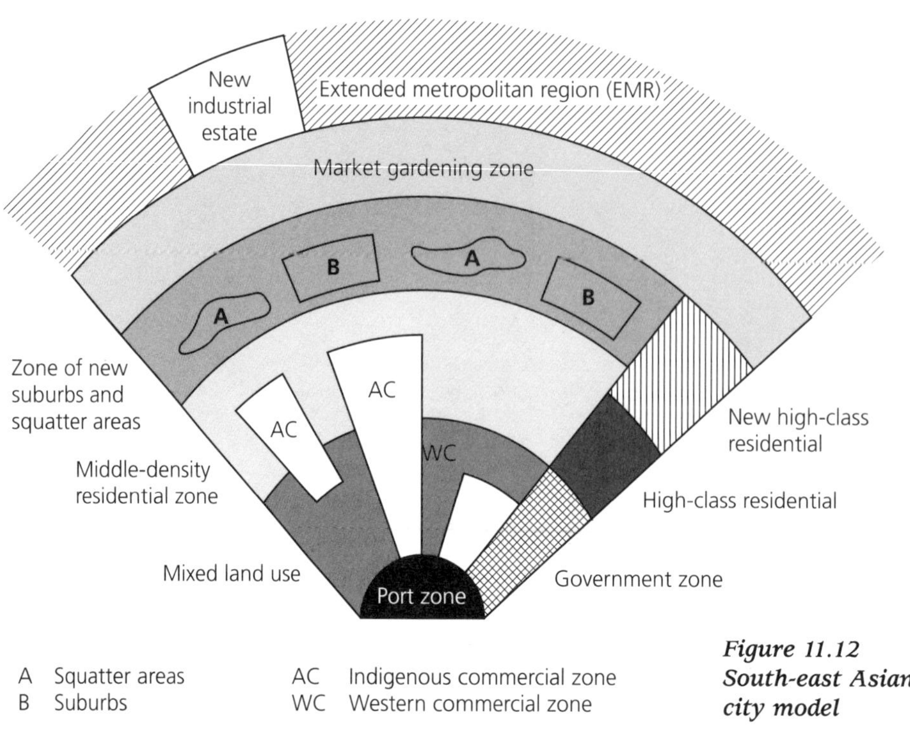

Figure 11.12 **South-east Asian city model**

occupy the periphery. Despite the westernisation of many south-east Asian cities, the bulk of the population live in unplanned, high-density residential districts that still lack modern infrastructure.

Latin American cities

Colonialism has also influenced the structure of Latin American cities. Both the Spaniards and Portuguese laid out their cities in similar style: a central square with a church or cathedral, with the main administrative buildings and homes of the colonial elite nearby. A grid-iron street pattern then spread out from the centre. The most distinctive feature of modern Latin American cities is the commercial spine that extends out from the CBD, as shown in Figure 11.13. Although suburbanisation of higher-income groups has occurred in many cities, the commercial spine also includes high-class residential areas and the city's main cultural amenities. Away from the spine, the urban structure is often zonal. Unlike cities in North America and Europe, social and economic status declines with distance from the centre. The zones of maturity are either areas of elite housing that have filtered downmarket or self-built housing areas that have been upgraded. Housing in the zone of *in situ* accretion is more modest and provision of infrastructure is patchy. The periphery is the zone of unimproved squatter settlements or favelas. Newly arrived migrants are most likely to live here. This is also a zone of disamenity, where many industrial and environmentally polluting activities locate.

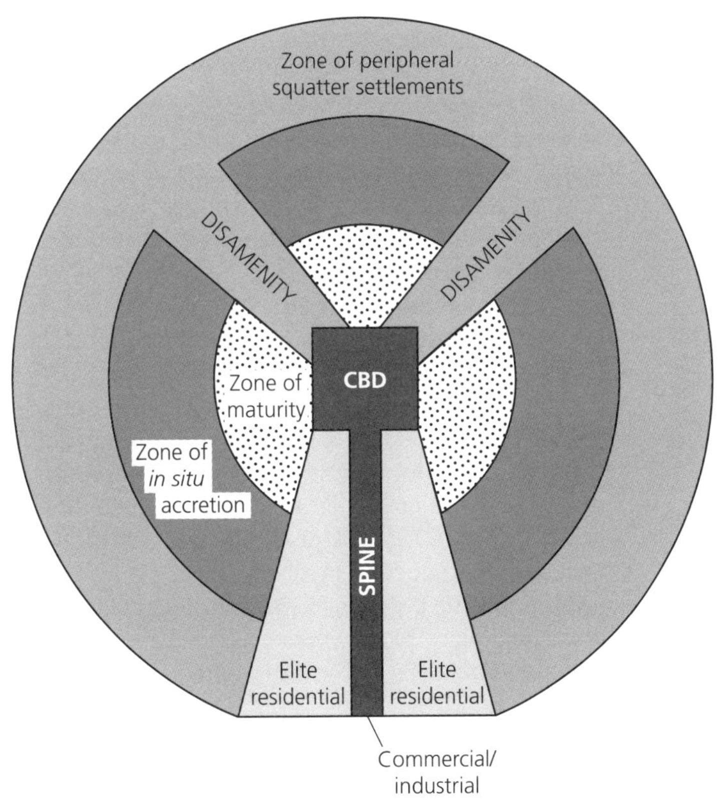

Figure 11.13 Latin American city model

8 Land use in the rural–urban fringe

The rural–urban fringe is the zone of land adjacent to the edge of the city's built-up area. It is a zone of distinctive land uses. Some, such as golf courses and water treatment plants, need large amounts of space that are either unavailable or too expensive within the built-up area. Others, such as sewage works, are noxious. They generate **negative externalities** that conflict with residential areas. None of these fringe uses is disadvantaged by

Cities expand in growth phases and often engulf the rural–urban fringe and its distinctive land uses. Many of these uses survive (e.g. parks, cemeteries) and become fossilised within the urban fabric.

peripheral locations. Indeed, for some (e.g. industrial estates, retail parks), a peripheral location gives access to modern roads and suburban consumers and is a positive advantage.

Rural–urban fringe land uses are strongly influenced by the proximity of the city. Woodland, country parks and other areas of parkland may be managed for urban visitors. Farms may be converted to livery stables, riding schools or smallholdings for hobby farmers. Full-time farmers may anticipate selling their land for development and may cultivate their land less intensively. Farmland sold for future development may remain derelict for several years.

9 *The social geography of cities*

The distribution of social, economic and ethnic groups within the city depends on the housing market. There are three dimensions to the housing market: the production of housing; the supply of housing; and the demand for housing.

House building tends to follow cycles that coincide with periods of strong economic growth. Each cycle adds a distinctive area of housing to the city (e.g. late-nineteenth-century terraces, interwar semi-detached, postwar peripheral estates).

9.1 The production of housing

The type of housing – its size, cost and location – has an important effect on where people live in the city. For example, high-quality Georgian housing is found adjacent to the CBD in Edinburgh's New Town, and this area has always attracted high-income residents. We therefore need to look at house building. This may result from self-help, individual contract production, large-scale contract production and speculative building.

- Self-help housing is common throughout urban areas in the economically developing world. People resort to building their own houses when they are too poor to rent or purchase housing, or when the existing housing stock is insufficient to meet demand. The most obvious examples of self-help housing are squatter settlements in cities in LEDCs.
- Individual contract production involves wealthy consumers hiring architects and builders to construct imposing villas and mansions.
- Large-scale house building occurs when individuals or institutions commission large numbers of dwellings. In nineteenth-century Britain, a number of wealthy and paternalistic entrepreneurs built 'model' villages and company towns for their workforces. Examples include Saltaire in West Yorkshire and Port Sunlight on Merseyside. In many European countries, the state has been directly involved in house production. In the UK by 1979, 35% of all housing was local authority owned.
- Speculative production involves private house building in advance of demand. Most private housing projects in North America and western Europe are speculative, and most are designed for owner-occupiers. Speculative building requires financial backing to provide builders with credit and consumers with mortgages.

9.2 Housing supply

Houses are very expensive in relation to most people's income. Few people can afford to purchase housing outright. To solve this problem, there are different types of tenure agreement: private renting, owner occupation and public renting.

- In private renting, a tenant purchases accommodation from a private landlord, who owns the building. The private rented sector in the UK accounts for only 5% of housing. Most private rented accommodation in the UK is in the inner cities.
- Nearly 60% of housing in the UK is owner-occupied. Governments have encouraged owner occupation by providing tax relief on mortgage interest payments, and since 1979 by selling off local authority houses to tenants.
- Local authority housing, built and subsidised by government, has traditionally met the housing needs of those who are too poor to purchase their own housing.

9.3 Housing demand

Three factors influence demand for housing: income; stage in the life cycle; and ethnicity.

Income

In the private housing market, housing is allocated on the basis of ability to pay. Thus, large expensive houses in desirable neighbourhoods will be available only to higher-income groups. In contrast, people with low incomes have little choice but to purchase smaller or older housing, often at high density in less attractive neighbourhoods. However, many countries in western Europe have social (local authority) housing programmes that allocate housing according to need rather than ability to pay.

Large public sector housing schemes distort the effect of income in determining who lives where in the city. In the UK, many local authority housing estates have peripheral locations that would otherwise be exclusive to high-income groups.

Stage in the life cycle

Most individuals follow a life cycle that involves setting up households and child rearing, as shown in Table 11.3. At critical stages in this cycle, their housing requirements change, and this may prompt a move to different accommodation. Thus, where an individual lives in the city may depend on the stage they have reached in their life cycle.

However, not everyone follows the cycle in Table 11.3. Some 35% of households in the USA are single-person households or households with no children. High rates of divorce in many western countries further undermine the simple life cycle model.

Stage in life cycle	Housing needs/aspirations
1 Pre-child stage	Relatively cheap, central-city apartment
2 Child bearing	Renting of single family dwelling close to apartment zone
3 Child rearing	Ownership of relatively new suburban home
4 Child launching	Same area as stage 3 or perhaps move to a higher-status area
5 Post-child	Marked by residential stability
6 Later life	Institution/apartment/live with children

Table 11.3 Housing needs at different stages of the life cycle

Ethnic status

Ethnic minority groups are often highly segregated within urban areas. Generally, the greater the racial and cultural distance between an ethnic minority and the majority population, the greater the degree of segregation. Segregated enclaves of the city dominated by ethnic minorities are known as **ghettoes**. Segregation arises from both positive and negative factors.

Positive reasons for ethnic segregation include:

- to share a common language and other cultural traditions;
- to have access to their own places of worship, schools and shops.

Negative reasons for ethnic segregation include:

- discrimination in the housing market;
- defence and security against racial/ethnic prejudice;
- poverty and high rates of unemployment, which often force ethnic minority groups to concentrate in low-cost housing areas.

INSET 5

Urban managerialism

The allocation of housing to individuals and families depends on decisions made by key managers in the housing system. They include public housing officials, estate agents, building society managers and bank managers. Their influence on who lives where in the city is considerable. Studies have shown that, in the past, managers and institutions have often practised discrimination. Building societies and banks may refuse loans on properties in some inner-city areas. Public housing managers may allocate more desirable housing to applicants who have been rated highly as tenants in the past.

9.4 The residential mosaic

The effect of the housing market in urban areas is to create a residential mosaic of different social, economic, demographic and ethnic groups. Figure 11.14 shows that each element of housing demand has a distinctive spatial pattern. Income has a sectoral pattern; stage in the life cycle is zonal; and ethnicity has discrete enclaves. If we superimpose these three patterns one upon the other against the spatial framework of the urban housing stock, the outcome is the residential mosaic.

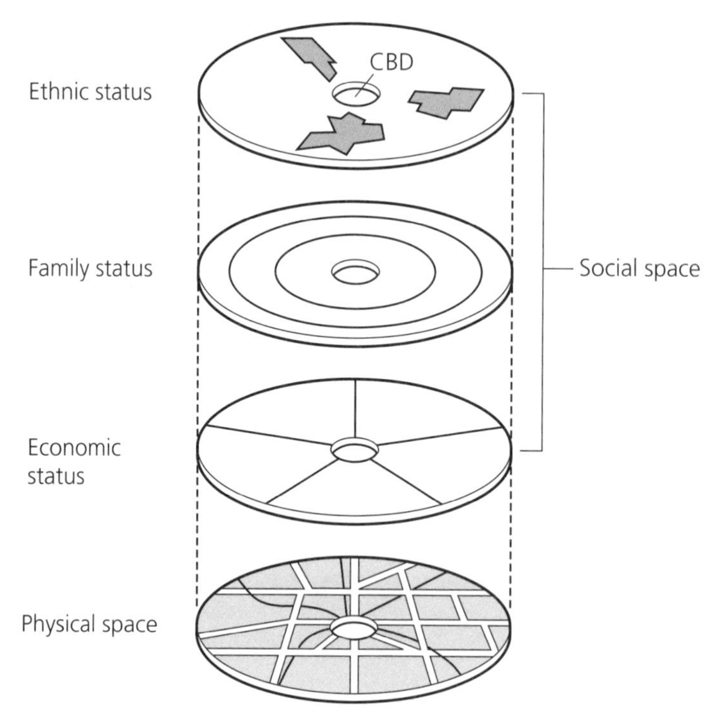

Figure 11.14 Spatial dimensions of urban structure

The residential mosaic is not static:

- New building adds to the housing stock. For example, the regeneration of many former dockland areas in British cities in the 1980s (e.g. London Docklands, Salford Quays) has brought higher-income singles and couples without children back to the inner city.
- **Gentrification** of traditional inner-city neighbourhoods causes an upward filtering of housing originally built for lower-income groups. As a result, many professional households (singles, couples and families) have relocated closer to the city centre, which offers good access to work and to a wide range of retail and leisure services.
- Ghettoes can expand and diffuse into more spacious suburbs surrounding the inner city. In Bradford in West Yorkshire, this diffusion process during the last 20 years has seen the Asian population expand northwards from inner-city areas such as Manningham into middle-class suburbs like Heaton and Frizinghall.

Remember:

- The urban built-environment changes only slowly.
- Today's urban housing stock and population densities often relate to past economic systems.
- Urban population density profiles have lower peak densities today than in the past and, as a result of urban growth, the density profile has a gentler gradient.

10 Population density

Given the variety of house types and land uses, it is not surprising that population density in towns and cities is highly uneven. Population density profiles that extend from the CBD to the outer suburbs are a convenient way to show urban population density (see Figure 11.15). The following factors influence crude population density in towns and cities:

- standards of living;
- societal traditions, values and preferences;

- spatial patterns of urban residential, commercial, industrial and recreational land use;
- transport technology and the mobility of society.

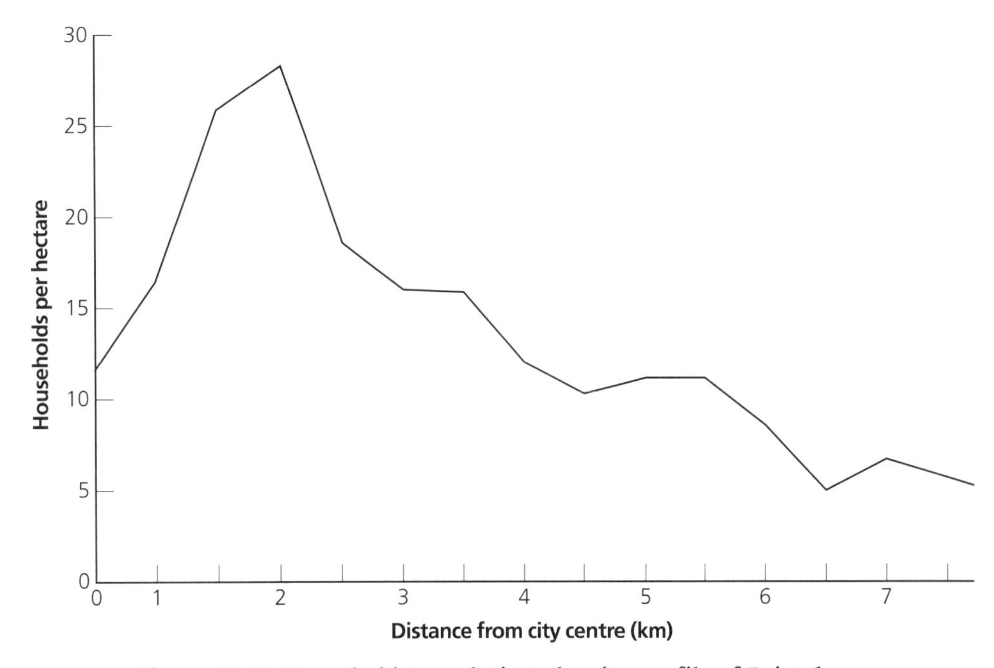

Figure 11.15 Household (population) density profile of Bristol

INSET 6

Measuring urban population densities

The crude density of population is simply the population of a unit, such as a ward or enumeration district, divided by its area. Because its value is influenced by non-residential land uses (e.g. industry, recreation), crude population density is often a poor indicator of housing conditions. Residential population density gives a more accurate picture. It is the ratio of population to the area of residential land use. Even residential density can be distorted, especially where apartments and high-rise blocks dominate the housing stock. In these circumstances, the best indicator of population density (and housing conditions) is the average number of people per room.

10.1 Population density in MEDCs

In MEDCs, urban population density profiles have three main features:

- low crude density at the centre (a density 'crater'), owing to the dominance of commercial land use in the CBD;
- high crude density in the inner suburbs, where nineteenth- and early-twentieth-century terraces, apartments and tenements comprise the bulk of the housing stock;
- low crude density in the outer suburbs, where housing mainly comprises detached and semi-detached houses with gardens.

Some cities in MEDCs vary from this standard density pattern. Many cities in continental Europe are more compact than those in the UK. They often have higher densities in the inner city, less extensive outer suburbs and significant residential populations in the CBD. Even within the UK there are variations: London, Edinburgh and Glasgow all have high-density residential districts in and around the central core.

10.2 Population density in LEDCs

In LEDCs, lower standards of living, less efficient transport systems and different social traditions give rise to much higher average urban population densities. The city centre and inner suburbs are often areas of very high density. Higher-income groups often live in multi-storey apartment blocks close to the centre. Towards the periphery, where land use is more extensive, crude densities fall. However, squatter settlements, which have mainly peripheral locations, have some of the highest densities of all.

Urban problems in MEDCs and LEDCs are more or less the same: poverty, pollution, traffic congestion, poor housing, etc. The difference is the greater scale and severity of these problems in cities in LEDCs.

11 Urban problems and urban planning in the UK

At the start of the twenty-first century, the major problems facing British cities are: urban sprawl; inequality and poverty; and traffic congestion.

11.1 Urban sprawl

Urban sprawl was a problem for most of the twentieth century. In the UK, planners favoured green belt policies as constraints to urban growth and to the loss of countryside. To some extent this policy succeeded: the total built-up area of the UK is still only 11.5%. However, in regions such as the south-east and East Anglia, where the demand for new housing has soared, green belts interrupt rather than stop urban growth.

On the Continent, urban sprawl is often controlled by green wedges rather than green belts (e.g. in Copenhagen). Corridors of urban development and green wedges of countryside radiate from the city. Urban growth concentrates along the corridors, where good communications give easy access to the city centre. Broad wedges of open land separate the growth corridors, allowing easy access to the countryside for everyone.

A report published in 1998 forecast that the UK would need 4.4 million new homes by 2016. Some of this projected increase is due to population growth, but most is down to demographic changes. These include marriage breakdown (40% of marriages end in divorce), old people living longer, and more single people wanting homes of their own.

Developers and builders prefer to build new homes at low density on **greenfield** sites. This has three main drawbacks:

- It leads to further loss of countryside.
- It means longer journeys to work, more commuting and therefore more traffic congestion in cities.
- It encourages the use of private cars (for journeys to work) and increases urban traffic congestion and pollution.

Despite these objections, many large new housing developments on greenbelt land were approved in the late 1990s (e.g. Gosforth in Newcastle, Silsden in West Yorkshire). Some of these are described in Figure 11.16.

INSET 7

An urban renaissance: the Rogers Report

In 1999 a government task force recommended policy changes to encourage people to return to cities. The main recommendations of the Rogers Report were:

- to give tax advantages to housing built in cities (housing on greenfield sites is exempt from VAT; conversions within cities pay the full VAT rate);
- to allow planners to approve housing developments at twice the currently accepted density;
- to create urban action zones – special low-tax areas where councils can use compulsory purchase to acquire urban land and buildings for regeneration.

The Labour government elected in 1997 wanted to encourage a movement back to towns and cities. Its target was to build 60% of new homes on **brownfield** sites (i.e. derelict land or land already in urban use) in cities. Many cities, particularly in northern Britain, have suffered huge population losses to their suburbs and exurbs in the last 40 years. This, together with deindustrialisation, has created vast swathes of derelict land (e.g. in east Manchester). In addition, there are an estimated 100,000 empty council houses in the UK.

British people, unlike most other Europeans, have preferred to live in the suburbs and exurbs at low density. Shortages of land, particularly in southern England, no longer make this an option. Living in apartments and terraces at high density in the inner city, with services, jobs, parks and plazas nearby, can give a high quality of urban life. This already happens in a few British cities, such as Edinburgh and London.

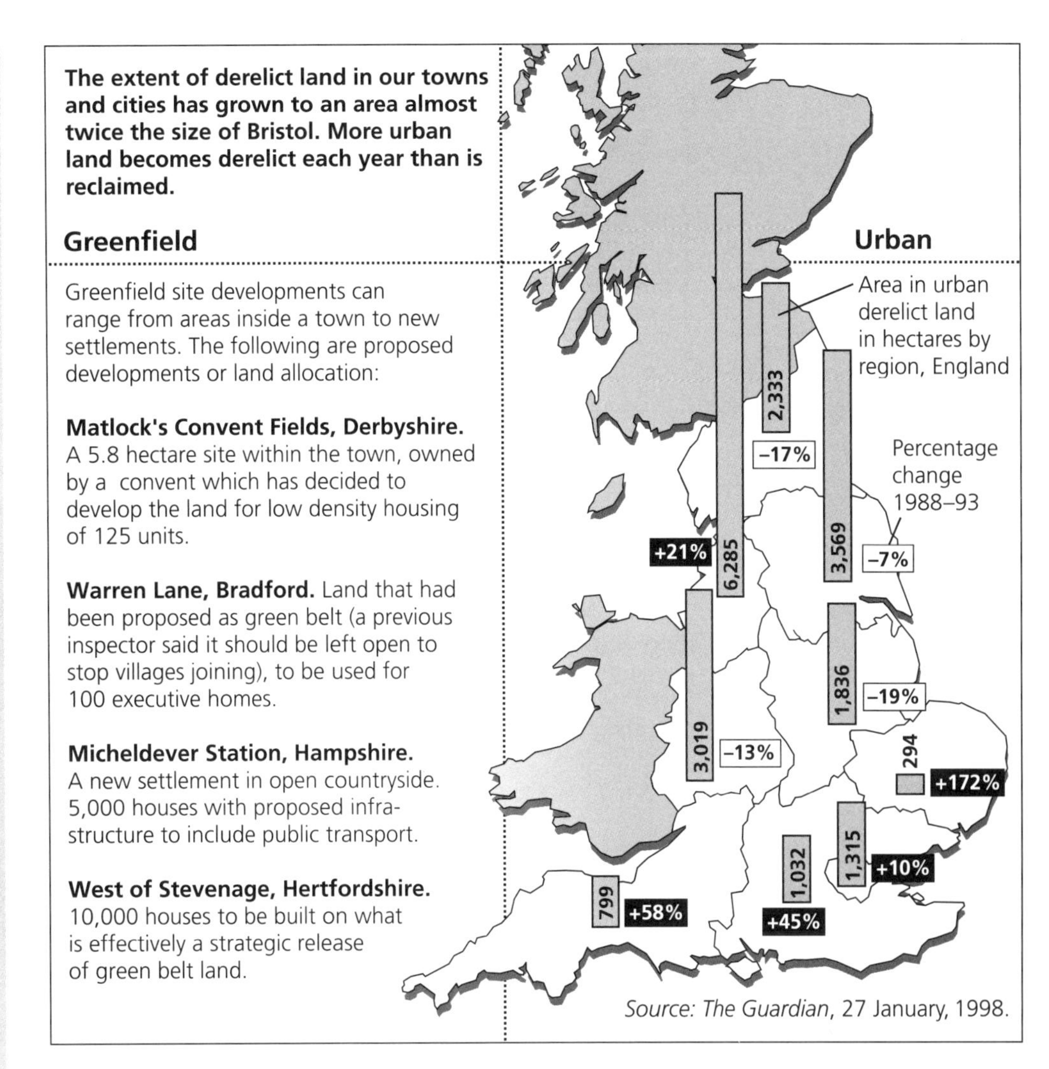

Figure 11.16 Derelict urban land and pressure on greenfield sites in England, 1998

11.2 Urban inequality and social exclusion

Inequality in the UK has increased significantly in the last 30 years. Between 1979 and 1995 the real incomes of the richest 10% of the population grew by 70%. Meanwhile, the incomes of the poorest 10% fell by 8%. The poorest groups have become increasingly concentrated in small areas of acute need, particularly in the inner cities and on peripheral council estates.

There are around 3,000 of these deprived neighbourhoods in British cities, with deep-seated problems of run-down and derelict housing. In these neighbourhoods, there is high unemployment, low educational attainment and high mortality rates. Their residents also suffer **social exclusion**. Many are old; many belong to ethnic minorities; many are under-educated; most do not own a car; and all are relatively poor. These people often do not have access to good schools for their children, and local shops provide a limited range of food products, often at high prices.

Government concern over the problem of social exclusion led to the launch of its £800 million New Deal for Communities programme in 1998. Initially, this targeted 17 of the most deprived urban neighbourhoods in the UK. They are to be the first of many. Public funding will be available for housing improvements, demolition of sub-standard housing, job creation, training programmes, better school and health care facilities, and crime reduction. In addition, 18 special action teams will tackle the most intractable problems in neighbourhoods around the country.

11.3 Traffic congestion in cities

The economic and environmental impact

Annual vehicle mileage in the UK increased ninefold between 1952 and 1995. The growth in car usage during this period was even higher. The result of this growth is chronic traffic congestion in virtually all large urban areas. Traffic congestion imposes both economic and environmental costs. Congestion has reduced average traffic speeds at peak time in London to just 18 kph. Meanwhile, the delays caused by congestion cost the country £15–20 billion a year.

The environmental costs of congestion are also high. In the UK, motor traffic is now the major source of carbon, nitrogen oxides and particulate matter in urban areas. This pollution poses the greatest risk to health during the summer months. In warm anticyclonic conditions, the pollutant gases from car exhausts react with sunlight to create photochemical smog. This lethal cocktail of sulphur dioxide, nitrogen dioxide and ozone is a particular hazard to people who suffer from asthma, bronchitis and other respiratory disorders. For two weeks in October 1997, a thick smog caused by vehicle exhaust gases settled over Paris. The city authorities were forced to take drastic action. They limited car usage to odd and even registration numbers on alternate days; drivers were asked to reduce their average speed by 20 kph; and on one day public transport was made free.

Planning responses

British planning authorities in large urban areas have policies for sustainable transport and must conform to the EU's Air Quality Directive of 1996.

INSET 8

Towards a sustainable transport policy in Norwich

Norwich in East Anglia has a population of 200,000 and a dependent population in its surrounding hinterland of 500,000. The city's transport plan aims for a dramatic reduction in car usage, as shown in Table 11.4.

The planners in Norwich aim to achieve these targets by: making more bus lanes; establishing seven park and ride sites; developing a comprehensive cycle network; improving safety measures for pedestrians; introducing traffic-calming measures in residential areas; restricting long-stay parking in the city centre; controlling land-use change in the city; and discussing commuter plans with major employers.

Mode of transport	1991	2001
Car	67	39
Bus/park and ride	9	16
Cycling	7	24
Walking	12	13

Table 11.4 Target percentage shifts in transport modes in Norwich, 1991–2001

In future, **road pricing** may reduce the demand for car travel. Studies based on London show that a charge of £12 for entering the central area of the city at peak time would increase traffic speeds by 26%. Similar findings have emerged from studies of Edinburgh.

In the UK, the building of new roads in towns and cities is largely ruled out as a solution to traffic problems. Experience suggests that building new roads simply increases car usage.

Another approach involves integrating land-use planning and transport. The UK government's policy of encouraging people to move back into cities would reduce journeys to work and congestion. If services and jobs were provided close to urban residential areas, this would also cut car journeys and promote walking and cycling.

Several cities in the UK have invested heavily in modern public transport systems. By offering a high-quality service, which is both fast and frequent, these cities hope to persuade people to leave their cars at home. The networks developed so far include trams (Sheffield, Manchester), light railways (West Midlands), rapid transit railways (Tyneside) and guided bus lanes (Leeds).

12 Urban problems and planning in LEDCs

Urban problems in LEDCs derive from poverty and rapid rates of urbanisation and urban growth. In-migrants cannot expect to have either housing or employment provided for them. Meanwhile, traffic congestion and pollution are even worse than in cities in MEDCs.

12.1 Housing

Urban populations in LEDCs are increasing rapidly and most urban dwellers are poor. For example, Delhi's population is increasing by 500,000 every year. The city needs to build 200,000 houses a year to cope with demand. In reality, it builds less than one-tenth of this number.

Today, most urban authorities in LEDCs recognise that self-help, through the construction of squatter settlements, is the only practical solution to the housing problem. In cities such as Nairobi and Dar es Salaam, more than half the population lives in squatter settlements. These settlements are illegal, unplanned and high density. Initially, they have no infrastructure (e.g. mains water supply, sewerage, drainage, electricity) and the houses are little more than shacks made of wood, brick, corrugated iron and other recycled materials.

In the past, many urban authorities regularly evicted squatters and destroyed the squatter settlements. The authorities saw them as hotbeds of crime, disease and political dissent. Now attitudes have changed. Squatter settlements are seen as a way forward. Once granted legal title to the land, squatters gradually upgrade their homes. Eventually, what was once a slum settlement often becomes a recognised suburb and a valuable addition to the city's housing stock.

Remember:

- Most urban authorities in LEDCs adopt a positive approach to squatter settlements.
- Squatter settlements reflect self-help, which the authorities aim to encourage.
- Squatter settlements have many advantages for residents.
- Living in a squatter settlement is often preferred to living in low-cost housing schemes or renting traditional housing in the inner city.

The location of squatter settlements depends on:

- the availability of land – vacant land is most often found on the edge of the city or in locations that have strong negative externalities (e.g. near polluting industries and landfill sites, flood-prone areas, or very steeply sloping sites exposed to landslides);
- proximity to centres of employment (e.g. port areas, near the CBD, close to peripheral industries).

12.2 Planning responses

- Most cities have low-cost housing schemes for the poor. For the urban poor, low-cost housing is often a less attractive option than self-built housing in squatter settlements. This is because squatter settlements are often more conveniently located in relation to employment; squatters live rent-free; squatters may have workshops and other sources of livelihood in their homes; there are strong social ties in squatter settlements; squatters may have sufficient political power to force the city authorities to upgrade settlements; and once granted legal title to the land, squatters will own their houses.
- In Delhi, 2.4 million people live in squatter settlements known locally as *jhuggies*. Most *jhuggies* have few amenities and services. Infant mortality in Delhi's *jhuggies* is twice the average for India. The city authorities hope to improve living conditions by helping the residents to help themselves. They grant squatters legal title to their land; provide essential infrastructure such as mains water, roads and electricity; and give loans to residents to purchase building materials and hire builders to improve their homes.
- Sites-and-services schemes are a popular, low-cost solution to the housing problem. The city authorities provide serviced plots with mains water, electricity, sewerage and roads. Residents build their own houses on the plots either from scratch or around a basic shell.

Although rates of unemployment in cities in LEDCs are officially low, under-employment is common. This means that workers are so numerous that they are not fully employed or work fewer hours than they would like.

12.3 Employment

Growth rates in manufacturing and service industries in cities in LEDCs have failed to keep up with population growth. Only a small proportion of workers can secure jobs in the modern or **formal sector**. But without any welfare support from the state, people cannot afford to be unemployed. As a result, people rely on self-help and create their own jobs. This process has spawned a huge **informal sector** in most cities. In Nairobi, most of the city's 40,000 small businesses are in squatter settlements. The informal sector consists of small-scale operations that are labour intensive and rely on traditional technology and skills. Much of the work in this sector is home-based and casual. Activities in the informal sector are extremely diverse. They include producers such as builders and various workshop manufacturers; retailers such as street hawkers; and service providers such as shoe cleaners and launderers. Some activities in the informal sector, such as drug dealing, smuggling, theft and prostitution, are criminal or socially undesirable. None the less, the informal sector is vital to the functioning of cities in LEDCs, soaking up huge numbers of workers who would otherwise be unemployed.

Urban environmental problems, such as air and water pollution, are worse in LEDCs than in MEDCs. However, given limited resources and the desperate shortages of housing and basic services, environmental problems have a relatively low priority.

12.4 Environmental issues

Traffic congestion and air pollution are major problems in large cities in LEDCs. About 72% of air pollution in Delhi comes from motor vehicles. Vehicle exhausts produce over 1,300 tonnes of pollutants a day. More than half of the city's children suffer from asthma, and the incidence of lung disease is 12 times the national average.

Mexico City's air pollution comes from its 4 million vehicles, 30,000 industrial plants and airborne dust from dried urine and faeces from dogs, rats and people. Ozone levels are well above safe limits set by the World Health Organisation (WHO). China's coal-based economy produces dense smogs in Beijing, with sulphur dioxide, ozone and particulate matter several times higher than WHO recommendations.

Attempts to deal with traffic problems and air pollution are hampered by limited financial resources and often by disregard for the law. Apart from a one-way system in the central area, Delhi has done little to avert gridlock and the air pollution that makes it the fourth most polluted city in the world. Plans for a mass transit system and bus corridors are some way off. In Mexico City, one-fifth of cars are banned from the roads each day according to the last digit of their numberplate. Catalytic converters have in theory been installed on all vehicles since 1991, but enforcement is difficult.

UNIT 12 Manufacturing

1 Manufacturing activities

Manufacturing is the production of goods by industrial processes. In the UK in 1998, manufacturing industries employed just over 4 million people or 18% of the workforce. Overall the manufacturing sector contributed around one-fifth of the country's **gross domestic product** (GDP).

In the last 100 years, the proportion of the workforce in manufacturing in leading industrial nations has shrunk by more than half. Figure 12.1 plots the trend for the UK since 1975. A similar, though much steeper decline, has occurred in agriculture. Employment in manufacturing and agriculture has been replaced by new jobs in services. Service industries currently account for nearly 80% of the British workforce. This employment shift from manufacturing and agriculture to services is known as **tertiarisation**.

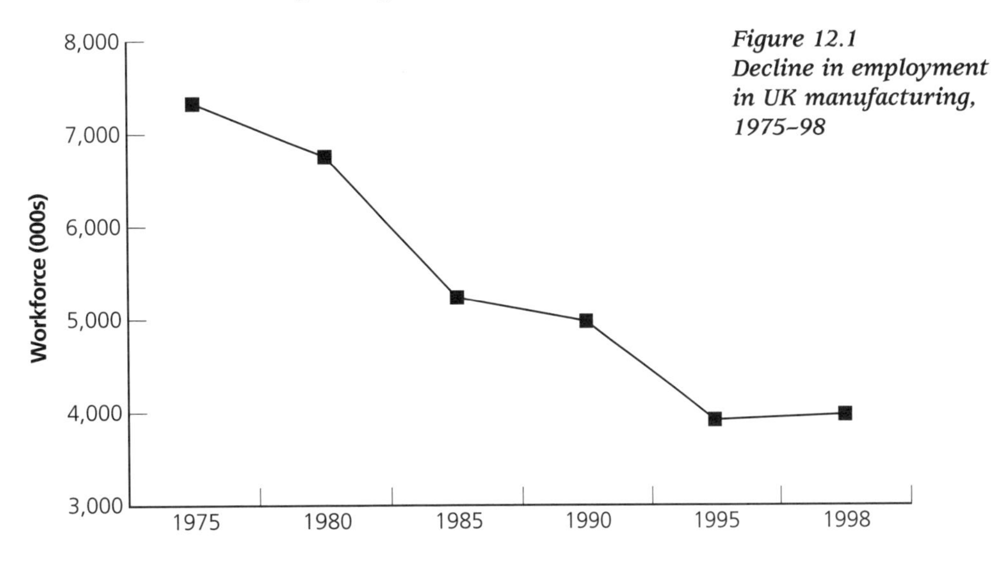

Figure 12.1 Decline in employment in UK manufacturing, 1975–98

INSET 1

The UK's classification of manufacturing industries

The Standard Industrial Classification (SIC) classifies all business establishments in the UK by economic activity. Manufacturing has a section (D) of its own. Each section is split into a hierarchy of sub-sections, divisions, groups, classes and sub-classes. The example of textiles is shown in Table 12.1.

Class name	Code	Activity	Employment
Section	D	Manufacturing	4,001,300
Sub-section	DB	Textiles and textile products	323,400
Division	17	Textiles	181,300
Group	17.4	Made-up textile articles except apparel	35,700

Table 12.1 Textile industry SIC

Any classification of industry is no more than convenient shorthand. Often just a single factor is used to summarise an industry's many characteristics.

Besides SIC, manufacturing industries are also classified in other ways. Some are explained below.

- Size and complexity of firms. Some industries (e.g. car making) are dominated by large firms that have factories in many countries and employ thousands of people: **transnational corporations** (TNCs). Other industries (e.g. clothing) are characterised by small firms based in one country and employing no more than a few hundred workers: **small manufacturing enterprises** (SMEs). TNCs are also classed as **multi-plant firms**, while most SMEs are **single-plant firms**.

- Relative importance of labour and capital. In **labour-intensive industries** (e.g. high-tech research and product design), labour costs are a large proportion of total costs. In **capital-intensive industries** (e.g. aerospace), automation and heavy investment in plant and machinery replace large numbers of workers.
- Locational influences. Some industries with heavy transport costs may be either **material-oriented** (e.g. iron and steel) or **market-oriented** (e.g. soft drinks). An industry such as aluminium smelting, which needs large quantities of cheap electricity, is **energy-oriented**.
- Manufacturing operations. Industries that refine raw materials (e.g. pulp manufacturing, iron and steel making) and provide semi-finished or finished products to other industries are known as **processing industries**. Most of these industries are **heavy industries**. **Assembly industries** (e.g. car making) take the fabricated products of other industries (e.g. car parts) and fit them together to make a finished product. Some assembly industries (e.g. manufacture of circuit boards) are **light industries**. Others, such as shipbuilding, are clearly heavy industries.
- Production methods. **Fordist industries** (e.g. car making) use **mass production** methods to make a small range of standard items in large volumes. They are often based on assembly lines. Many jobs in Fordist industries are broken up into small, repetitive tasks. **Flexible production** requires workers to have more varied skills and take on a range of tasks. Industries with this type of production are able to respond quickly to changes in demand.

2 *General locational influences*

The choice of location for a manufacturing industry can have an important bearing on its profitability. The factors influencing location decisions are economic, social, political and environmental.

- In a **free market economy**, most locational factors are likely to be economic. At the simplest level, firms survive only if in the long term they make a profit. Large companies will be driven by the market and the need to make profits for shareholders. Smaller private firms have more latitude in their decision making, and here non-economic factors may come into play.
- Because costs and revenues vary in geographical space, we might expect firms to make hard economic choices and locate where they can maximise profits. In reality, this rarely happens. Even the largest companies may have insufficient resources to make the optimal locational choice. Instead they may be satisfied with a level of profit below the maximum. Of course, other non-economic factors, such as inertia and personal preferences, may also figure.
- Governments may influence locational decisions for social, political and environmental reasons. By offering financial incentives such as grants and tax concessions, governments may persuade firms to locate in areas of high unemployment. In a **command economy** such as China's, most locational decisions are taken centrally by government. While such governments cannot ignore basic economic principles, locational decisions reflect the interests of the state rather than profit *per se*. Thus,

Governments in free market economies often divert investment to poorer regions for reasons of social justice and, on occasion, political self-interest (i.e. to secure votes in an election).

INSET 2

Spatial profit margins

Spatial profit margins are the geographical boundaries of the area in which a firm can operate profitably, as shown in Figure 12.2. Within this area there is in theory a point of maximum profit. As distance increases from this optimal point, transport costs rise and profits fall. Eventually, a point is reached where revenue and costs are the same. This is the **spatial margin of profitability**. In a free market economy, firms must locate somewhere within these spatial margins. However, in exceptional circumstances, a firm may locate a factory outside the area of profitability. Examples are where there are government subsidies and where firms are willing to subsidise loss-making plants in order to establish a foothold in a market or compete with a rival manufacturer.

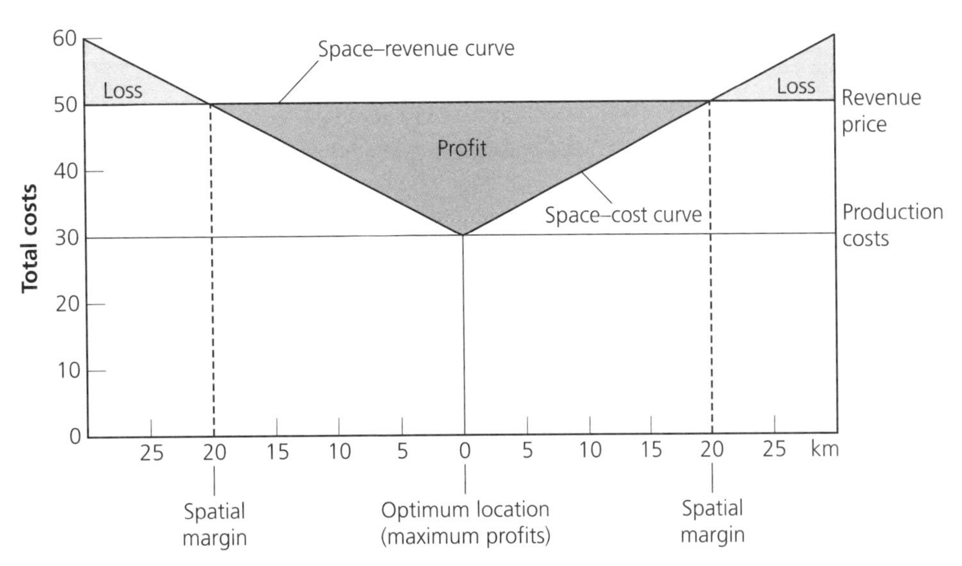

Figure 12.2 Spatial margins of profitability

considerations such as security and long-term planning may figure prominently. At a local scale, environmental considerations may affect locational decisions. In the UK, planning authorities have policies and structure plans that may force firms to locate on **brownfield** sites in cities rather than **greenfield** sites in the country.

3 Industrial location factors

3.1 Raw materials

Only a small proportion of industries (e.g. metal refining, food processing) use raw materials directly. Raw materials are often heavy, bulky and expensive to transport. Thus, in order to minimise transport costs, industries that rely on raw materials often locate at the material source (see Inset 3).

INSET 3

The material index

The material index shows whether an industry is likely to be material- or market-oriented. It assumes that the optimal location for a factory is where transport costs are minimised. The index only takes account of localised materials (i.e. those available only at specific locations). Ubiquitous materials that occur everywhere (e.g. water) are excluded.

$$\text{Material index} = \frac{\text{Weight of localised materials}}{\text{Weight of finished product}}$$

An index of more than 1 means that materials lose weight in manufacturing. Therefore, to reduce transport costs the industry should locate at the material source. An index of less than 1 indicates a finished product that weighs more than materials (e.g. beer and soft drinks). In this situation, the industry should have a market orientation.

The 'pull' of raw materials (and energy) explains the growth of heavy industrial complexes at tidewater (e.g. Europoort, Teesside). These deep-water harbours give access to raw materials such as iron ore, crude oil and coal transported by sea in bulk. This attracts processing industries such as metal refining, oil refining and petro-chemicals.

Tidewater locations have other advantages. They often have large areas of flat, cheap, reclaimed land, which is ideal for processing industries such as steel making and oil refining. Coastal locations also facilitate the disposal of pollutant gas and liquid waste.

3.2 Energy

Coal shaped the industrial geography of the nineteenth century. Before the development of canals and railways, coal was expensive to transport, so industries were drawn to coalfield sites. In western Europe, nearly every major industrial region before 1900 was based on a coalfield.

Declining demand for coal has led to the closure of most coalfields in western Europe (e.g. South Wales, Nord Pas-de-Calais). Yet coalfields remain important centres of population and industry. The reasons for this are:

- the immobility of fixed capital invested in plant, machinery and infrastructure, which leads to **industrial inertia**;
- the **acquired advantages** of linkages between firms (i.e. external economies) and local pools of skilled labour.

A few 'energy hungry' industries are constrained to locate close to supplies of cheap energy. They include aluminium smelting, electro-chemicals and electricity generation itself.

Today, electricity is the principal source of energy for most manufacturing industries. Thanks to transmission grids, electricity is available almost everywhere. Thus, for most industries, energy is no longer a significant locational factor. This, together with the decline in the importance of transport and materials, gives modern industries much greater freedom in their choice of location. We refer to this as **footlooseness**.

3.3 Transport

Industries need cheap and efficient transport to procure materials and deliver manufactured goods to markets. Most MEDCs (unlike LEDCs) have comprehensive road and rail networks, major ports and airports. In these countries, efficient transport systems have contributed to the footlooseness of many industries. However, within MEDCs, at both regional and local scales, access to transport systems varies, and may influence the location of industry. Hence the clustering of industrial and service activities around motorway intersections (e.g. M6/M62), deep-water estuaries (e.g. Teesside) and international airports (e.g. Heathrow).

In LEDCs, transport infrastructures comparable to those of MEDCs may be confined to just one or two regions. Such a region is south-east Brazil. Its modern transport infrastructure is one reason why cities such as São Paulo, Rio de Janeiro and Belo Horizonte have been targets for huge investments by foreign TNCs in the last 20 years.

INSET 4

The structure of transport costs

Transport costs are made up of two components: terminal costs and haulage costs.

- **Terminal costs** include charges for handling freight, storage, docking in seaports, and airport taxes etc. These costs are fixed regardless of journey length.
- **Haulage costs** cover the cost of fuel and wages for the crew. They increase with distance.

Variable haulage costs and fixed terminal costs mean that the average cost of transporting freight per tonne per kilometre is higher for shorter journeys than for longer journeys. Also any transfer of freight between different transport media (i.e. break-of-bulk) adds extra handling charges and results in higher total transport costs. This explains why break-of-bulk points such as seaports are attractive locations for many industries.

3.4 Markets

Markets are where manufactured goods are sold. In LEDCs, traditional low-technology industries, such as textiles, pottery and basket making, serve local markets. In contrast, the products of TNCs are geared increasingly to the global market.

Locational theorists in the first half of the twentieth century said that industries whose products gained weight or bulk (see Inset 3) could minimise their costs by locating at the market. Industries making perishable products would also choose market locations. Many industries, such as brewing, soft drinks and bread making, are indeed market-oriented. But production is no longer tied to the point of consumption. Technological advances in transport and refrigeration mean that a single brewery or bakery may serve a whole region.

The **globalisation** of industry is about firms supplying markets worldwide. Usually this is done by locating production in several different countries and continents. One reason for organising production in this way is to be near markets. Proximity to markets allows manufacturers to respond quickly to changes in demand. Thus a Hong Kong firm making jeans in China for the US market may be at a disadvantage compared to a similar operation in Mexico. The Mexican manufacturer can respond to fashion changes and deliver a new product to market in days. Compare this to Hong Kong, where the transport time (by container ship) may be two or three weeks.

3.5 Labour

On average, labour accounts for nearly one-quarter of total costs in manufacturing. The influence of labour on industrial location depends not only on its cost, but also on its quality and availability.

Labour costs

At the global scale, there are huge spatial differences in labour costs. TNCs have used these differences to their advantage. In the process, they have given a major impetus to globalisation. In Mexico, close to the border with California, a huge sprawl of foreign-owned *maquiladora* factories has arisen. Over 4,000 firms (American, Japanese, Korean and Taiwanese) have grown up here to take advantage of wages that are just one-quarter of those in the USA. Apart from cheap labour, the *maquiladoras* have one other advantage: proximity to the US market. It's a similar story in south-east China. In the Pearl River delta, 5 million Chinese work in factories owned by Hong Kong businesses. Hong Kong businesses have invested over $70 billion in China in recent years, nearly all of it in manufacturing. The attraction is low labour costs: wages in China are barely one-tenth of those paid for similar work in Hong Kong.

Labour quality

Labour quality is about skills. The labour employed by TNCs in Mexico and China is relatively unskilled. But large companies also require highly skilled workers for management, engineering, research, design and product development (R & D). These skills are mainly found in MEDCs. Thus, the location of company headquarters and R & D for a Hong Kong firm will be in Hong Kong, not in China (see Figure 12.3).

Those branches of high-tech industry focused on product design, research and development locate not only in MEDCs, but in culturally and environmentally attractive regions within them (e.g. California, Bavaria). This reflects the high level of demand for skilled workers, who are in short supply.

Labour availability

High rates of unemployment in a county or region indicate a surplus of labour. Such a reservoir of cheap labour may be attractive to firms where wage levels are very low, as in China and Mexico. However, this is not the case in MEDCs. Despite government grants and subsidies over the last half-century, the gap in unemployment levels between rich and poor regions in western Europe remains as high as ever.

3.6 Economies of scale

There are two kinds of economy of scale: internal economies and external economies.

Internal economies

Internal economies occur when increasing plant size leads to lower unit costs. Savings arise because:

- fixed costs (e.g. R & D, local taxes, investment in plant) can be spread over a larger number of units of output;
- greater specialisation of labour and machinery is possible in larger enterprises;
- discounts may be obtained for buying or transporting materials in bulk.

In industries that have high fixed costs, such as iron and steel and car making, large size matters. In others, such as fashion clothing and footwear, size has little significance. This has implications for industrial location. Industries that need to operate

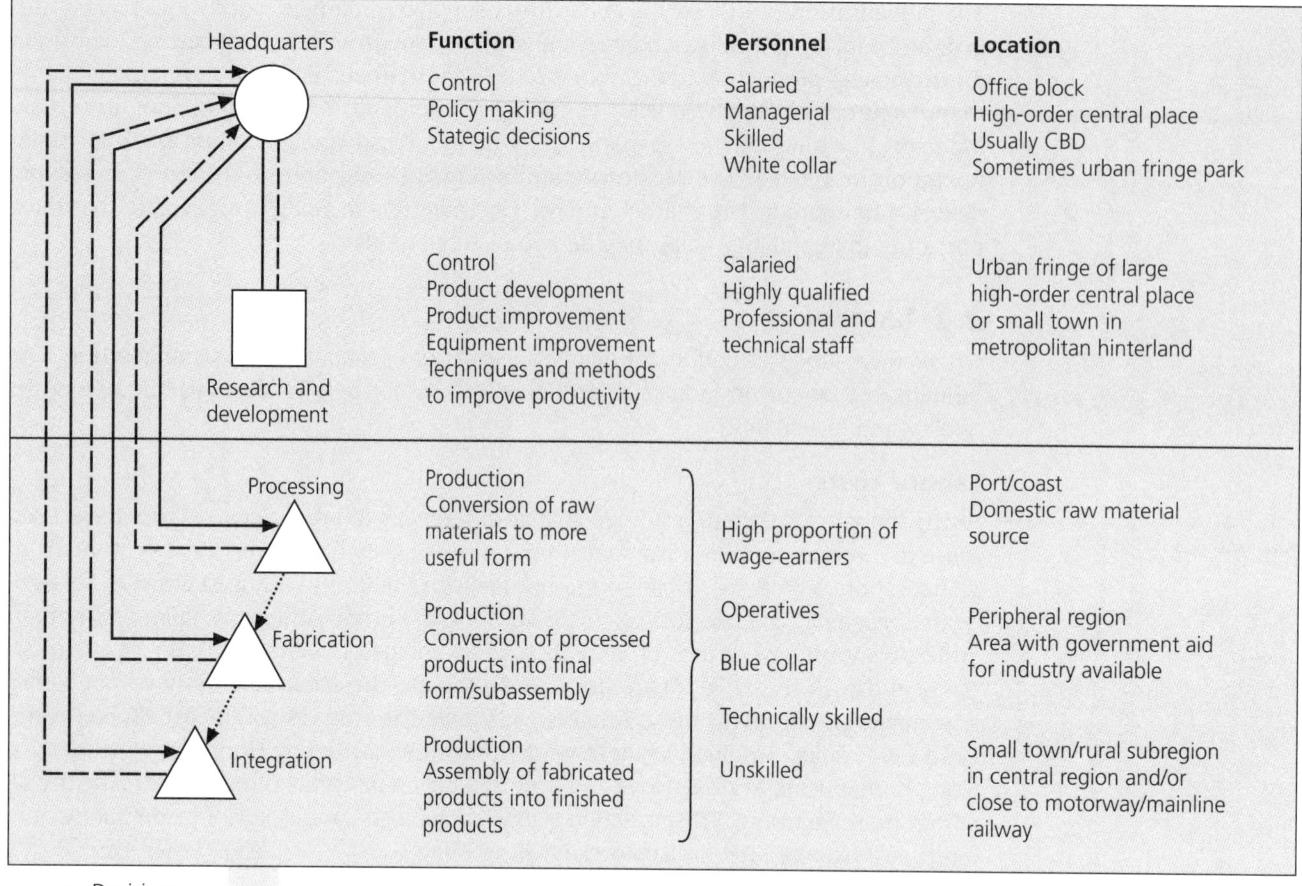

Figure 12.3 Spatial organisation of large multi-plant firms

at a large scale have a more limited choice of location than small-scale industries. For example, a modern iron and steel works operates most efficiently with an output of around 8 million tonnes of steel a year. To achieve this, it needs a large, flat site (up to 10 km^2), access to tidewater and access to a workforce of several thousand. The availability of locations that meet these requirements is at a premium.

External economies

Inter-firm linkages may be either **backward linkages** or **forward linkages**. These terms describe stages in the production chain. For example, petrochemical industries have backward linkages with oil refineries and forward linkages with plastics, paint and cosmetic firms.

External economies arise from outside the firm. They are the savings made when firms cluster in space. Clustering promotes **linkages** between firms. These linkages include the movements of materials, semi-finished products and components between suppliers and consumers. Clustering also allows firms to exchange information and have face-to-face meetings more easily. Most industrial clusters are in or close to large urban areas. Urban areas provide external economies to firms (known as **urbanisation economies**). Savings include:`

- access to a wide range of producer services (e.g. banking, accounting, advertising) and a large labour market;

INSET 5

Industrial clustering in Emilia-Romagna

Clusters of SMEs dominate manufacturing in Emilia-Romagna in northern Italy. Firms in industries such as textiles and footwear are bound together by a complex web of interlinkages in the production chain. Production processes are often simple and the industries are export-oriented. Firms derive external economies from being part of a cluster that smoothes the relationships between manufacturers, customers and suppliers. Clusters also promote innovation and provide pools of highly skilled labour. SMEs can tune into customer needs more rapidly: an important advantage in an era of mass customisation.

- the use of economic infrastructure (e.g. roads, factory space, water and electricity grids);
- the availability of social infrastructure (e.g. housing, schools, hospitals) at minimal cost to the firm.

4 The influence of government on industrial location

Government influence on industrial location operates at continental, national, regional and local scales, as shown in Table 12.2. In the free market economies of the EU and North America, government influence is mainly through financial incentives such as grants and loans. Government has a more direct role when industries are state owned. Today few state-owned manufacturing industries survive in most market economies, but in economies such as China, Cuba and North Korea the state controls and directs all industries.

Scale	Direct	Indirect	
		Positive	Negative
International (EU)		Structural funds: ERDF, ESF; joint international ventures (e.g. aerospace)	
National	Nationalised industries	Regional policies; *ad hoc* grants to attract foreign direct investment	
Regional/local		Promotional measures; Rural Development Agencies in Wales and Scotland; Regional Development Agencies in England, Wales, Scotland and N. Ireland	Local authority structure plans and land-use zoning

Table 12.2 Government influence on the location of industry in the UK

4.1 EU STRUCTURAL FUNDS

A number of industrial regions in the UK get financial assistance from the EU's two structural funds – the European Regional Development Fund (ERDF) and the European Social Fund (ESF). Five types of area are eligible for funding, but only two – Objective 1 and Objective 2 areas – include urban and industrial problem regions (see Inset 6).

INSET 6

Objective 1 and Objective 2 areas in the UK

- Objective 1 areas cover Northern Ireland, north-west Scotland and Merseyside, as shown in Figure 12.4. The EU describes these areas as 'substantially lagging behind the rest of Europe'. Merseyside's problems include industrial decline, high long-term unemployment, an economy overdependent on large TNCs and government employment, urban deprivation, out-migration and environmental stress. Between 1994 and 1999 Merseyside received EU grants worth nearly £650 million. The money targets new inward investment, the development of SMEs, high-tech industries, and cultural and leisure industries.
- Objective 2 areas have been seriously affected by industrial decline. They have unemployment levels above the EU average; have an above average dependence on employment in industry; and have suffered an absolute fall in industrial jobs in recent years. Objective 2 areas in the UK have 17.7 million people and received £1.7 billion in EU grants between 1994 and 1996. The grants aim to encourage diversification of employment, develop new technologies, create jobs, improve infrastructure and promote SMEs and tourism.

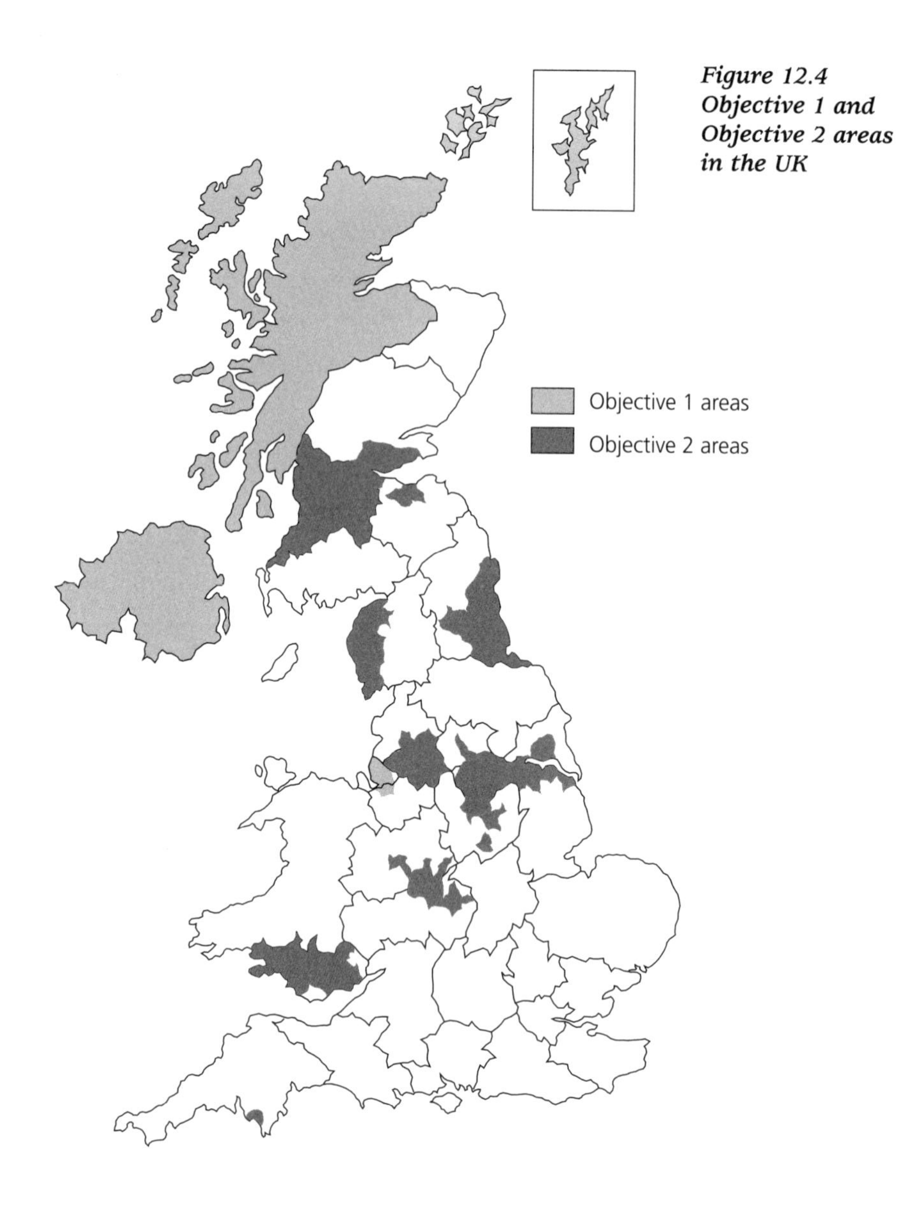

Figure 12.4 Objective 1 and Objective 2 areas in the UK

Governments review regional policy at frequent intervals. Changes of government, harmonisation with EU regional policies, and the economic performance of the regions all contribute to these changes.

4.2 UK regional policy

The origins of the UK's regional policies date back to the Great Depression of the 1930s. Since then successive British governments have developed policies aimed at reducing regional economic differences, particularly in unemployment. Even so, Figure 12.5 shows that considerable differences in wealth between the regions still remain.

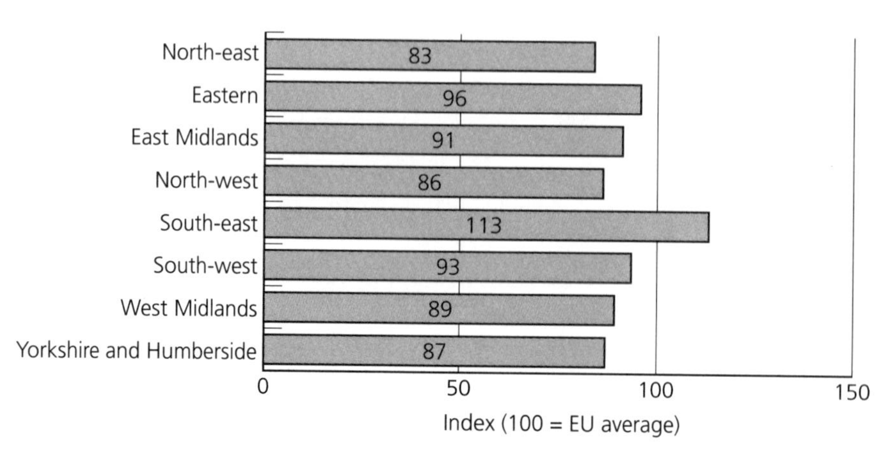

Figure 12.5 Regional disparities in GDP per head: England, 1998

Current regional policy identifies two types of assisted area: **development areas** and **intermediate areas** (see Figure 12.6). Both have problems of above average unemployment and economic decline, though the problems are more acute in development areas. The main tool of regional policy is the **regional selective assistance scheme** (RSA). Its purpose is to attract new investment and safeguard jobs, especially in assisted areas.

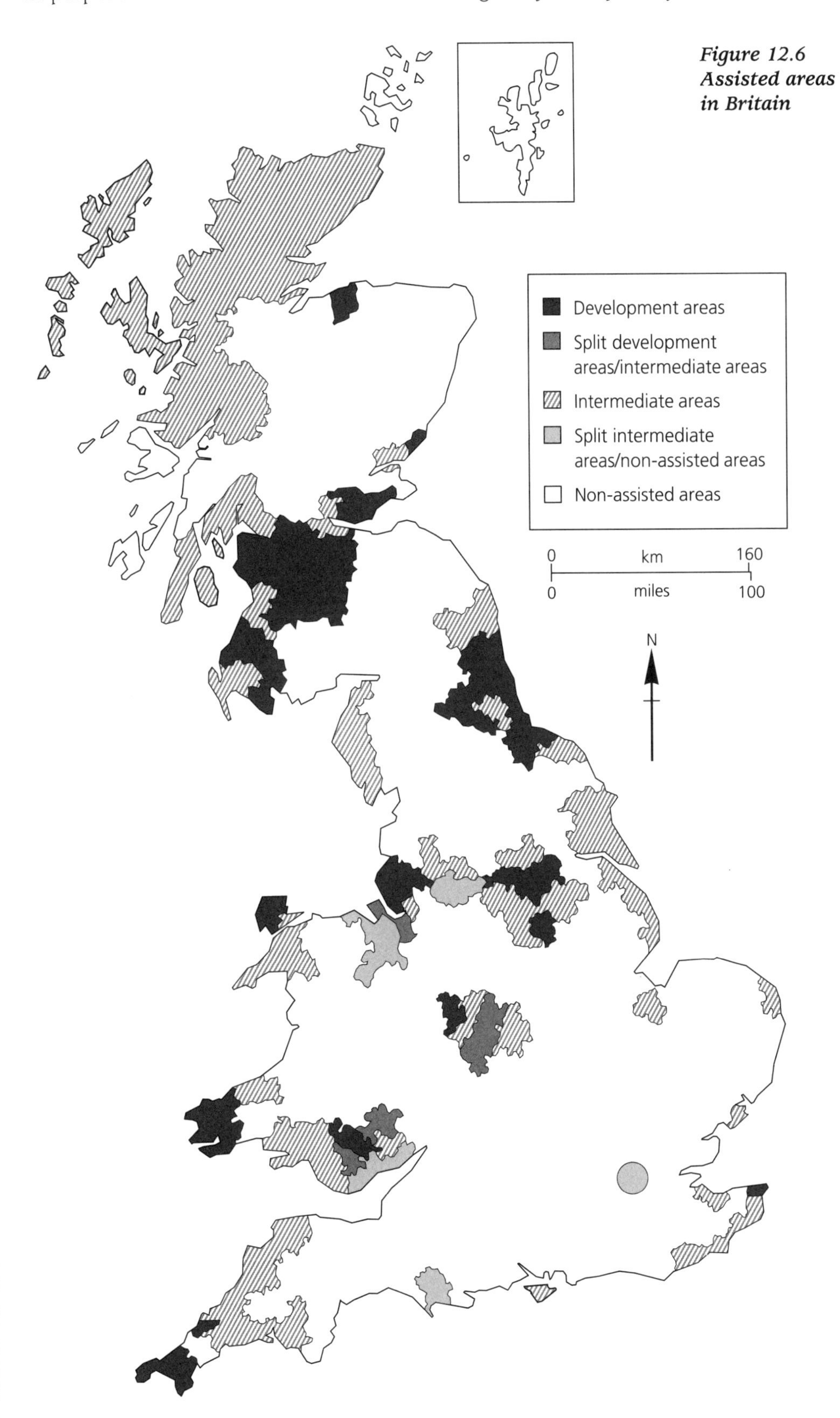

Figure 12.6 Assisted areas in Britain

At the discretion of the Department of Trade and Industry, RSA grants are available that cover up to 15% of the cost of new investment in plant, machinery, buildings and land preparation. Firms do not need to be in an assisted area to qualify for a grant, but it is easier to get a grant in such areas.

In 1999 the UK government set up Regional Development Agencies (RDAs) for the English regions. Previously only Scotland, Wales and Northern Ireland had their own development agencies. As a result, they received more generous funding than the English regions. The RDAs will have a funding of £1 billion a year. They will have responsibility for closing the wealth gap between the regions, as well as building factories and clearing derelict land.

4.3 Government grants for foreign investment

Compared to other MEDCs, the UK has been very successful in attracting FDI. Foreign TNCs find the UK an attractive location because of its flexible labour market and relatively low labour costs, and the positive attitude of government.

Governments also provide grants and subsidies to attract **foreign direct investment** (FDI). Such investments generate jobs and exports, and are keenly sought after. In the UK, most FDI has gone to poorer regions such as central Scotland and south Wales. However, the cost to the taxpayer is considerable: as much as £250,000 per employee. The UK government has also given TNCs grants to expand existing investments in the country. In 1999 BMW threatened to move car production from its Longbridge plant in Birmingham to Budapest unless the government contributed £110 million to the company's £1 billion expansion programme at Longbridge. The government eventually agreed a deal with BMW.

5 The changing location of manufacturing industry

In the last 30 years, the location of manufacturing industry has undergone major change. Locational change has occurred at global, regional and local scales.

5.1 The globalisation of manufacturing industry

Manufacturing has increasingly become a global activity. At the forefront of this **globalisation** of industry are TNCs.

Transnational corporations (TNCs)

Today, North American, European and east Asian TNCs dominate the world economy. Large firms with production units in more than one country have been around since the early years of the twentieth century. However, it is only in the last 30 years that the organisation of these firms has become truly global. For example, Ford used to be a collection of regional companies based in several continents. Each regional company would produce models for its own geographical market and source components locally. Now Ford designs and produces cars on a worldwide basis and has a global supply chain. These changes enable Ford to benefit from economies of scale by producing fewer models in greater numbers. They also allow the company to source parts and employ labour where they are cheapest.

The organisation of most TNCs has a spatial dimension (see Figure 12.3). Tasks that require highly skilled workers, such as top management, strategic planning, design and R & D, are based in MEDCs. Once a given product is in the mature stage of its life cycle, as shown in Figure 12.7, production will be transferred to the company's **branch plants**, often in low-wage areas.

Transport and telecommunications

Global manufacturing chains rely on modern telecommunications, such as e-mail, fax and video conferencing. They also rely on global transport networks, such as international airlines, for the movement of key personnel, and on specialised shipping services, such as containers and car carriers, for the transport of parts and finished goods.

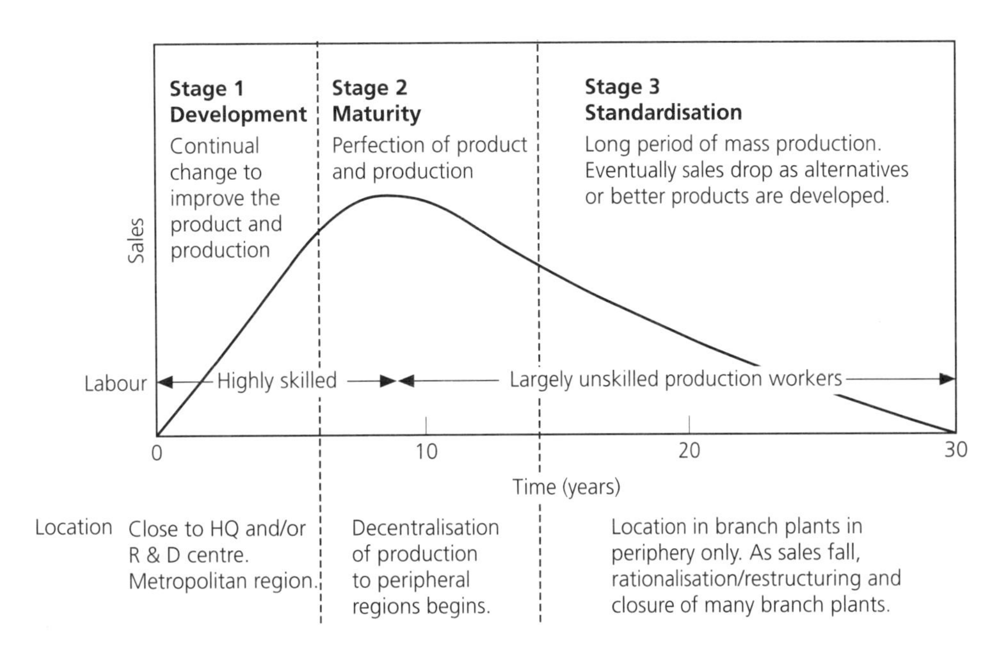

Figure 12.7 The product life cycle and the need for skilled labour

INSET 7

Acer: a Taiwanese electronics giant

Acer is the world's third largest manufacturer of personal computers. Rising labour costs in Taiwan forced Acer to establish its first overseas branch plant in 1976. It now has branch plants in China, the Philippines, Mexico, Malaysia, Singapore and Indonesia. Nine-tenths of its personal computers are made outside Taiwan. In future, Acer's Taiwan operations will concentrate on research and product development.

Acer has also built factories in the UK, Italy and France. Despite the disadvantage of high labour costs in Europe, these factories are close to the market. Close contact with the market allows the company to respond rapidly to changes in demand.

Barriers to trade

Although most countries support the principle of free trade, significant trade barriers remain in place to protect national and international (e.g. EU, NAFTA) markets. One way for TNCs to get round these trade barriers is to establish production in these markets. This is why three major Japanese car makers (Nissan, Toyota and Honda) built assembly plants in the UK between 1984 and 1991. The cars made in the UK by Japanese firms were classed as British and given free entry to the EU market.

5.2 The impact of globalisation

- Globalisation has produced a shift of manufacturing from North America, Europe and Japan to LEDCs in Asia and Latin America. The decline of traditional manufacturing industries such as textiles, steel and shipbuilding in the UK in the 1970s and 1980s was due partly to competition from lower-cost producers in newly industrialising countries (NICs), such as Taiwan and South Korea, and LEDCs.
- Foreign direct investment by TNCs creates jobs, improves the trade balance and in LEDCs may introduce new skills. Some regions in the UK have attracted huge investments by foreign TNCs since 1980. In Scotland, 30% of manufacturing jobs are in foreign-owned firms.
- However, over-reliance on FDI creates **branch plant economies**. Jobs are routine and require limited skills. Moreover, TNCs have no lasting commitment to the workers and regions in which they locate. These factories and regions are vulnerable to **disinvestment** (see Inset 8). Thus, any downturn in world demand often means that branch plants are the first to close.

INSET 8

Samsung: investment and disinvestment in North Yorkshire

February 1994	Samsung, the world's 14th largest TNC, acquires a modern steel-fabricating factory at Flaxby Moor near Harrogate in North Yorkshire to assembly excavators. Export problems from South Korea to the European market have forced Samsung to establish a European assembly base. The factory is on a greenfield site close to the A1(M) and A59 junction. Skilled labour is available locally and Samsung negotiates an attractive deal: £3 million for a factory worth £17 million and an incentive package worth £500,000.
October 1995	Production begins. Samsung hopes eventually to employ up to 500 workers. Kits are imported from South Korea and assembled in the factory. Only engines are made in the UK. The input of components from the UK will increase over time, giving spin-off benefits to local engineering firms.
10 November 1997	Samsung announces that it is to restructure its overseas operations and close its Flaxby Moor factory.
15 November 1997	Samsung announces that it is likely to transfer production from Flaxby Moor to the Czech Republic. MP for Harrogate: 'I'm bitterly disappointed ... it demonstrates quite clearly how vulnerable British industry is when it is dominated by TNCs and how simple it is for them to move to another part of the world where manufacturing costs are cheaper.'

5.3 Regional change: the urban–rural shift of manufacturing

In the last 30 years, the proportion of manufacturing activity in small towns and rural areas in MEDCs has increased at the expense of conurbations and cities. This change is known as the **urban–rural shift of manufacturing**. As an example, between 1979 and 1990, SMEs grew by just 3% in inner London compared to 23% in the outer metropolitan area and 51% in the rural south-east.

The urban–rural shift is not the result of firms migrating from urban to rural areas. Rather, it reflects the closure of many factories in large urban areas; the more rapid growth of firms in small towns and rural areas; and a relatively greater investment in new businesses in small towns and rural areas.

Constrained location theory gives the best explanation for the urban–rural shift of manufacturing industry. The theory suggests that physical limits to the growth of industry in urban areas are the main reason for the shift. These physical limits include:

- outdated factory buildings (e.g. multi-storey buildings), unsuited to modern production methods;
- shortages of space for on-site expansion;
- shortages of land for industrial development;
- the high cost of reclaiming brownfield sites for development;
- high land prices owing to competition from commerce and housing.

5.4 Local change: inner-city decline and suburban growth

For most of the twentieth century, the outer suburbs of cities have increased their share of industry, while inner-city areas have suffered prolonged decline. Historically, the inner city had a strong attraction for manufacturing industry.

- It was a zone of factories and housing, giving industry good access to its workforce.
- It was highly accessible: railways, docks, canals and roads gave access to materials and markets.
- The concentration of firms in the inner city gave important external economies through linkages in the production chain.

The suburbanisation of industry in MEDCs is part of a much wider process that has affected most economic activities in the last 50 or 60 years. It has led to the growth of edge-of-town retail parks, shopping malls, office parks, science parks and industrial estates.

However, since the mid-twentieth century the inner city has becoming increasingly unattractive for industry. Instead, industry has preferred investment in the suburbs. Apart from the problem of constrained locations, some of the factors that account for this change are listed below.

- The decentralisation of higher-income groups to the suburbs has left behind unskilled, poorly educated and elderly populations in the inner city. The workforce available in the inner city has little attraction for most firms.

- Inner-city areas are often congested, with poor accessibility by road. The nineteenth-century infrastructure of railways, canals and docks has little value to modern industry. In contrast, the suburbs offer easy access to trunk roads and motorways, as well as greenfield sites and purpose-built industrial estates.
- With factory closures in the inner city, the nexus of inter-firm linkages in this area no longer exists.
- Inner-city urban renewal in the UK in the 1960s and 1970s forced the demolition of many inner-city factories.
- The physical and social environments of inner cities have deteriorated. Derelict land, ageing infrastructure, slum housing, high rates of crime and poor schools have created an unattractive environment for firms.

INSET 9

Reviving the inner city: Urban Development Corporations

Between 1981 and 1998 (when they were wound up), the Urban Development Corporations (UDCs) were the UK government's main initiative for reviving the economic fortunes of inner cities. Twelve UDCs were set up across the UK. They covered the worst areas of inner-city decay. The UDCs were independent of local planning authorities. Their brief was to acquire derelict land, make it fit for development and sell it on. UDCs were a partnership between the state (which provided initial funding) and private business, responsible for the bulk of investment.

It is estimated that the UDCs created 150,000 jobs, built 27,000 homes, reclaimed 2,400 hectares of derelict land, and built 900 kilometres of road and 5.4 million square metres of industrial and commercial floorspace. None the less, the UDCs did attracted criticism. Most schemes, including London Docklands, provided few jobs for local people in the inner city. Job creation was expensive (an average of £56,000 per job) and the overall cost of UDCs to the tax-payer was high (at least £3 billion). It is argued that much of the investment in UDCs, attracted by generous subsidies, was simply transferred from elsewhere. Some UDCs were more successful than others. While the success of London Docklands and Sheffield's Don Valley is undeniable, the UDCs in Plymouth and Bristol, for example, have had only a limited impact.

6 The environmental impact of manufacturing industry

All economic activities generate a range of benefits and costs known as **externalities**. In manufacturing industry, externalities are the spill-over effects that are felt beyond the factory site.

- Positive externalities include the jobs and local prosperity that industry provides.
- Negative externalities are the adverse effects of industry on the environment and people.

Environmental pollution is the most obvious negative externality caused by manufacturing industry. Pollutants are unwanted outputs from manufacturing processes (see Table 12.3). They contaminate environmental resources, such as air, water and soil; enter food chains; threaten wildlife; and affect people's health and safety. For the most part, manufacturing firms bear only a tiny fraction of the costs of negative externalities. Most of the costs fall on the environment and on the people who live near polluting factories.

Pollutant	Output (m tonnes/year)
Sulphur dioxide	1.28
Nitrogen oxide	0.65
Carbon monoxide	0.17
Particulates	0.05

Table 12.3 Major pollutants from industries in the UK

INSET 10

Industrial pollution on Teesside

Teesside has the highest concentration of polluting industries in the UK. The major polluters are chemicals, steel and power stations. Studies have shown that the costs of pollution fall heaviest on low-income groups. These people are most likely to live in low-cost accommodation close to industry. For example, one postcode area on Teesside has 17 large factories.

Routine air pollution from heavy industries on Teesside is blamed for high levels of respiratory illness. Mortality from lung cancer, bronchitis and asthma is three to four times greater than the national average. However, it is difficult to prove a causal link between pollution and ill health. Lifestyle, diet and poverty also influence mortality and morbidity (ill health) rates.

Chemical effluent containing alkylphenols is routinely discharged into the River Tees from the Wilton petrochemical works. These have a toxic effect on larvae, shrimps and other invertebrates at the base of the food chain. They also disrupt the development and reproduction of fish. Meanwhile, accidental leaks of toxic chemicals into the heavily populated urban environment of Teesside occur from time to time. In 1997 a leak of titanium tetrachloride from ICI's Tioxide plant caused breathing problems for many local people and caused the plant to be shut down.

UNIT 13 Agriculture

1 Agriculture and its importance

1.1 The importance of agriculture

Agriculture is the control and use of plants and animals for the production of food, fibre and raw materials. Agriculture is an important economic activity for the following reasons:

- It is the principal source of food.
- It provides direct employment for over a billion people, including one in every two working adults in LEDCs.
- It is the starting point of the human food chain and indirectly provides millions of jobs in food manufacturing and food retailing in MEDCs.
- It makes a major contribution to economic output and wealth.
- As the largest user of land (around one-third of the world's land surface is farmed), agriculture has a huge influence on the physical environment (landscapes, wildlife, habitats, etc.).

1.2 The spatial distribution of agriculture

The importance of agriculture varies with scale:

- At the global scale, agriculture is the world's leading economic activity.
- Agriculture makes a far greater contribution to employment and output in LEDCs than in MEDCs.

The spatial distribution of the world's agricultural workforce is highly uneven. Some 95% of farmers and farm workers live in LEDCs, the vast majority in Asia. However, LEDCs account for only 59% of all agricultural land. This suggests that a great deal of farming activity in these countries is (a) labour intensive and (b) based on very small farms. There is a similar mismatch at the global scale between agricultural land area and the value of output. Thus Europe, with just 3.5% of the world's agricultural area, accounts for nearly 20% of the value of world agricultural production. In contrast, Africa has 17.5% of the world's agricultural area, but contributes only 5.5% to the value of agricultural production. These regional differences between area and output are due to:

- the variable quality of physical resources for agriculture;
- variations in levels of farming technology and farm management, including automation and the use of agro-fertilisers;
- the relative importance of commercial agriculture (where crops are sold for cash) and subsistence agriculture (where most crops are for consumption on the farm);
- the greater demand for high-value crops (e.g. meat and horticultural products) in MEDCs.

2 Agriculture as a system

Agriculture operates as both an economic and a biological system. We can define agricultural systems at all scales, from the continental (e.g. the EU) to the local (e.g. an individual farm). A basic agricultural system consists of a group of **objects** (farm buildings, land area, etc.) linked by a series of **inputs**, **outputs** and **flows**.

2.1 Economic systems

The purpose of any farming enterprise is to make a profit or a surplus. To achieve this the farm system needs resources, such as land, buildings, machinery, labour and capital (see Figure 13.1). In an economic system, capital (in the form of machinery, fertiliser, pesticide, etc.) and labour are the main inputs. When applied to the land, these inputs yield outputs such as crops and livestock products. In commercial farming, most of the output is sold for cash, which should cover the farm's running costs and provide a reasonable profit. Governments often support farmers with subsidies, guaranteed prices and tariff protection against foreign imports. Today, governments play a key role in the agricultural economic system in most MEDCs.

INSET 1

Some characteristics of farming systems

Enterprise	
Arable	Farming that produces crops, such as cereals, sugar beet and oilseed.
Livestock	Farming based on livestock enterprises, such as cattle, sheep and pigs.
Mixed	Farming enterprises that combine both arable and livestock production.
Intensity	
Labour intensive	Farming that uses large amounts of labour per hectare. Labour-intensive systems (e.g. wet rice cultivation in south-east Asia) give high yields per hectare, but relatively low yields per person. Most labour-intensive systems make limited use of capital and machinery.
Capital intensive	Farming that uses large amounts of capital (e.g. machinery, fertiliser, pesticide) per hectare and produces high yields per person. Capital-intensive farming in the EU also gives high yields per hectare. In North America, yields per hectare from capital-intensive systems are lower.
Technology	
High-tech	Capital-intensive farming that uses sophisticated machinery, veterinary services, biotechnology, etc.
Low-tech	Farming based on simple technologies, such as hand labour and ox-drawn ploughs.
Markets	
Commercial	Farming for cash: where most farm output is for the market (food wholesalers, supermarket chains, etc. in MEDCs).
Subsistence	Farming where most production does not leave the farm. Crops feed the farmer and his family, and only a small proportion of output is sold in local markets for cash. This is most typical of farming in LEDCs.
Settlement	
Sedentary	The permanent farming of a given tract of land with fixed locations for farms and outbuildings.
Nomadic	Mainly livestock herding where, because of limited resources of grazing and water, farmers follow a cycle of movement throughout the year.
Shifting	The cultivation of land for just a year or two. Initial clearance and burning of vegetation raises the soil's nutrient status and permits cultivation. The rapid exhaustion of soil fertility causes farmers to move on and clear fresh plots.
Moisture control	
Rain-fed/dry	Farming that relies on rain as its only source of water.
Irrigation	Farming that relies mainly on water diverted from aquifers and rivers.
Tenancy	
Owner-occupier	Where the farmer owns the farm, farm buildings, machinery, livestock and farm inputs (e.g. seed, fertiliser).
Tenant	Where a farmer pays rent to a landlord.
Sharecropper	Where a tenant pays a proportion of farm output as rent.

2.2 Agro-ecosystems

Agro-ecosystems are ecosystems (see Unit 8) that have been modified for agricultural purposes. As Figure 13.2 shows, agro-ecosystems consist of crops and livestock and their interaction with the physical environment. Natural inputs to the farm ecosystem include solar energy, rainfall, gases and nutrients (from weathering and from the atmosphere). Added to natural inputs are human inputs such as labour, energy (e.g. use of machinery) and agro-chemicals. Leaving agro-ecosystems as outputs are heat, water (run-off and evapotranspiration), gases, farm waste, crops, livestock and livestock products.

As long as there is a balance between inputs and outputs, agro-ecosystems are sustainable. Most agro-ecosystems in MEDCs are sustainable only because they are heavily subsidised with energy (e.g. diesel for farm machinery), fertilisers (e.g. nitrates, phosphates) and pesticides from outside.

Organic farming is an attempt to develop a more sustainable agriculture in MEDCs. As far as possible, organic farming maintains soil fertility by recycling the farm's organic waste products. It avoids the use of agro-chemicals.

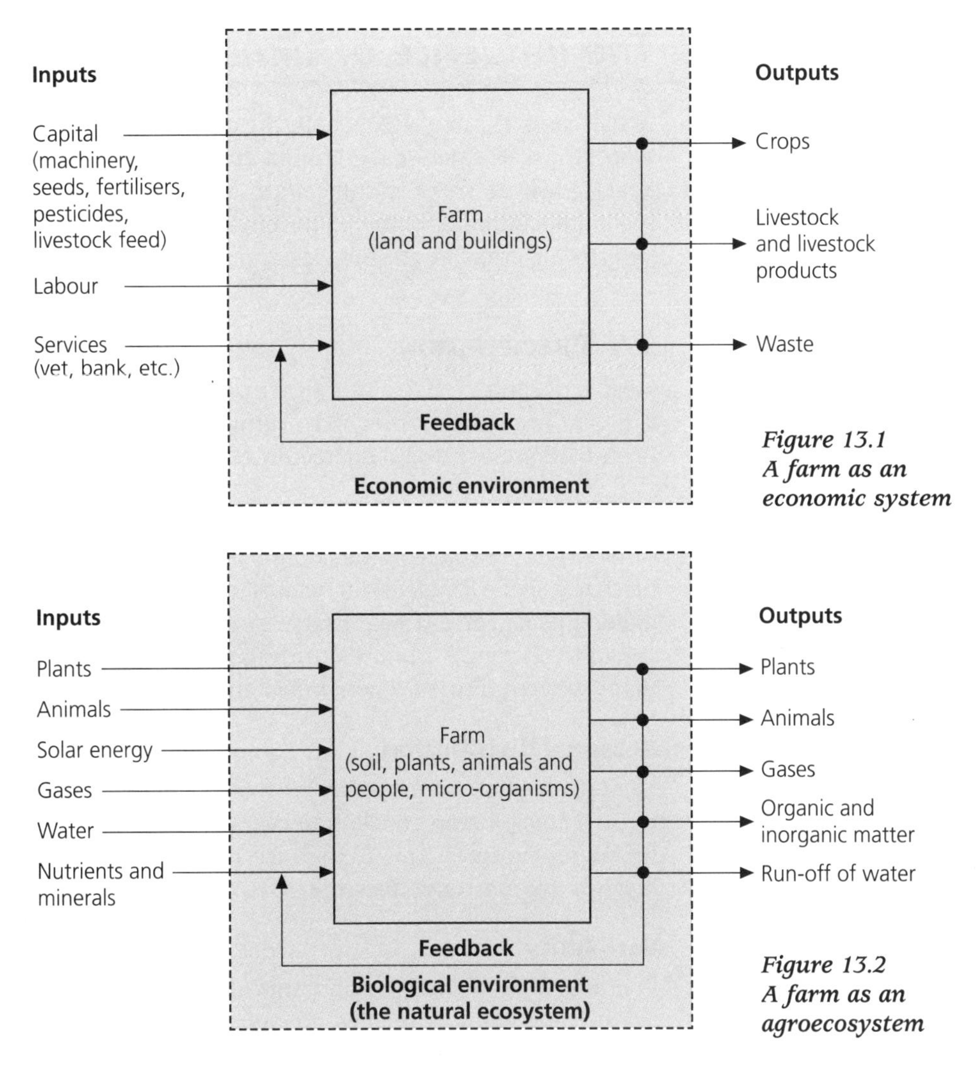

Figure 13.1 A farm as an economic system

Figure 13.2 A farm as an agroecosystem

	Natural ecosystems	Agro-ecosystems
Productivity	Efficient use of available energy. Where there are few limiting factors, productivity is high.	Inefficient use of available energy. Productivity usually lower than natural ecosystems in the same environment.
Species diversity	High. Biodiversity provides many niches for fixing solar energy in photosynthesis.	Low. Often only one species (monoculture). Much solar energy is wasted.
Food chains	High biodiversity, therefore complex food chains/food webs with several trophic levels.	Low biodiversity. Food chains are short. Crops may be consumed by domestic animals. Livestock and livestock products are consumed by people. Food crops are consumed directly by people.
Nutrient cycling	Efficient cycling of dead organic matter. Few nutrients lost from the system. Self-sustaining.	Nutrients removed by crops. They are replaced by organic and chemical fertiliser. Chemical fertilisers must be imported to the system. Heavy losses of some nutrients through leaching.
Stability	Stable. Able to respond to change and restore equilibrium.	Unstable. Change often leads to positive feedback and degrading of the system (e.g. soil erosion).

Table 13.1 Comparison of natural ecosystems and agro-ecosystems

3 The influence of climate on agriculture

At all scales, climate affects both the spatial distribution of agriculture and the types of crop grown. Farmers have limited control over climatic inputs such as moisture and heat. However, some modification is possible through: irrigation to compensate for moisture shortages; drainage to reduce excess moisture; and raising air temperatures by growing crops in glasshouses and cloches.

3.1 Precipitation

Most agriculture relies on moisture from direct precipitation (**dry farming**). In the tropics, it is soil moisture (rather than temperature) that determines the growing season. Precipitation has several characteristics that have an impact on agriculture.

Irrigation may impose costs as well as benefits:

- It is often capital intensive and therefore not an option for many farmers in LEDCs.
- It is often wasteful in its use of scarce water resources.
- It may facilitate the spread of water-borne diseases (e.g. bilharzia).
- Over-irrigation may lead to salinisation, lower yields and land abandonment.

Annual amount

Amounts of precipitation may be too little (e.g. the deserts of the south-west USA) or too much (e.g. in the Pennines) for successful cultivation. Food crops often have specific moisture requirements. For example, arable crops thrive in eastern England where mean annual precipitation ranges from 550 mm to 800 mm. However, arable crops are not suited to many western districts where mean annual precipitation often exceeds 1,000 mm.

Seasonal distribution

The effectiveness of precipitation for agriculture depends partly on its seasonal distribution. Precipitation concentrated in winter is more effective than precipitation falling mainly in summer. This is because most summer precipitation evaporates before it reaches the root zone for crops.

Variability

In arid and semi-arid environments, amounts of precipitation are highly variable from year to year. Without reliable precipitation, dry farming is not possible. Thus, in Africa and the Middle East, the limits of cultivation correspond to 250 mm mean annual isohyet and an annual variability of 40%.

Intensity

High-intensity precipitation (i.e. showers, thunderstorms) is less effective for crop growth than low-intensity precipitation spread over several hours or days. High-intensity events allow only a small amount of moisture to infiltrate the soil.

3.2 Temperature

In middle and high latitudes, temperatures, rather than precipitation, set climatic limits to agriculture. In lowland Britain, the **thermal growing season** on average lasts between 250 and 275 days, as shown in Figure 13.3. This means that from late October to early March, temperatures are too low for crop growth. Temperature influences agriculture at the global, regional and local scales.

Farmers have only limited scope for modifying the temperature environment. Only where demand and prices are high (e.g. flowers, fresh fruit and vegetables) are the capital costs of glasshouse cultivation justified (e.g. Westland in the Netherlands).

Global scale

Most crops have strict temperature requirements. For example, rice, maize and millet need temperatures of at least 15–18 °C throughout the growing season. Optimal temperatures for their growth are between 31 and 37 °C. As a result, these crops are largely confined to tropics and sub-tropics.

Regional scale

Temperatures decrease with height at an average rate of 6.5 °C/km. This means that upland regions usually have a shorter thermal growing season than adjacent lowlands.

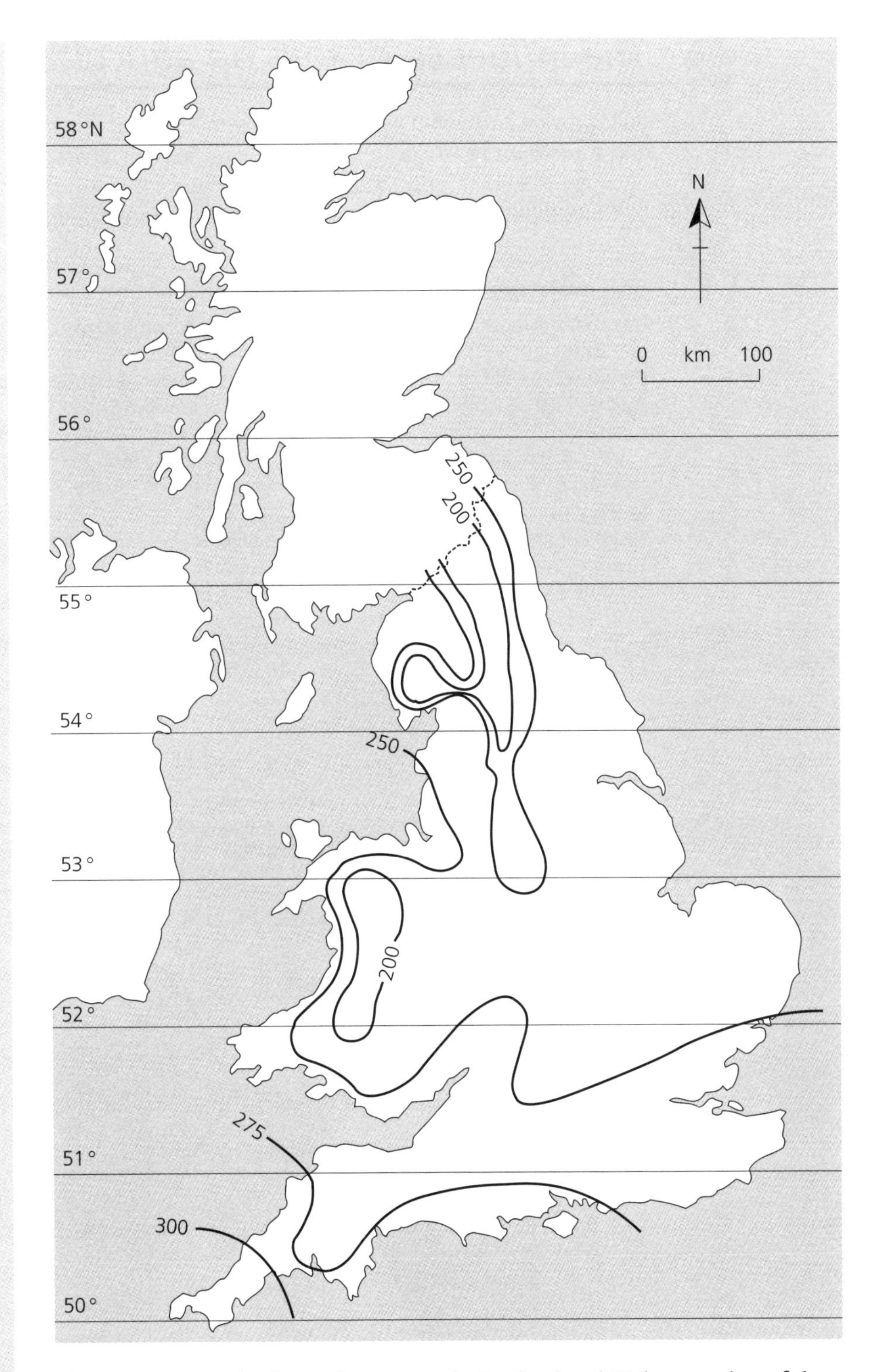

Figure 13.3 Length of growing season in England and Wales: number of days when soil temperatures (at 30 cm depth) exceed 6°C

Cloudiness also increases with altitude, reducing sunshine levels and lowering temperatures in the uplands.

Local scale

At a local scale in valleys, **aspect** (the direction in which a slope faces) is a major influence on temperatures. Sun-facing or **adret** slopes receive the most intense insolation and the longest hours of direct sunlight. In the Alps, warm south-facing slopes are cultivated, while the colder north-facing or **ubac** slopes are often forest-covered.

4 The influence of soils on agriculture

Soils provide crops with water for photosynthesis and transpiration; nutrients for growth; and a medium in which to root. Soils vary in their physical and chemical characteristics (pp. 109–112), and these often influence agriculture. Farmers are able to modify some of these characteristics to make soils more productive.

INSET 2

Soil moisture budgets

Levels of soil moisture depend largely on the interaction between precipitation and temperature. Most crops cannot tolerate either prolonged water shortage or waterlogging. The maximum amount of water the soil can absorb is known as its **field capacity**. When the soil reaches field capacity, it becomes unworkable. In lowland Britain, most soils are normally at field capacity from October to March. During this period, cultivation comes to a standstill.

We can analyse soil moisture budgets by plotting the monthly distribution of precipitation and evapotranspiration on a chart, as shown in Figure 13.4. Soil moisture budget charts show four distinct periods:

- Late autumn and winter: precipitation exceeds evapotranspiration; soil is at field capacity.
- Spring: evapotranspiration exceeds precipitation; soil moisture is lost, but there is sufficient moisture in the soil for the loss not to affect crop growth.
- Summer: evapotranspiration exceeds precipitation; a moisture deficit restricts crop growth.
- Late summer and autumn: precipitation exceeds evapotranspiration; the soil is recharged until it reaches field capacity.

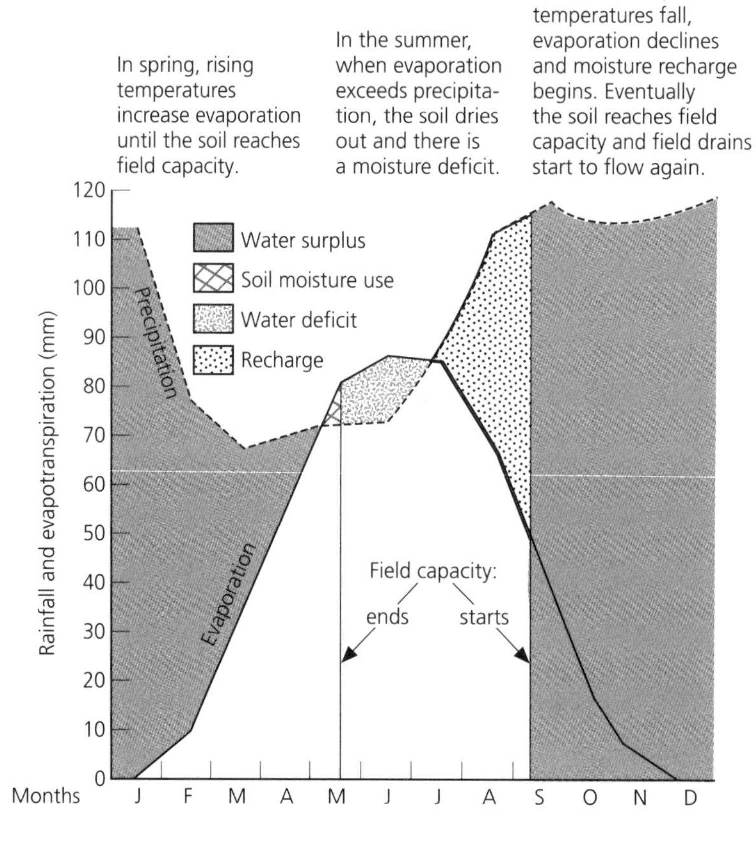

Figure 13.4 A soil moisture budget

4.1 Soil texture

Soil texture describes the size of particles that form the mineral fraction of the soil. There are three textural classes: sand (coarse); silt (medium); and clay (fine).

- Sandy soils are free draining and easy to cultivate, but often suffer from drought in summer.

- Clayey soils are heavy, poorly drained and difficult to work. These soils are better suited to pasture than to arable.
- Soils that comprise a mixture of sand, silt and clay are known as **loams**. Loamy soils are ideal for farming. They are easy to cultivate and well drained, and retain sufficient moisture for crops.

4.2 Soil structure

Soil structure describes the way that humus and mineral particles stick together to form larger aggregates or **peds**. A well-structured soil provides good drainage and allows water and air to reach the root zone of crops. However, soil structure can be damaged by farmers using heavy machinery in wet conditions, and by **overcultivation**, which depletes the soil's humus.

4.3 Soil acidity

Soil acidity is an indication of hydrogen ion concentration in the soil. Measured on the pH scale, soil acidity normally ranges from 3 to 9. A pH value around 7 gives neutral conditions. Soils with pH values below 7 are acidic; those above 7 are alkaline. Ideally, cultivated soils should have acidity levels between 6.5 and 7.5.

4.4 Soil nutrient status

Crops require a wide range of chemical elements or nutrients. Some, such as oxygen and carbon, are available from the atmosphere. However, most nutrients, such as calcium, magnesium and potassium, come from the soil. The most productive soils have a high nutrient status. A soil's nutrient status will depend on several factors, including its texture and structure, and the chemical composition of its parent rock.

Problem	Response
Poor drainage	Underdraining using clay pipes. Digging dykes and drainage ditches.
Nutrient deficiency	Addition of organic (manure) or inorganic (nitrate, phosphate, etc.) fertilisers. Growing nitrogen-fixing crops such as clover and lucerne.
Moisture deficiency	Irrigation.
Acidity	Addition of lime.
Poor structure	Addition of organic material. Sowing rotational grass that has a dense root network.
Hard pan formation	Deep ploughing.

Table 13.2 How farmers modify the soil environment

5 The environmental impact of agriculture

The relationship between agriculture and the environment operates in two directions. While environmental factors set broad limits on what can be grown where, agriculture has a huge impact on cultural landscapes, rural settlement, wildlife and soils.

Agriculture depends on natural resources and occupies nearly one-third of the world's total land area. As a result, its impact on the natural environment (vegetation, wildlife soils, surface water, groundwater, etc.) has been profound. Agriculture has had both positive and negative effects on the environment. Its main positive effect has been landscape development: cultural landscapes consisting of villages, fields, hedgerows and copses reflect the operation of agriculture over hundreds of years. The negative environmental effects of agriculture are numerous. They include land degradation, reductions in biodiversity, deforestation and water pollution.

Land degradation is a clear indication that agriculture is unsustainable. In extreme cases, the misuse of resources leads to declining yields and ultimately to land abandonment.

5.1 Land degradation

Land degradation is a general term encompassing processes such as soil erosion, salinisation and desertification that affect soil, plant and water resources for agriculture.

Soil erosion

Accelerated soil erosion by run-off and wind is usually induced by human activity. It occurs when the rate of soil destruction exceeds the rate of soil formation. Soil erosion is widespread in both MEDCs and LEDCs. Current estimates suggest that worldwide up to 26 million tonnes of topsoil are lost every year. The most common causes of erosion are:

- destruction of the soil's protective vegetation cover through deforestation and overgrazing;
- overcultivation, which exhausts the soil and depletes the humus responsible for the soil's structure;
- poor management, which leaves the soil without any crop cover for long periods.

The consequences of soil erosion are not just the loss of topsoil. Run-off may carve deep gullies across fields, which then become uncultivable. Soil erosion also increases sediment loads in streams and rivers, causing problems of siltation in irrigation canals and drainage ditches, and increasing the flood risk downstream.

Some measures to counter soil erosion are listed in Table 13.3.

Contour ploughing	Ploughing across slopes reduces run-off and erosion. (Downslope ploughing creates artificial channels that increase run-off and erosion.)
Afforestation	Planting trees on steep slopes increases interception and reduces run-off.
Shelter belts and hedges	Shelter belts and hedges reduce wind speeds and protect the soil from erosion.
Strip cropping	Crops that ripen at different times are grown in belts across fields. This ensures at least partial crop cover all year round.
Allow stubble to remain after harvest	The stubble slows wind speeds and provides protective cover against run-off throughout the winter.
Maintain soil fertility	Soils depleted of humus lose their structure and are easily eroded by wind and water.
Grow autumn-sown crops	These crops (e.g. wheat) provide protective cover throughout the winter.

Table 13.3 Soil conservation measures

Salinisation

Salinisation describes the build-up of chloride, sulphate and carbonate salts of sodium, calcium and magnesium in the soil (see Figure 13.5). Crop yields are seriously reduced

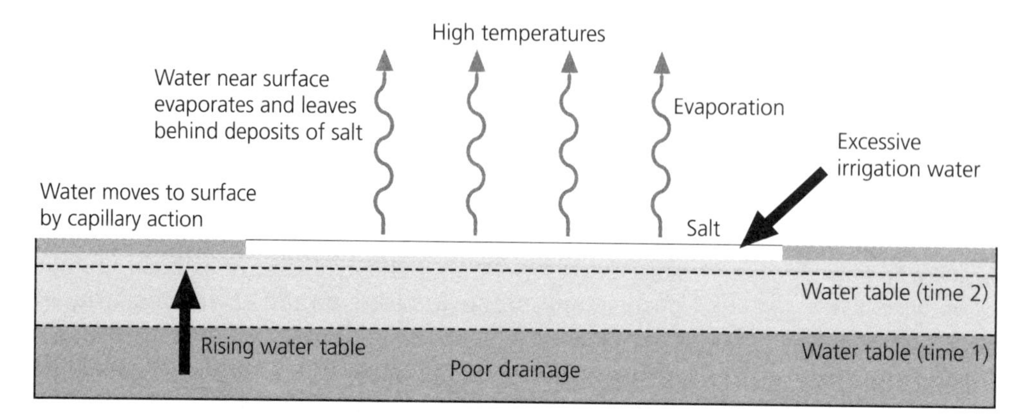

Figure 13.5 The process of salinisation

by salinisation. Salts reduce the soil's capacity to hold air and nutrients, and are toxic to many plants. Large areas of farmland in arid and semi-arid regions have been abandoned because of salinisation. A common cause of salinisation is the over-irrigation of crops.

Responses to salinisation include: land abandonment; the installation of drainage systems to lower the water table; and the conversion of land use from crops to pasture, or crops that have greater tolerance to salt, such as barley, wheat and cotton.

Only in the most extreme conditions does once-productive farmland become desert. Most often desertification describes a situation where significant reductions in production result from diminishing pasture, water and soil resources per capita.

Desertification

Desertification describes human and climatic processes that degrade the environment and create desert-like conditions. This form of land degradation occurs in many dryland environments and affects around 1.2 billion people. It is caused by:

- periodic droughts, such as those that hit the Sahel between 1968 and 1973 and in the mid-1980s;
- overcultivation of soils, which weakens their structure and increases their susceptibility to wind and water erosion;
- overgrazing of pastures (especially around waterholes), which exposes the soil to erosion;
- deforestation by overgrazing and the destruction of forests in dryland regions in LEDCs for firewood.

The impact of agriculture on biodiversity has been most severe in the humid tropics. Peasant farmers have cleared large areas of tropical rainforest in South America, replacing it with a monoculture of poor-quality grassland (for extensive ranching).

5.2 Reduction in biodiversity

The impact of capital-intensive arable farming has had a disastrous effect on the countryside in the UK and other EU countries in recent years. The EU's common agricultural policy (CAP) (see Inset 6) encouraged farmers to increase production with little regard to the environmental impact.

The increased use of pesticides eradicated many wild plants, creating a monoculture of arable crops. Insects that relied on wild plants disappeared and this had a knock-on effect on populations of birds and small mammals. Meanwhile many diverse habitats, such as hedgerows, wetlands, ancient woodlands and chalk downlands, have been destroyed to create more arable land. The dramatic decline, during the 1980s and 1990s, in the populations of some birds normally associated with arable farming areas – skylarks, lapwings, corn buntings, etc. – is attributed to these changes.

INSET 3

Agriculture and conservation programmes in the UK

- Farmers in **environmentally sensitive areas** (ESAs) receive grants for following traditional, low-intensity farming methods. These grants compensate them for lower output. Farmers in ESAs have to limit their use of agro-chemicals; maintain hedges and walls; and make silage or hay only after most wild flowers in meadows have flowered and set seed. There are 22 ESAs in England, covering nearly 10% of all farmland.
- The **Countryside Stewardship Scheme** operates outside ESAs. Farmers who join the scheme are paid to conserve particular landscapes and habitats, such as old meadows and chalk and limestone grassland. The scheme covers 143,000 hectares.
- **Set-aside** allows farmers to withdraw at least 17.5% of their land from arable cultivation for five years. Farmers are compensated by the CAP for their lost production. Set-aside fields are left fallow, although farmers have to maintain a green cover. The scheme has positive environmental effects, providing habitats for plants and animals, and promoting biodiversity.
- **Nitrate sensitive areas** (NSAs) cover areas where groundwater resources are used to supply drinking water. Farmers in NSAs receive financial incentives to reduce their use of nitrates. Nitrates pollute groundwater and surface water supplies. This pollution threatens human health as well as aquatic life in streams and rivers (eutrophication).

6 Factors of production

Agriculture, like other economic activities, depends on land, labour, capital and entrepreneurship. These are the **factors of production**.

6.1 Land

- In LEDCs the amount of agricultural land has increased since 1960. This is because new land has been brought into production, often as a result of population growth.
- In MEDCs the area of agricultural land has fallen. Most of this decrease is due to urban growth, as towns, cities and commuter settlements have expanded into the countryside.

Farmers may either own their farms (i.e. owner-occupiers) or pay rent to a landlord (i.e. tenant farmers). In many LEDCs, farmers have a particular type of tenancy arrangement known as **sharecropping**. This means that tenant farmers pay a proportion of their harvested crops as rent. Farms vary in size from a fraction of a hectare to thousands of hectares (see Inset 4). Farm size affects the crops grown and methods of cultivation.

INSET 4

Some factors influencing farm sizes

- Population pressure. Countries with low population densities (e.g. Canada) often have large average farm sizes; those with very high densities often have small average farm sizes.
- Economies of scale. In commercial agriculture, economies of scale in purchasing machinery, inputs of seed, agro-chemicals, etc. often make large farms more profitable than small farms.
- Land quality. Output per hectare on low-quality land is lower than on high-quality land. Thus, the minimum economic size of a farm unit is much larger on poor-quality land.
- Inheritance practices. On the death of a landowner, farms may be divided equally among heirs. Often the outcome is tiny, fragmented farms.

6.2 Labour

The agricultural workforce in the UK and other MEDCs has declined massively in the last century. Today, agriculture accounts for less than 2.5% of the UK's workforce. The causes of this decline are: mechanisation; larger farm units and economies of scale; and low wages and poor conditions in agriculture compared to other sectors of the economy. The relative importance of part-time farming has increased as more farmers have developed sources of off-farm income (holiday accommodation, horse livery, etc.). Meanwhile, in common with most other MEDCs, the UK's farmers are ageing. Young people have little interest in farming, especially in marginal hill areas.

6.3 Capital

Capital in agriculture means all of the materials and financial resources used for production. There are three types of farm capital:

- fixed capital, comprising land, farm buildings, roads and drains;
- standing capital, which includes farm assets such as machinery;
- working capital, such as seed, fertiliser, pesticides and animal feed.

Farming in MEDCs is usually **capital intensive**, relying on machinery and investment in technology to raise output. Although subsistence and peasant farmers have capital assets such as ploughs, oxen and carts, crop farming in LEDCs is mainly **labour intensive**.

Because farms have a fixed location, the decision making of farmers is different to that of most other entrepreneurs. If economic conditions change, farmers do not have the choice of relocating their business. Their options are limited to changing farm enterprises and diversifying into off-land activities.

6.4 Farmers as entrepreneurs

Farmers are entrepreneurs who either own or manage agricultural enterprises. In their role as entrepreneurs, farmers are decision-makers. The decisions that farmers routinely make are:

- type of enterprise (e.g. arable, livestock, mixed farming);
- types of crop and livestock;
- location of crops and livestock on the farm.

Although farmers need to make sufficient surplus to make a living (or survive), their decisions are not entirely determined by economic goals. Social, cultural and personal factors (preferences, experience, etc.) also play a part in farmers' decision making.

A farmer's freedom to make decisions is limited by the physical environment (climate, soils, relief, etc.), the economic environment (e.g. prices), access to markets, existing investments in expensive plant and machinery, and risk and uncertainty. Like other entrepreneurs, it is a farmer's **perceptions** of the weather, the economy and risk that are important. Invariably, these perceptions do not correspond accurately with reality. There are several reasons for this:

- lack of information on which to base decisions;
- personal factors, such as social background, income, age and education;
- psychological factors influenced by personality, values, beliefs, traditions, etc.;
- the ability to assimilate and use information;
- experience and past perceptions.

7 The diffusion of innovations

The willingness of farmers to adopt innovations, such as new machinery, new crop rotations and government subsidies, depends on the availability of information, personal background, age, psychological factors, ability and experience. Over time, the curve of adoption for any innovation follows an S-shaped trend, as shown in Figure 13.6.

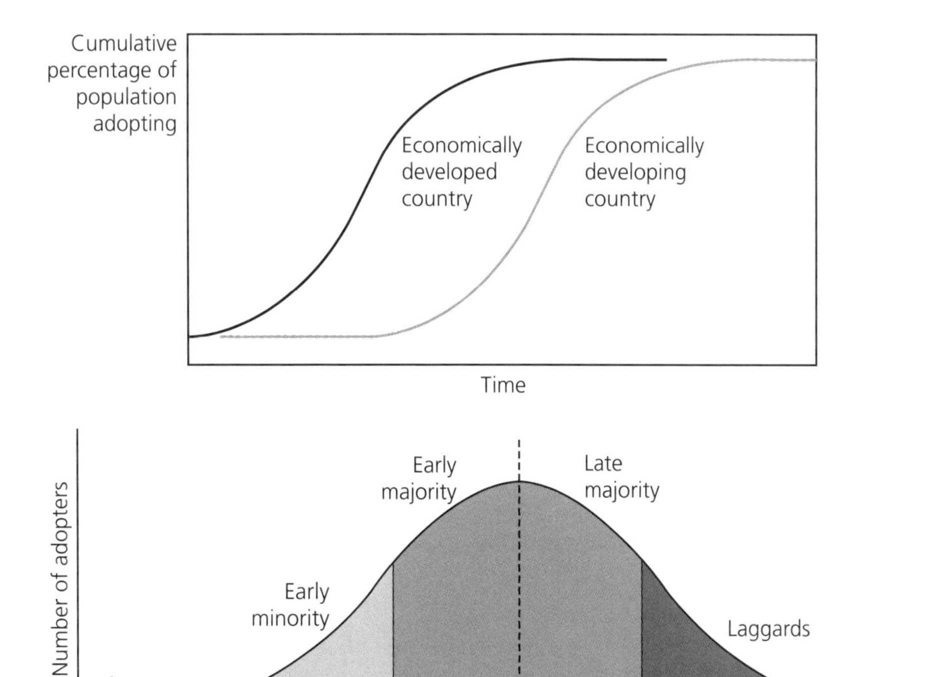

Figure 13.6 Adoption curves for innovations

- The early adopters are often younger farmers who are well educated and prepared to take risks.

- The success of the early adopters encourages more conservative-minded farmers to take up the innovation, so numbers rise rapidly.
- Eventually the rate of acceptance slows; the curve of adoption flattens out as all the farmers willing to accept innovation have done so.

Location plays a key part in the adoption process. Where information is largely spread by word of mouth, the likelihood of farmers hearing about the innovation depends on their distance from the information source. This is the so-called **neighbourhood effect**. It causes new ideas to spread across space like a ripple on a pond. We refer to this process of spread as **diffusion** and an example is shown in Figure 13.7.

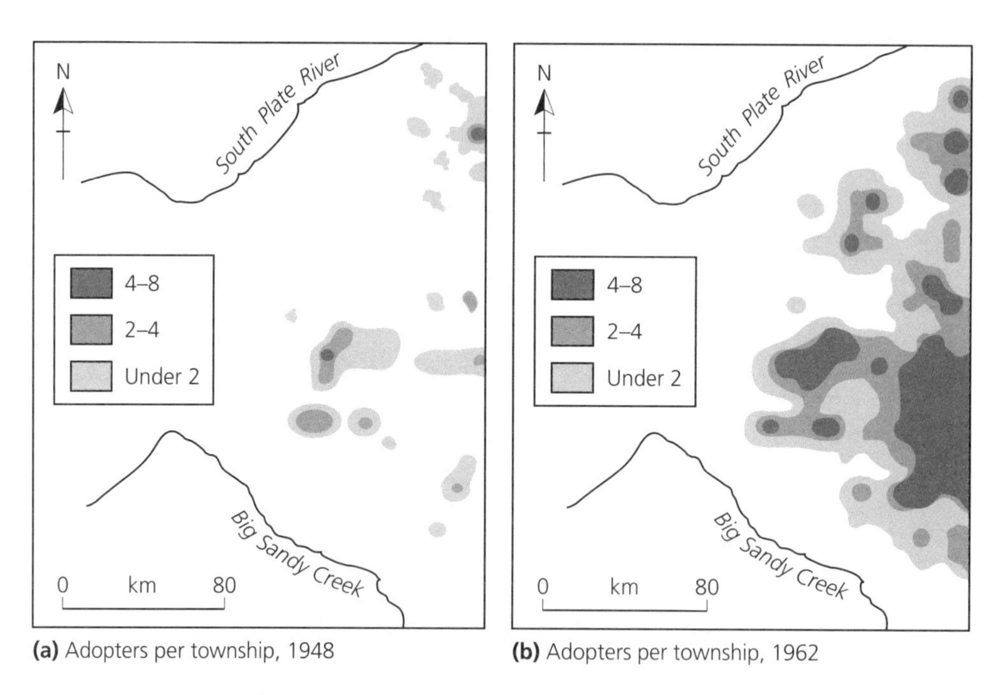

Figure 13.7 Diffusion of irrigation wells in Colorado, 1948–62

8 Selling agricultural products

Remember:

- Farming is the first stage (the production stage) in the human food chain.
- Increasingly, farming is controlled by organisations in the later stages of the food chain, such as food-processing industries and food retailers.
- Food-processing industries and food retailers have a major input into what is grown and how it is grown.

The immediate destination of farm products may be street markets or livestock markets in small towns, food wholesalers, food manufacturers, and retailers such as supermarkets. Food manufacturers and food retailers play an increasing part in the early stages of the **food chain**. Contracts between food manufacturers, supermarkets and farmers account for a high proportion of agricultural output in the UK. Farmers may be contracted to deliver a given quantity and quality of crop. Contract farming favours large farms that can keep prices low through economies of scale.

Direct marketing has become popular on farms in the UK and EU located close to large centres of population. Farmers sell directly to consumers, bypassing wholesalers and retailers, and increasing their profits. Many farmers have set up their own farm shops and stalls. Pick-your-own (PYO) schemes for soft fruits such as strawberries and raspberries are very popular in rural–urban fringe areas.

9 Agricultural land use and markets

Proximity to market is one of many factors that affect agricultural land use. For instance, the location of sugar refineries in England largely determines the geographical distribution of sugar beet growing. Similarly, the location of freezer factories will influence where vining peas (which must be frozen within 40 minutes of harvesting) are grown. Some of the best-known models in human geography seek to explain how towns and cities, as markets for farm products, influence agricultural land-use types and intensity (see Inset 5).

INSET 5

Von Thünen's model of agricultural land use

This early theory (1826) isolates the effect on agricultural land use of distance to market. To do this the theory makes a number of simplifying assumptions:

- Farmers aim to maximise their profits.
- The area farmed is an isolated, self-sufficient state with a single, centrally placed market (i.e. town).
- The area farmed is a plain of uniform fertility.
- The market is equally accessible from all parts of the plain, and transport costs are a function of weight and distance.

The theory says that the **locational rent** of each crop will determine the pattern of land use. Locational rent is the difference between the market value per hectare for a crop and the costs per hectare of cultivation and transport to market. Thus:

$$R = E(p - a) - Efk$$

where:
R = locational rent per hectare
k = distance from the market (km)
E = yield of crop (tonnes per hectare)
p = market price (£ per tonne)
a = cultivation costs (£ per hectare)
f = transport costs (£/tonne/hectare)

Because transport costs increase with distance, locational rent decreases away from the market as shown in Figure 13.8. Eventually, a point is reached where the locational rent is zero. This point marks the spatial limit of cultivation for that crop. Plotting the locational rent curves for several crops and rotating them through 360 degrees produces a zonal land-use pattern (i.e. concentric rings). This zonal pattern can be modified by relaxing some of the model's assumptions. The effect of a navigable river, which offers lower transport costs, can be seen in Figure 13.9.

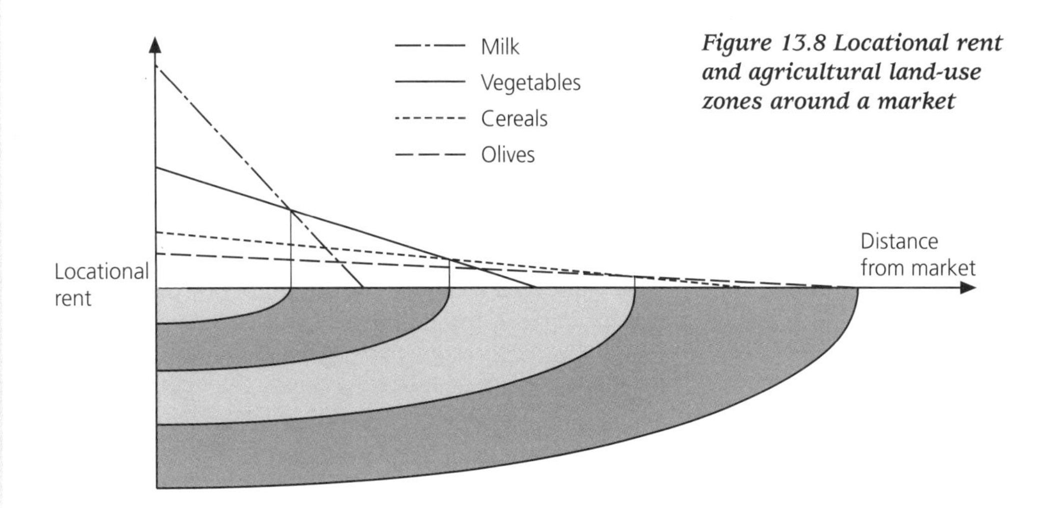

Figure 13.8 Locational rent and agricultural land-use zones around a market

Von Thünen's model does not aim to predict actual land-use patterns. It merely shows the patterns that should emerge, given the desire of farmers to maximise their profits, in a simplified world of fixed economic and environmental conditions.

A development of Von Thünen's theory suggests that the location of the market also affects farming intensity and the location of perishable crops. Towns and cities provide labour and generate waste materials that intensify farming in the rural–urban fringe areas. Meanwhile, dairying and market gardening (products that before refrigeration were highly perishable) must locate close to the market.

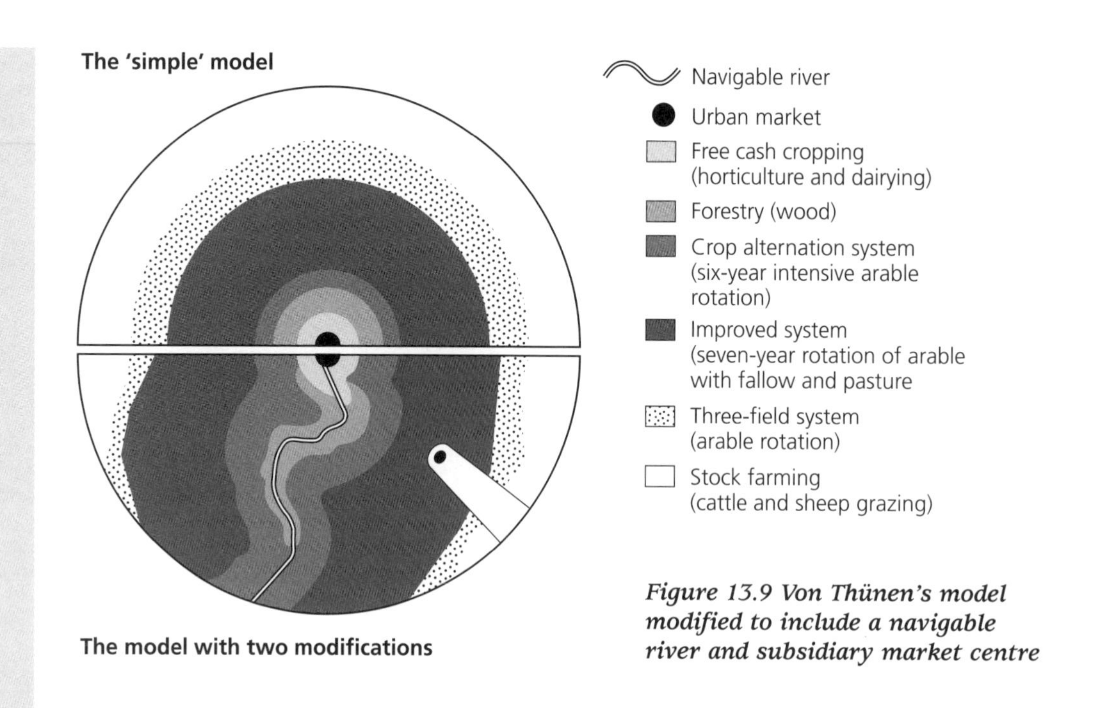

Figure 13.9 Von Thünen's model modified to include a navigable river and subsidiary market centre

10 Agriculture in the rural–urban fringe

Agriculture in the rural–urban fringe has to compete for land with housing, industry and service activities. These non-agricultural land uses normally have higher locational rent values than agriculture. Thus, in the absence of any planning control, farmland will eventually be converted to urban use. Anticipating change, farmers may cut back their investment in the land. As a result, farmland in the fringe belt may be left fallow or cultivated less intensively, with reduced inputs per hectare.

11 Government policies and agriculture

Governments often give agriculture a level of financial support denied to other economic activities. The reasons for agriculture's special status are:

- the need to ensure an adequate food supply;
- the uniquely vulnerable position of farmers, who have no control over prices and weather conditions.

11.1 The EU's common agricultural policy (CAP)

The CAP is a common farm policy that controls agriculture among the EU's member states. It has been the dominant influence on European agriculture in the last 30–40 years. First introduced in 1963, the CAP's aims were:

- to increase farm productivity;
- to ensure a fair standard of living for farmers;
- to stabilise prices of agricultural products;
- to maintain food supplies;
- to ensure reasonable food prices for consumers.

11.2 The costs and benefits of CAP

The CAP has in some respects been highly successful. It has guaranteed food supplies, greatly increased the productivity of agriculture, protected farmers from foreign competition and modernised agriculture in peripheral regions such as southern Europe.

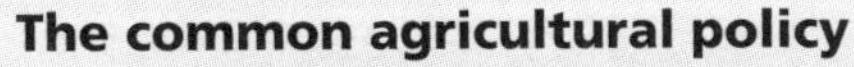

INSET 6

The common agricultural policy

The CAP has undergone several reforms since its inception. However, there are three essential parts to the CAP: price guarantees; funds to help restructure agriculture; and import levies.

- **Price guarantees**. Minimum prices are set for arable crops such as cereals and oilseed. If the market price falls below this minimum price, the EU purchases the crops, and in so doing stabilises market prices. Farmers also receive direct payments (price support per tonne) for arable crops. Price guarantees absorb around round 90% of the CAP budget.
- **Structural funds**. Farmers receive funding for modernisation, diversification, farm reorganisation and so on. Part of the purpose of this funding is to reduce disparities between core and peripheral regions. In difficult environments (less favoured areas) such as uplands and drylands, farmers receive livestock subsidies (payments per head of sheep or cattle).
- **Import levies**. Levies on imports protect EU farmers from foreign competition. The levy is the difference between the price of imported foodstuffs and the minimum price determined by CAP.

At the same time, the CAP has imposed a number of costs:

- **Overproduction**. Price guarantees based on tonnage led to massive overproduction of cereals, dairy products, beef and wine in the 1980s. The costs of buying and storing surplus food put a huge strain on the CAP.
- **Environmental damage**. Price guarantees encouraged farmers to extend the area of cultivation. Wetlands and woodlands were 'reclaimed' for agriculture, and hedgerows removed to allow more efficient use of machinery. Even poor-quality land was brought into cultivation. Meanwhile, farmers intensified production. In the lowlands, they used more agro-chemicals; in the uplands, they increased stocking densities. The environmental impact was disastrous: a loss of habitat and wildlife; changes to the cultural landscape; and pollution of water supplies.
- **Food prices**. The huge costs of subsidising the farming industry have meant higher prices for consumers.
- **Free trade**. The EU countries belong to the World Trade Organisation (WTO), which encourages the expansion of free trade. Relations between the EU and its global neighbours have been strained by its protective import levies. Export subsidies have also made some EU foodstuffs artificially cheap on world markets.
- **Inequality**. The guarantee prices of the CAP have favoured the large, wealthy arable farmers, thus increasing the income gap between core and more marginal farming regions in the EU.

11.3 The changing CAP

The costs of the CAP have prompted several major reforms. Problems of surpluses have been tackled by:

- production quotas for some products (e.g. dairy products in 1984);
- lowering guaranteed prices – a policy set to continue in future;
- set-aside – reducing the arable area under cultivation by making direct payments to farmers who left 20% (now 17.5%) of their land fallow for a minimum of five years.

Environmental problems have been given greater priority since the mid-1980s. There is an emphasis on the deintensification of agriculture:

- the shift of direct payments (and headage payments for livestock) away from tonnage to the area cultivated;
- long-term set-aside (20 years), which has environmental benefits as well as reducing production;
- promoting organic farming and a reduction in the use of agro-chemicals;
- diversion of farmland to other uses (e.g. forestry) and funds for the conservation of the environment and reduction of pollution (e.g. nitrates).

UNIT 14 Tourism

1 The importance of tourism

Tourism may be defined as 'people taking trips away from home and the industry that has developed in response to this activity'. Although tourism mainly involves travel for recreation and pleasure, it also includes trips for business, health and religious reasons. Tourism has an elaborate support infrastructure that includes transport, accommodation, promotion and marketing.

The following facts underline the economic importance of tourism.

- Tourism is the world's largest industry.
- In 1996 tourists took some 595 million trips abroad – 77% more than 10 years earlier. By 2010 the number is forecast to reach 937 million.
- The economic value of goods and services generated by tourism in 1996 was $3.6 trillion or 10.6% of global product.
- Tourism sustains more than one in ten jobs around the world. It provides work for 255 million people, a figure that could rise to 385 million by 2006.

2 The growth of tourism

The fashion for tourism and tourism destinations has often been pioneered by the upper classes. As tourism became more accessible, these exclusive resorts and other destinations were often abandoned by upper-class groups and filtered down to lower social and economic groups.

2.1 Before 1850: spas and bathing resorts

In Britain, tourism began in the eighteenth century. Inland spas such as Bath and Tunbridge Wells became fashionable resorts for the aristocracy and upper classes. This early tourism was based on the supposed curative properties of mineral waters. In the later eighteenth century, the focus of tourism shifted from inland spas to seaside resorts as doctors promoted the health-giving properties of sea bathing and even drinking sea water. As a result, a string of fashionable seaside resorts such as Scarborough and Brighton developed. Early tourism was economically and socially exclusive, i.e. confined to those who had money and leisure time. Eventually, the attractions of inland spas and bathing resorts filtered down to the middle classes. But **mass tourism** involving the working classes did not take off until the second half of the nineteenth century.

Patronage of seaside resorts by the aristocracy and upper classes gave coastal environments a new and positive image. In a similar way, the romantic poets and writers of the early nineteenth century such as Wordsworth and Byron changed public attitudes towards mountain landscapes. Previously regarded as fearful and forbidding, in the popular imagination mountains such as the Alps and the Lake District acquired a new picturesque and inspiring image.

2.2 1850–1900: mass tourism and seaside resorts

The period from 1875 to 1900 saw the start of mass tourism in the UK. No longer exclusive to the upper and middle classes, tourism underwent rapid growth. Most of this growth centred on seaside resorts close to large urban populations (e.g. Blackpool, Southend, Margate). Several factors contributed to the growth of mass tourism:

- the development of the railway network, which by shortening journey times and reducing travel costs brought seaside resorts within the range of large urban centres;
- the development of new resorts to accommodate the rising demand for tourism;
- the provision of cheap accommodation (small guest houses and boarding houses), places of entertainment (e.g. piers) and service industries at resorts;
- more leisure time for the working classes, including statutory paid holidays, better wages and larger disposable incomes.

INSET 1

The growth of a British seaside resort: Blackpool

Until the 1830s, Blackpool in north-west England was a small, exclusive resort that catered for middle- and upper-class visitors. They came for the supposed health-giving properties of sea bathing and sea water drinking. Then in 1846 the railway linked Blackpool with the industrial areas of the north. Cheap and rapid travel by rail opened up the resort to mass tourism.

Blackpool was the first resort for the working class. Its purpose was to provide pleasure and entertainment for the factory workers of northern England and the Midlands. As the resort's popularity boomed, the necessary tourism infrastructure was provided. Streets of purpose-built boarding houses appeared in large numbers around the railway stations after 1860. Development was piecemeal and the local authority often ignored health and safety regulations. Attractions for visitors included the sandy beaches, three piers, steamer trips to the Isle of Man, the Winter Gardens (1878), the tower (1892) and the promenade.

By the 1890s, Blackpool had 1.25 million visitors a year. The staggered holidays of the northern industrial towns allowed the resort to accommodate the large numbers of visitors throughout the summer.

2.3 The decline of traditional resorts

Seaside resorts remained the principal attraction for mass tourism in the UK until the mid-twentieth century. The steep decline in their popularity began in the early 1960s. The reasons for this were:

- cheap air travel, which opened up new international destinations, especially in the western Mediterranean;
- rising real incomes which opened up alternative foreign destinations to more people;
- the development of rural tourism in areas such as national parks;
- new forms of tourism based on outdoor activities such as hiking and camping;
- competition from urban-based tourism in cities focused on historic buildings, museums, shopping, restaurants, theatres, etc.;
- lack of investment in traditional seaside resorts as visitor numbers and tourism income declined, giving many resorts a run-down image.

2.4 Reinventing traditional resorts

Traditional resorts have responded to decline by:

- promoting more short-stay and out-of-season visits;
- providing improved facilities for the conference market;
- investing in new attractions and infrastructure (e.g. indoor leisure centres, theme parks);
- converting hotels and guest houses to retirement and nursing homes.

INSET 2

Butler's tourism evolution model

Butler's model, shown in Figure 14.1, suggests that the development of tourism follows several stages.

1. The initial discovery of a tourism destination, often exclusive to a social and economic elite, leads to slow growth (e.g. Mallorca before 1950).
2. As the destination becomes more widely known and more accessible, growth accelerates rapidly (e.g. Mallorca from the early 1960s to the 1980s).
3. Tourism reaches 'maturity' and the destination's popularity stagnates or declines (see Inset 5) (e.g. Mallorca in the 1990s).
4. The future of tourism at the destination depends on the response. Some places continue to decline and lose their tourism function (e.g. former seaside resorts in the UK, such as New Brighton and Redcar). Others reinvent themselves, invest in new attractions, appeal to a different market, etc.

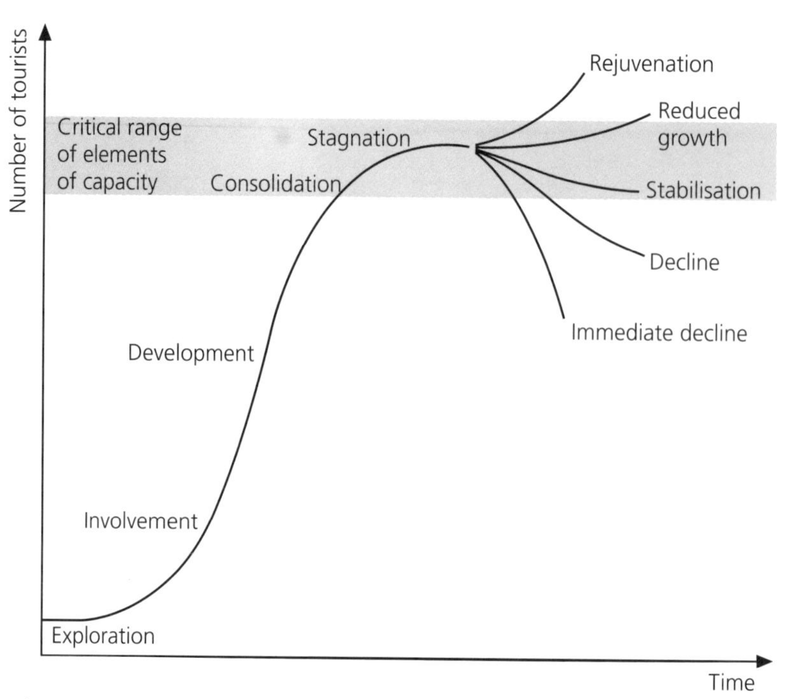

Figure 14.1 Butler's model of tourism development

3 International tourism

Before 1945 most tourists travelled only within their home country. This situation changed dramatically in the second half of the twentieth century. Between 1950 and 1994 the number of international tourists increased from 25 million to 528 million. This upward trend will continue in future.

International tourism owes its spectacular growth to a number of factors:

- The establishment of a mature travel industry. This includes high street travel agents that arrange and sell foreign holidays. Most international holidays are package tours with transport, accommodation and services included. This simplifies foreign travel and makes it more attractive to customers. The travel industry also provides holiday guides in the resorts and promotes international tourism through brochures and advertising.
- The jet plane. Modern air travel has transformed time–distance relationships. Wide-bodied airplanes and charter companies have reduced the costs of air travel. Between 1970 and 1995 the number of passengers carried by scheduled planes increased from 307 million to 1.15 billion. Today, no part of the world is more than 24 hours' flying time from any other part.
- Rising disposable incomes. As a majority of people in MEDCs have become better off, foreign travel has become more affordable. In Europe, political stability since 1945 has been a further incentive to international travel.
- A greater awareness of foreign countries through the media (TV, radio, newspapers, magazines, etc.).
- Educational improvements. As a result of improved education, language is less of a barrier to travel and personnel in the tourism industry are better trained.
- Standardisation. The use of credit cards, telecommunications, standard forms of accommodation (e.g. international hotel chains that ensure consistent standards everywhere) and car rental all help to promote international tourism.
- The use of information technology (IT). Airlines use computer reservation systems; travel agents find cheap tickets and package tours on their computer screens.

INSET 3

The changing nature of tourism in Mallorca

The Balearic island of Mallorca, shown in Figure 14.2, accounts for 6% of total EU tourism. The island's attractions include its warm sunny climate, sandy beaches, impressive mountain ranges and medieval buildings. Tourism began in the late nineteenth century. However, until the 1950s Mallorca was an exclusive destination, attracting mainly upper-income groups, as well as writers and artists.

All this changed in the 1960s. Rising prosperity in western Europe, the advent of cheap air travel and package tours led to a huge increase in tourism on the island. Mallorca was especially popular with British and German visitors. High-rise hotels sprang up along the sea front in popular resorts close to the airport, such as Palma Nova, El Arenal and Magaluf. At this stage, planning and concern for the environment were minimal. Mallorca soon became synonymous with cheap holidays for the mass market, providing sun, sand and sea.

By the 1990s, Mallorca's tourism industry had reached stagnation (see Figure 14.1). Mass tourism was in decline. The reasons were a downmarket image and competition from more exotic destinations, such as the eastern Mediterranean and Florida, for the sun-and-sea package-tour market.

In the 1990s, the island attempted to broaden its appeal and move away from dependence on mass tourism. More emphasis was placed on Mallorca's natural environment, historical sites and cultural conditions. Activities such as golf, hiking, cycling and bird watching are being encouraged, and planning and conservation are being given greater priority. Mallorca is in the process of reinventing itself, creating a new image that corresponds to the rejuvenation stage in Butler's model.

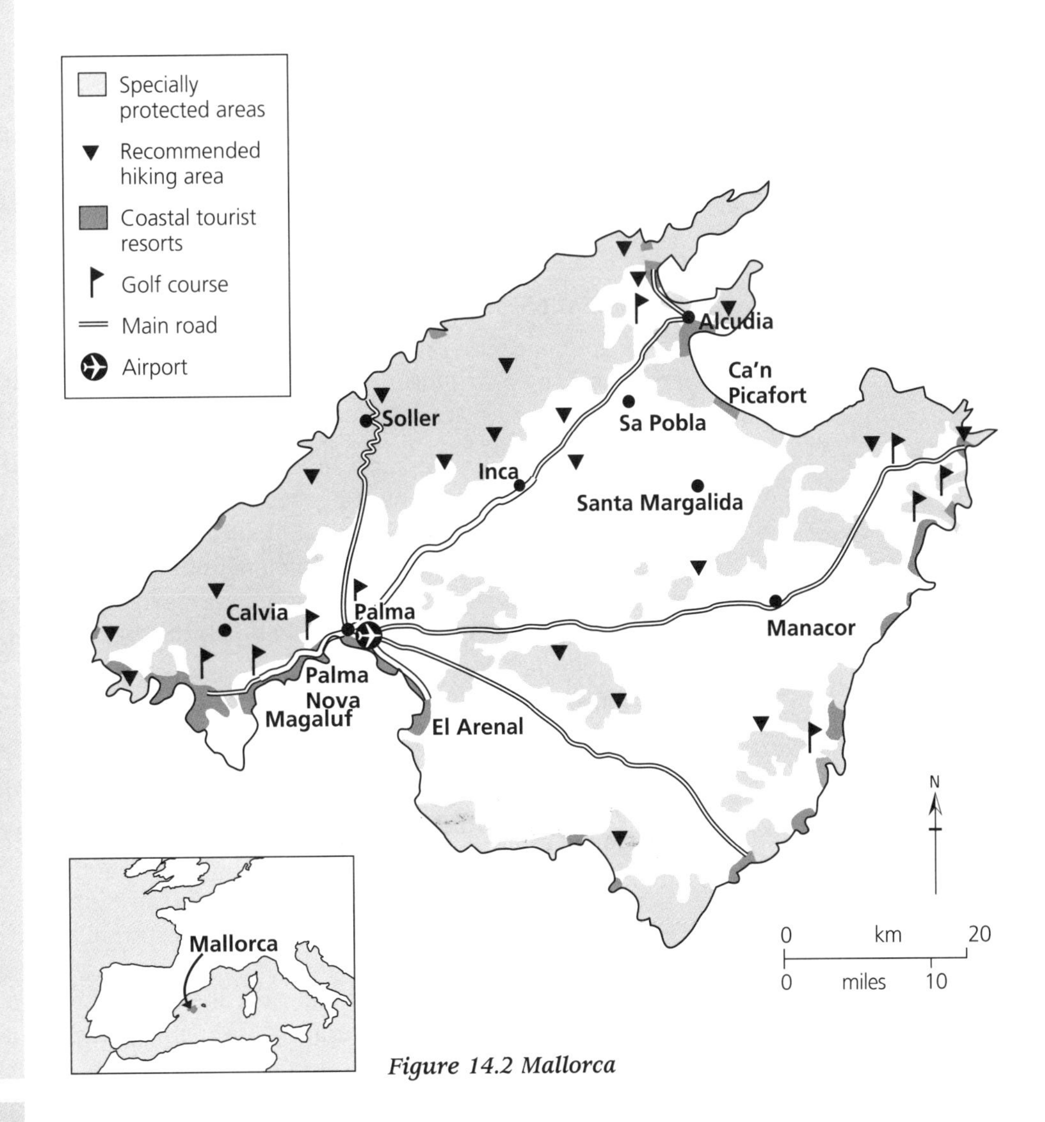

Figure 14.2 Mallorca

4 Physical factors influencing the development of tourism

4.1 Resources

Tourism is a resource industry. Some tourism resources are natural; others are historical and cultural.

- Natural resources: warm climates, beaches and the sea (e.g. western Mediterranean); spectacular mountain and canyon landscapes (e.g. national parks in the western USA); wildlife (e.g. safari tours in east Africa).
- Historical and cultural resources: museums, galleries, theatres, restaurants, markets, battlefields, historic buildings such as cathedrals and castles, and shops (e.g. major cities such as Paris and London).

4.2 Infrastructure

Tourism development requires infrastructure, such as accommodation, transport facilities and public utilities. Accommodation will depend on the target market, but is likely to include a range of hotels, self-catering apartment blocks, and caravan and camping sites. Foreign tourism relies on an efficient transport infrastructure: an international airport close to the main tourism destinations; harbours; tarmacked roads to allow sightseeing; and car rental services. Meanwhile, investment in public utilities such as electricity, water supply and sanitation is a pre-requisite of tourism development.

5 Forms of tourism development

Maturity in a country's tourism industry often has spatial expression:

- In LEDCs, tourism is often confined to small enclaves and resorts.
- In MEDCs, tourism often extends over entire regions, e.g. the Côte d'Azur in Mediterranean France.

Three common types of modern tourism development are enclaves, resorts and zones.

5.1 Enclaves

Enclaves are concentrated areas of tourism development. This type of development is largely confined to LEDCs where: limited funds are available for investment in infrastructure; investment is mainly overseas; the target market is a small elite group; and tourist activity is focused around localised resources such as beaches.

Often tourist enclaves are physically separated from and closed to local communities. Contact between foreign tourists and the local population will be minimal. Their isolation from local populations offers a safe environment for tourists. Enclaves often occur at an early stage in tourism development. For LEDCs, enclaves make it possible to provide the high-quality facilities demanded by foreign tourists at moderate cost.

5.2 Resorts

Resorts are the oldest type of tourism development. The first resorts were inland spas and seaside resorts. Most resorts are highly concentrated, developing around key natural resources such as beaches (e.g. St Tropez) and mountains (e.g. Banff in the Canadian Rockies). However, the world's biggest resort – Las Vegas – is located in a desert and its attractions are completely man-made (see Inset 4).

5.3 Tourism zones

In regions with a mature tourism industry, the scale of tourism development is such that extended **tourism zones** emerge. In coastal regions, tourism zones usually have a linear growth that reflects the importance of coastline as the principal resource.

This type of extended linear development is found in Mediterranean Spain, where it forms tourism zones such as the Costa del Sol (see Inset 7).

INSET 4

Las Vegas: the world's biggest resort

Las Vegas has no natural advantages for tourism. Located in the Nevada Desert, in 1900 Las Vegas had a population of just 30. In 1931 the legalisation of gambling in Nevada changed all this. Gambling became the bedrock of the city's growth. Today, Las Vegas has a population of over 1 million and is the USA's fastest-growing city. It attracted 32 million visitors in 1997. The remoteness of Las Vegas means that most visitors travel by air.

Unlike many long-established resorts, Las Vegas has retained its popularity. Growth has not levelled out, as Butler's model predicts. This is because the resort has diversified away from its core activity of gambling. Las Vegas is now one of the USA's top convention centres. Meanwhile, massive and continuous investment in lavish hotels, casinos and new attractions (e.g. the Mirage hotel cost $700 million) has meant that Las Vegas has retained its popularity. Most hotels and tourism attractions have been built along 'the strip', the city's commercial and entertainment spine. Apart from gambling, hotels offer restaurants, theatres, night club entertainment, shopping malls and indoor theme parks. Today, less than half of the revenue of the big hotels comes from gambling. In recent years, Las Vegas has also broadened its appeal to families and children.

6 The economic impact of tourism

Tourism has both positive and negative economic effects.

6.1 Positive economic effects

- Tourism earns foreign currency and therefore helps a country's balance of payments. Egypt's tourism industry is worth $3 billion a year and is the country's single biggest earner of foreign currency. Furthermore, tourism in most LEDCs is largely in one direction only: the spending of Egyptian tourists abroad is negligible compared to what foreign tourists spend in Egypt.
- Tourism attracts inward investment to finance capital projects. In 1997 a large part of the $2.2 billion inward investment received by Egypt was for tourism-related projects, such as beach resort development on the Red Sea coast.
- Tourism may help to regenerate and diversify regional economies. Many hill farmers in national parks such as the Lake District and Yorkshire Dales have generated new income streams with enterprises such as farmhouse holidays, bed and breakfast, bunk barns, and caravan and camping sites. Meanwhile, large industrial cities such as Liverpool and Bradford have developed sizeable tourism industries in the last 20 years. Liverpool's tourism industry generates £335 million annually and employs around 14,000 people.
- Tourism has a multiplier effect as the spending of tourists cascades through local economies.
- Tourism, being labour intensive, is an important source of employment. People directly employed in tourism include those working in hotels, restaurants, bars and tourist information centres. However, there are many more who indirectly benefit from tourists' spending.

Remember:

- Tourism has both benefits and costs.
- Tourism's true worth to a country or region can be measured only by its economic, environmental and societal impact.

6.2 Negative economic effects

The negative economic effects of tourism are most strongly felt in LEDCs.

- Tourism is vulnerable to economic changes such as a recession in tourist-generating countries (see Inset 5), competition from emerging tourism areas, changes in transport costs, political instability and civil war.

- Tourism is often highly seasonal, which causes significant unemployment out of season in tourism-dependent regions.
- Tourism in LEDCs may increase levels of dependency on MEDCs and foreign companies.
- In many LEDCs, foreign ownership dominates the tourism industry. As a result, a large part of the income generated by tourism 'leaks' abroad to MEDCs. Travel agents, airline operators and hotels chains are most likely to be based in MEDCs.
- Much employment in tourism is poorly paid, unskilled and overdependent on female labour. These jobs are filled by local labour. Better-paid jobs that require higher levels of skill and training often go to foreign workers.

Cornwall is one of the most popular tourism destinations in the UK. But tourism brings high seasonal unemployment, making the county one of the poorest in the UK. As a result, Cornwall qualifies for government financial help as both an assisted area and an Objective 2 area.

INSET 5

Short-term economic problems in Hawaii's tourism industry

Between 1990 and 1993, Hawaii experienced its worst slump in tourism since 1945. Visitor arrivals fell by 12% and expenditure fell by $2 billion. The slowdown in tourism was particularly serious as tourism powers about one-quarter of Hawaii's economy directly, and an even greater share indirectly. Visitor arrivals to Hawaii from 1990 to 1996 declined by 0.4% per year on average.

The major cause of this slump was the erosion of Hawaii's competitive position in the USA. As a sun-and-surf destination, Hawaii has had to face stiff competition from new resort destinations in Florida, Mexico and the Caribbean. A prolonged recession in California, which provides nearly one-third of American visitors, also contributed to decline. While visitor arrivals from the USA declined by nearly 18% between 1990 and 1996, the number of Asian visitors continued to increase through this period. However, financial instability in Japan, South Korea and other east Asian countries (which represent nearly 40% of Hawaii's market) threatened further decline in visitor numbers in the late 1990s.

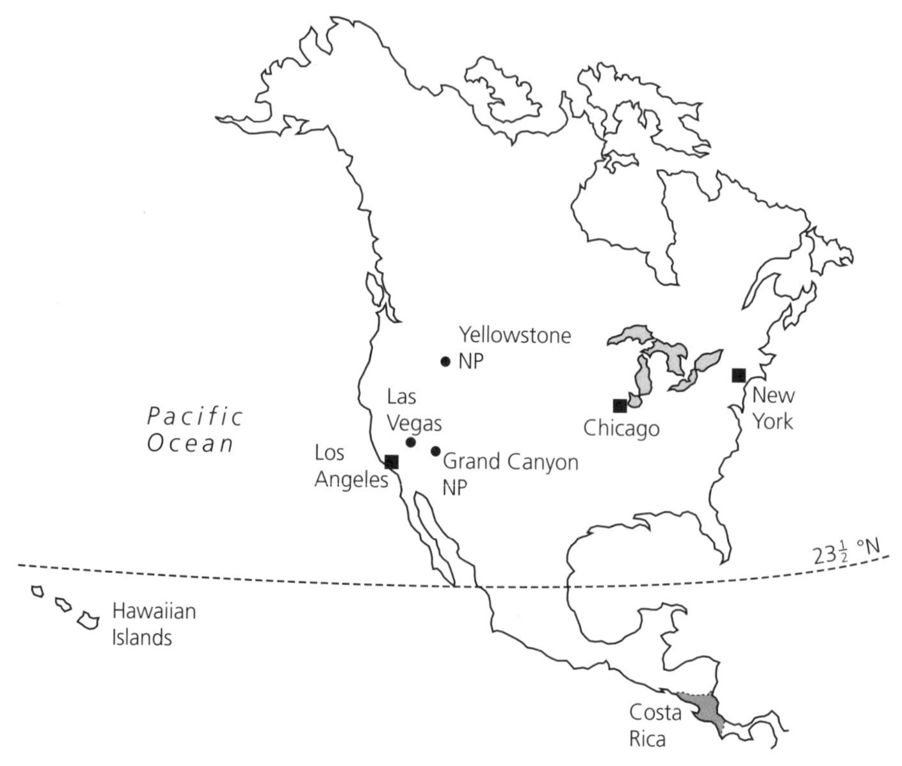

Figure 14.3 Location of tourism destination case studies

7 The environmental impact of tourism

Tourism often has an adverse impact on the environment, degrading the resources on which it depends. Damage results from the overuse and misuse of resources together with poor management and planning. Tourism that permanently degrades the

Unsustainability is particularly serious in tourism because it leads to a decline in the quality of the industry's key resource – the environment.

environment and reduces its value for future generations is said to be **unsustainable**. Fragile natural environments, such as mountains, deserts and sand dunes, are especially vulnerable to pressure from tourism.

INSET 6

Yellowstone National Park: the environmental impact of tourism

Yellowstone is the sixth most visited national park in the USA. In 1997 it received nearly 3 million visitors. Nearly 70% of tourists visit the park in the three months from June to August. The result is overcrowding at 'honeypot' sites, such as the Old Faithful geyser, Mammoth Springs and Yellowstone Grand Canyon. Most tourists travel to Yellowstone by car and this leads to traffic congestion, air pollution and noise. The tourists' experience is far removed from the original aims of national parks: to encourage the peaceful enjoyment of nature. Other problems caused by visitors include trampling of alpine meadows, footpath erosion on popular trails, and snowmobiling in winter, which disturbs hibernating mammals. The recent development of two marinas on Yellowstone Lake is a further threat to the ecology of the park.

The adverse environmental effects of tourism include: a reduction in biodiversity; accelerated erosion and physical damage; pollution; resource depletion; and loss of visual amenity.

7.1 Biodiversity

The pressure of visitor numbers on fragile ecosystems can reduce the diversity of plant and animal species. Trampling of alpine meadows by visitors who leave designated trails and footpaths is widespread in the Alps and the Rockies. Skiing can have a similar damaging effect on alpine plants. The building of hotels and roads in mountain environments also reduces biodiversity. On the positive side, through the designation of conservation areas, tourism may encourage the protection of species that would otherwise be at risk from hunters and collectors.

7.2 Erosion and physical damage

The destruction of plant cover on steep slopes and sand dunes, through misuse, often causes erosion. Footpath erosion in mountain environments may cause permanent damage. Not only is regeneration slow, but eroded debris often causes further damage by smothering healthy vegetation. Trampling in sand dune environments leads to massive wind erosion and blow-outs. Apart from damaging the ecology of sand dunes, excessive dune erosion may increase the risk of coastal flooding.

7.3 Pollution

Lack of adequate sewerage infrastructure may cause pollution along popular tourist coasts. Poor-quality water may detract from recreational and visual amenity, and may threaten human health. The EU's Blue Flag programme encourages clean beaches and sustainable tourism. But while the initiative has brought a steady improvement in levels of cleanliness of British beaches, many leading resorts still fail to achieve the qualifying standard.

7.4 Resource base

Seasonal drought is common in many popular tourism regions (e.g. Mediterranean). Demand for water during the tourism season, for swimming pools, golf courses and tourist consumption, may be unsustainable. The result is falling water tables and damage to local ecosystems. Summer drought is especially problematic in the Mediterranean because it coincides with peak water demand from tourism. In Mallorca, this has led to the overpumping of groundwater. As a result, the falling water table has allowed incursions of sea water.

The physical growth of resorts may also cause a loss of habitats. In Mallorca, heathlands, pine forests and wetlands have suffered to accommodate the growth of the island's tourism industry.

7.5 Visual and structural changes

Mass tourism in parts of the western Mediterranean has led to rapid and unplanned urbanisation. In resorts such as Torremolinos, high-rise blocks dominate the sea front (see Inset 7). As well as being visually intrusive, much of the building for tourism has been poorly constructed.

INSET 7

Unplanned mass tourism: Torremolinos

The development of low-cost package tours in the early 1960s fuelled the rapid growth of tourism in the resort of Torremolinos on the Costa del Sol in southern Spain (see Figure 14.4). Much of the urbanisation that followed was haphazard. During the 1960s, 21 hotels catering for mass tourism were built. Luxury hotels were downgraded for mass tourism, and huge investment in self-catering flats, hotels and apartments dominated the sea front. The result was an ugly built environment without any architectural merit. Until the late 1980s, only minimal infrastructure was provided. There were few green spaces, no promenade along the sea front and only a limited sewerage network. The experience of Torremolinos shows an imbalance between economic growth and conservation. Tourism which degrades the environmental resources that caused it to thrive in the first place is now recognised as unsustainable.

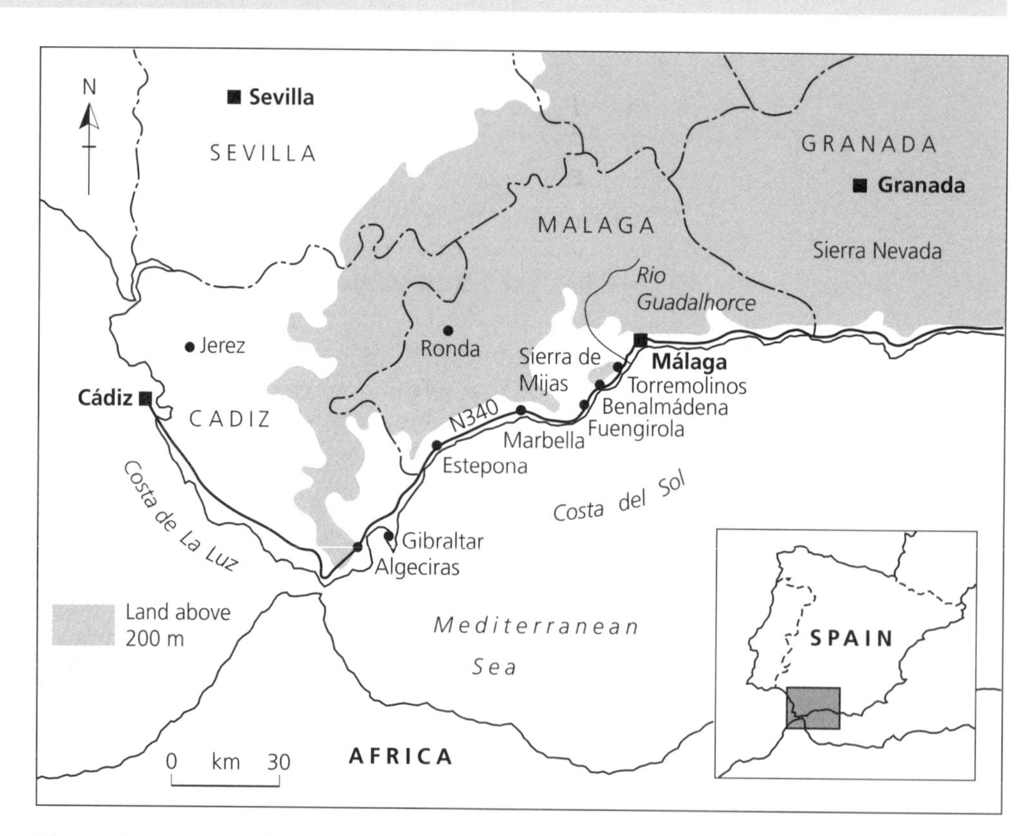

Figure 14.4 Torremolinos and the Costa del Sol

8 Sustainable tourism

The World Commission on Environment and Development in 1987 defined **sustainable tourism** as 'development that meets the needs of the present without compromising the ability of future generations to meet their own needs'. The uncontrolled growth of mass tourism in parts of Europe in the 1960s and 1970s promoted the idea of sustainable tourism. Sustainable tourism aims to balance economic growth with conservation of the environment (see Inset 8).

Ideally, sustainable tourism should:

- improve the quality of life of the host community;
- provide a high-quality experience for visitors;
- maintain the quality of the environment on which tourism depends.

INSET 8

Sustainable tourism in Costa Rica

Costa Rica (Figure 14.3) is a small Central American republic with a population of around 3 million. Tourism only developed in Costa Rica in the 1980s. The country's diverse natural environment – volcanoes, rainforest, cloud forest, high plateaux – is the principal attraction for tourists. Visitors come to Costa Rica to experience its habitats , scenery and wildlife (**ecotourism**); and for activities such as fishing, surfing, wind surfing and mountain biking. One-quarter of the territory comprises protected conservation areas, including national parks.

The government has pioneered a sustainable approach to tourism. It promotes limited development that aims to respect the environment and culture of local people. Hotels are small (only 5% have more than 100 rooms) and a significant number are owned and operated by Costa Ricans.

So far, tourism has not degraded the environment or local cultures, and has brought significant benefits to native Costa Ricans. Tourism is now the leading sector in the economy. It employs 75,000 people, it was worth $925 million in 1999, and it generates nearly 9% of the country's GDP.

9 Planning for tourism

9.1 The value of planning

The example of Torremolinos (Inset 7) shows that, without planning, tourism is haphazard and inefficient, and often has adverse social and environmental consequences. Effective tourism planning can:

- control development;
- co-ordinate the resources and infrastructure needed for tourism development (e.g. accommodation, attractions, transport, marketing);
- promote sustainability and biodiversity, conserve environmental resources, protect native cultures and maximise the benefits to local people;
- influence the distribution of wealth within a country by investment in tourism in particular regions.

A common approach to planning at regional and local scales is to establish protected areas, such as national parks. Within these protected areas, strict controls operate to prevent inappropriate development. The primary aim of planning control is to maintain the landscape, habitats and biodiversity of protected areas, and to ensure the sustainability of tourism.

9.2 Planning scales

Tourism planning takes place at national, regional and local scales.

National scale

Economic issues are the main focus of tourism planning at the national scale. This includes the broad contribution of tourism to employment, inward investment, balance of payments and so on. Often tourism at a national scale figures in government five-year plans. Targets for growth, foreign currency earning and employment, and strategies for achieving them (investment in infrastructure, promotion, etc.), are set out in such plans.

Regional scale

At this scale, there is more emphasis on development issues, such as the impact of tourism on regional economies and employment, investment in infrastructure, the management of visitors, the environmental effects of tourism and marketing the region.

Local scale

At the local scale, physical planning is most important. This often means controlling the type, size and location of accommodation; planning infrastructure, such as the road and sewerage network; and managing resources, such as water supply, beaches and wildlife.

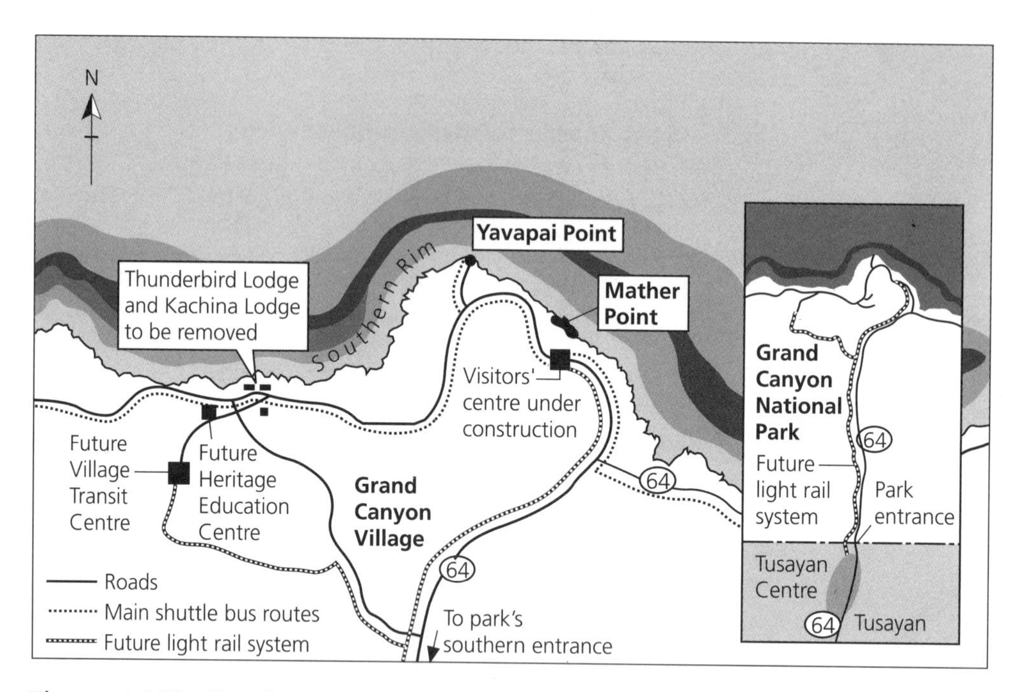

Figure 14.5 The Grand Canyon's plans to control visitor impact on the park

INSET 9

Visitor pressure and planning at Grand Canyon

The Grand Canyon in Arizona is the second most popular national park in the USA and a World Heritage Site. Visitor numbers increased from 2.5 million in 1980 to 4.7 million in 1998. About 80% of visitors travel to the park by car. Forecasts suggest a 50% growth in visitor numbers by 2050. Problems of traffic congestion, parking, noise pollution and air pollution have increased significantly in recent years. The quality of experience of visitors has been further eroded by noise from light aircraft, which fly tourists over the Canyon; the development of tacky hotels and gift shops in the park; and trampling of fragile vegetation by visitors. On the park boundary at Tusayan, unplanned clusters of hotels, motels and retailers offer accommodation and services for tourists. The growth of Tusayan has increased the demand for water, depleting local aquifers and affecting the flow of springs in the park.

The Grand Canyon park authorities have responded with a radical plan to tackle these problems and accommodate the expected growth in visitation (see Figure 14.5). Most cars will be banned from the park (the exception is those visitors who have booked accommodation in the park). Visitors will park at Tusayan and will travel by a light rail system to a new exhibition centre. From here, shuttle buses will take them to viewpoints on the South Rim. A new tourist village will be built within the park. The stress will be on sustainability. Even water will be brought into the village from outside.

The plan is likely to meet opposition from tour bus operators, companies providing air tours and even car-borne visitors reluctant to abandon their cars. A more serious obstacle is the plan's cost. Currently, the Grand Canyon national park receives an annual grant of $12 million from the National Park Service (NPS). At $310 million, the cost of the plan is equal to one-quarter of the NPS's entire budget (which provides for 54 national parks) for one year.